SCIENTISTS AGAINST TIME

Official Photo U. S. Army Air Forces

Symbol of a new age

Scientists
AGAINST TIME

by James Phinney Baxter 3rd

27583

WITH ILLUSTRATIONS

AN ATLANTIC MONTHLY PRESS BOOK

LITTLE, BROWN AND COMPANY · BOSTON
1946

FIRST EDITION

Published November 1946

ATLANTIC–LITTLE, BROWN BOOKS
ARE PUBLISHED BY
LITTLE, BROWN AND COMPANY
IN ASSOCIATION WITH
THE ATLANTIC MONTHLY PRESS

PUBLISHER'S NOTE

Under the terms of the contract for the publication of *Scientists Against Time* and of the various volumes to be included in the long history of the activities of the Office of Scientific Research and Development, to be entitled *Science in World War II*, the publisher has agreed to waive its right under the copyright of each separate volume after ten years from the date of publication of such volume. Thereafter the volume in question will be in the public domain and dedicated to the public.

*To the Scientists of the United Nations
who gave their lives in the
cause of freedom*

FOREWORD

THIS is the brief official history of the Office of Scientific Research and Development. It is the history of a rapid transition, from warfare as it has been waged for thousands of years by the direct clash of hordes of armed men, to a new type of warfare in which science becomes applied to destruction on a wholesale basis. It marks, therefore, a turning point in the broad history of civilization.

It begins in 1940, when this country was still asleep under the delusion of isolation — when only a few realized that a supreme test was inevitable, to determine whether the democratic form of government could survive; when none could see clearly the full revolution in the art of war that impended.

It recites the extraordinarily rapid evolution of weapons, as the accumulated backlog of scientific knowledge became directly applied to radar, amphibious warfare, aerial combat, the proximity fuze, and the atomic bomb.

But it tells also of something that is more fundamental even than this diversion of the progress of science into methods of destruction. It shows how men of good will, under stress, can outperform all that dictatorship can bring to bear — as they collaborate effectively, and apply those qualities of character developed only under freedom. It demonstrates that democracy is strong and virile, and that free men can defend their ideals as ably in a highly complex world as when they left the plow in the furrow to grasp the smoothbore. This is the heartening fact which should give us renewed courage and assurance, even as we face a future in which war must be abolished, and in which that end can be reached only by resolution, patience, and resourcefulness of a whole people.

Not that the great accomplishment of girding a nation for war was automatic or simple, even in this phase. On one hand were military men, burdened with the extreme responsibility that only military men can carry of ordering great numbers of their fellows into strife where many of them must die, harassed by an unreasonable load of work, determined to get on with the tough and appalling job and get it over. On the other hand were the scientists and engineers, realizing from their background that much they saw was obsolete, forced to learn overnight a new and strange way of life and set of human relations, driven to the limit by the keen realization of the scientific competence of the enemy and the consequent desperate nature of the race. And in between were industrialists, faced with the production of unprecedented quantities of strange devices, wary of the abrupt changes that would wreck the mass production in which this country excelled. These diverse groups and points of view could not collaborate unless they were forced to do so artificially and ineffectively by arbitrary orders from above, or unless they learned a new partnership. They accomplished the latter, and the accomplishment was greater than the mere creation of new weapons, and made such creation possible on a scale which determined the outcome.

There were no disloyalties, or so few as to be negligible. There were few who quailed at the heavy responsibilities. But in every group there are the small men, those whose selfishness persists, those whose minds are frozen, those whose pride is false. There were blocked programs, and futile efforts. There was also plenty of hearty disagreement, and vigorous argument in conference. But these were all incidents. Out of it evolved, toward the end, an effective professional partnership of scientists, engineers, industrialists, and military men, such as was never seen before, which exemplified the spirit of America in action at its strongest and best.

This is the story of the development of weapons of war, but it is also the story of an advance in the whole complex of human relations in a free society, and the latter is of the greater significance.

It is also the story of the advance of medicine under war stress. As man's knowledge of his environment extends, that is as science advances, it is well that it should be applied to ease man's lot and fend off the harshness of nature. This is not the greatest goal of the extension of knowledge, but it is a very great one. It was kept in view even in war, while the great weight of science became applied to destruction; in fact it was accelerated. Surgical techniques, blood substitutes, anti-malarials, penicillin, these and others were advanced at far beyond the peacetime rate. In fact, in the long run, it is probable that the medical advance of the war will save as many lives as were lost by military operations during its continuance. This is the mission of the medical profession, to save lives and mitigate suffering, and it was well done.

The same group of scientists and engineers who banded themselves together in 1940 stayed together and finished the job. Most of them have now returned to the peacetime tasks which were interrupted, to the extension of knowledge and the training of the next generation. They take with them a justifiable pride in the history which is here recited, and many deep and abiding friendships, forged under stress, among themselves and with their partners of the Army and Navy. Many have specific accomplishments to cherish, successes for which they took full responsibility; for the entire success of OSRD depended upon extreme decentralization and great autonomy of individual units. All have the satisfaction of having been members of one of the finest teams of men ever assembled in a great cause.

To President Baxter, who without compensation has given his energy and his historian's acumen to the difficult task of ordering and consolidating so complex and ramified a story, and to the Trustees of Williams College, who made it possible for him to undertake the assignment, the Office of Scientific Research and Development and the readers of this history owe their gratitude.

VANNEVAR BUSH

WASHINGTON, D.C.
January 21, 1946

CONTENTS

ILLUSTRATIONS

SCIENTISTS AGAINST TIME

Part One: The Race for Superiority in New Weapons in the Second World War

CHAPTER I

ORGANIZATION SAVES TIME

THE MAN in the laboratory and the man in the pilot plant touched almost every phase of operations in the struggle against Germany, Italy, and Japan. They transformed tactics and powerfully affected strategy. Their knowledge and methods were enormously productive of new weapons and devices of war, and of decisive countermeasures. They provided answers to the submarine, whose defeat was the first requisite of victory, and to the flying bomb, which Germany introduced in desperation as success began to slip through her fingers. Radar, at first conceived in defensive terms, for location of attacking planes and guidance of interceptors, became an offensive device of unrivaled versatility which has changed the nature of warfare in more ways than any other weapon. The atomic bomb, fruit of the most amazing co-operative enterprise in the history of science, shortened the war and bids fair to end warfare itself, unless mankind prefers to see what is left of its civilization in ruins.

The scientists of the United Nations, the plant engineers and skilled labor who were their partners, as they labored to provide the fighting forces with better weapons and devices, were daily conscious that time was the deciding factor of the conflict. Given time and sufficient scientific manpower, adequately organized to meet service needs, any major industrial power can produce new weapons that will help to tip the scales in its favor. The physicist or chemist engaged on war research knows that he is matching his wits against physicists or chemists in enemy laboratories, equally bent on giving to their national forces that measure of technological superiority on which success in modern war largely depends. It is small wonder that he works with feverish energy, and that his imagination responds to the challenge of his opportunity.

Although the skill and valor of the fighting man remain the most important element in warfare, he has become increasingly dependent on the equipment needed to give him information, mobility, and fire power. An historian of the services of supply remarked late in 1944 that God was no longer on the side of the big battalions, but on the side of the big factories. When the Russians smashed through the German lines on a wide front in January 1945, it seemed more likely that the winning side would have the big battalions backed by the big factories. Behind the big factories stood the laboratories and the pilot plants.

In peace, aggressor nations like Germany showed how easy it is to accumulate stockpiles, tool up war industries, improve old weapons, design new ones, and provide for an overwhelming superiority of force at the moment they choose to strike. Adding a technological superiority to the superiority of numbers mobilizable on M-Day, they counted on a quick victory over powers whose unrealized war potential would far exceed theirs if given time to develop. For them a quick victory was indispensable. Time is just as important to the innocent victims of their aggression, who, starting late and often ill-organized, must develop their latent resources of men and materials, and come from behind to win the race.

When technology was less developed than it is today, nations fought their wars with weapons of the types they had developed before the outbreak of war, expanding the volume of production, improving equipment when that was possible, but making few radical innovations. The World War of 1914–1918 saw the wide-scale use of aircraft, submarines, and toxic gases, but the only weapons of importance developed after hostilities began were poison gas and the tank. It was generally assumed, by those concerned with the application of science to war, that it took at least four years to produce a new weapon, from the first idea, through the stages of research, development, testing, and quantity production. It might take even longer before men were trained to use the weapon and commanders learned all the possibilities of its tactical use and its strategic implications. A great menace might, it is true, speed up the tempo. The stalemate of trench warfare led the Germans to try gas and the British to introduce the tank, just as the deadly challenge of the submarine set British and American scientists to work on new methods of detection. But the old idea that no new weapon could be introduced in a short war still prevailed in 1939 and led the Germans into what was perhaps their most costly blunder.

The speed with which a new weapon can be introduced and the extent to which science can contribute to victory are conditioned by a number of factors, including the readiness of the services to adopt new ideas, the state of technology, and the quantity and quality of scientific manpower available. There was a time in British history when the Admiralty preferred to leave radical improvements of material to the lesser maritime powers. As the Controller of the Navy, the equivalent of the Chief of our Bureau of Ships, stated in 1858, it was not to the interest of Great Britain to adopt any important change in the construction of ships of war until it was forced on her by foreign powers. Confident of their superiority in technology and production, the British assumed in the second quarter of the last century that they could give potential foes the advantage of a head start and then overhaul them with ease. Today these ideas are as obsolete as the crossbow. The British did more thinking to good purpose about new weapons for this war than did any of their enemies.

Churchill's splendid words after victory in the Battle of Britain applied to British physicists as well as to the Royal Air Force. If never in history had so many owed so much to so few, they owed it not merely to the magnificent skill, courage, and endurance of British fliers but to the little group of scientists who had developed the radar warning system that enabled the British to detect each incoming raid in time to throw fighters against it. As their numbers were inadequate for the maintenance of constant airborne patrols, the British fliers were in great danger of being destroyed piecemeal on the ground. They needed to know the range, direction, altitude, and number of enemy attackers, and to know them soon enough to get their interceptors off the ground and in position to strike. Not only did radar protect Britain with a curtain through which only low-flying planes could pass undetected, it enabled the R.A.F. to locate the enemy before they were halfway across the North Sea, or as they rose from their bases on the French and Belgian coasts. On September 15, 1940, the Nazis lost 185 planes out of 500 attackers. When they abandoned their costly daylight raids and turned to night bombing, airborne radar and ground control of interception led the British night fighters to their targets and helped to blast the invaders from the sky.

When eventually the German High Command realized that the *Luftwaffe* was destined to lose the command of the air to the British and Americans and be forced to abandon the bombing of England from aircraft, their scientists were forced to devise a new alternative. Flying bombs and long-range rockets were well within the competence of any major industrial nation, but it was one thing to make them and another thing to endow them with sufficient accuracy to make their manufacture worth the cost in materials and skilled manpower. Aware that these *Vergeltungswaffen* were weapons of the weak, inferior in accuracy to the bombers destined to rain destruction on German industry in the closing years of the war, they reasoned nonetheless that they had within easy range a target of unparalleled size and importance, and that whatever the inaccuracy of the V-1 and V-2 might be, the bombs could, if produced in time and in sufficient quantity, destroy London and rain down upon the ports of departure, decimating the huge forces which were being assembled to cross the Channel and to smash their way into the European Fortress.

German security measures were good enough to keep many of their scientific developments a secret from us until the close of hostilities, but Allied intelligence found out most of what we needed to know about the V-1 flying bombs and V-2 long-range rockets before the close of 1943. Thanks to large-scale Allied bombings of launching sites and production centers the output of these formidable weapons was greatly delayed and our forces were well ashore in Normandy before the first V-1 fell on British soil on June 12. The sorely tried British people mustered fresh supplies of fortitude from their inexhaustible store, and Allied scientists, who had given this problem top priority for many months, made a priceless contribution. The menace was not completely ended until the capture of the remaining launching sites by our advancing ground forces. But the problem of shooting down the V-1 bombs had been solved weeks before by the combination of three remarkable inventions, all developed in the United States under the sponsorship of the National Defense Research Committee.

These devices to shoot down bombs flying at 350 miles an hour were not produced to order in the space of a few months. No scientific wizard had waved a magic wand. Progress had been slow and painstaking. It had begun long before the first intelligence of the buzz-bombs had reached our shores and had proceeded by parallel research and by many a false step. Science had provided only the foundation of knowledge upon which inventors and designers had built with infinite patience and great engineering skill. If a miracle had been accomplished anywhere along the line, it was in the field of organization, where conditions had been created under which success was more likely to be achieved in time.

The first requisite of a satisfactory organization of science for war is that it must attract first-rate scientists. One outstanding man will succeed where ten mediocrities will simply fumble. In creative thinking there are no substitutes for imagination and resources. These will flourish only when the scientist has ample funds and a large measure of freedom. At the same time he cannot work alone in an ivory tower. Many of the problems involved must be attacked by teams of men with different skills and angles of approach, and on all of them effective liaison must be provided with the armed services. The organizational problem at this point becomes one of great difficulty. Armies and navies are operated on the principle of the chain of command, not on the principle of consultation and discussion. Their systems are well adapted to the conduct of military operations and to the production and methodical improvement of standardized equipment. They are anything but favorable to the conditions under which scientific inquiry best thrives, and the reconciling of the two is a matter of the utmost importance.

Here the Germans made almost every conceivable blunder. They were convinced of their ability to win the war quickly, with the excellent weapons they had produced in peacetime. If the war was to be a short one, they needed no great organization for the development of new weapons, no mobilization of their vast resources of scientific personnel, no experiments to ensure the scientist freedom to create within the meshes of their huge military system. German academic scientists could be left to their peacetime researches with the expectation that these would prove of value to the State after the war, helping in the

reconversion of industry and in the keen international competition of
the postwar years. It has been suggested that the Germans excluded
academic scientists from war research because they did not believe them
sufficiently imbued with Nazi doctrines, but of this we cannot yet be
certain.

German war research in the early years of the war was therefore with
few exceptions confined to the laboratories operated by the armed forces
and those of the war industries. What fundamental research had been
carried on in them in peacetime was greatly curtailed if not entirely
dropped. By Hitler's orders basic research on radar, for example, was
stopped in 1940, and was not renewed until 1942. The heavy hand of
bureaucracy forced industrial as well as government laboratories to
concentrate their efforts on the improvement and testing of existing
weapons.

The fixed belief in a short war had serious effects over the whole field
of German industrial production. In war research it cost Germany the
lead acquired in peacetime. Industry in America had long since learned
that to subordinate the research staff to the production department is
the shortest road to failure. Germany made this faulty conception the
basis of her system. Not only were her industrial scientists deprived
of the co-operation of academic chemists and physicists, diverted from
fundamental research and placed under the control of production men
far down in the hierarchy of the war effort; they were not furnished
with effective liaison with the armed services. They were given specifications and told to fill them, but were not afforded opportunity for
that constant and fruitful collaboration with Army and Navy officers
which contributed so markedly to the success of the British and American war effort. Under German regimentation there was no room for
such an uprush of useful ideas from industry as took place in the English-
speaking democracies. A representative of a great German electrical
firm testified bitterly that only one of their engineers had been permitted to see in actual operation the best of the radar sets they manufactured.

Scientists by the thousand, moreover, were drafted for military service. Even when it became clear that neither Britain nor Russia was to
prove an easy conquest, and when the entry of the United States aroused
apprehension for the future and memories of the results of American

intervention in an earlier war, the Germans persisted in holding these men under arms and putting more and more scientists into uniform.[1]

Early in 1942 the Germans made belated efforts to improve their organization for war production and to draw academic scientists into war research. By this time the hope of a short war had gone glimmering. In May 1942, Professor William Osenberg, of the Technische Hochschule at Hannover, became head of a committee to review the availability of research personnel at German universities, engineering schools, and other research institutes for work on problems of the German Navy. In January 1943, he was assigned to the *Reichsforschungsrat*, an agency somewhat similar to the Office of Scientific Research and Development but long inactive. In the welter of overlapping jurisdictions which characterized the German production effort, the RFR was never able to play effectively the role assigned to it. Just before the German surrender Osenberg complained that "Germany lost the war because of incomplete mobilization and utilization of scientific brains."

There is no question, however, that German war research was prosecuted far more effectively in the last half of the war than in the first, that it achieved important results, especially in aerodynamics and ordnance, and that, at the time of the German surrender, it was within measurable distance of other notable advances. Here was no case of the hare and the tortoise, for all three runners, Britain, Germany, and the United States, were endowed with tremendous potential speed. When one considers the manifold faults of the German war organization, many of which persisted to the end, it is remarkable that their scientists were able to do so much. They made a strong bid on the last lap but were still far behind when their rivals crossed the finish line.

Japan's organization of science for war was even more faulty than Germany's. Although the industrial laboratories of Japan were far inferior to those of the United States, and her Army and Navy establishments tended to attract second-rate men, her top-flight civilian scientists were men of great ability who could, under proper conditions, have made important contributions. But by British and American standards her utilization of academic scientists was only 10 per cent effective.

---

[1]Several thousand scientists were eventually released to the laboratories in 1943; too late to have much effect.

Prior to World War II Japan had expended large sums on grants-in-aid of science, chiefly through the Japanese Society for the Promotion of Scientific Research and the National Research Council. Early in 1942 a third agency, the Board of Technology, was created on the pattern of the OSRD. Its head reported to the Prime Minister, but found it impossible to co-ordinate the research of the Army and Navy, whose heads were responsible only to the Emperor. The three civilian agencies disposed of about 44,000,000 yen a year, a sum which, thanks to the extremely low pay of Japanese scientists, was roughly equivalent to as many American dollars. Research in aeronautics was entrusted, as in the United States, to a separate organization. This had an annual budget of 6,000,000 yen.

The Japanese setup had several fatal defects. The first was the under-mobilization of scientific manpower, which left the greater part of the academic scientists outside the war effort. Instead of placing contracts with universities, which would have permitted mass attacks on war problems, the Army and Navy dribbled out funds in small grants-in-aid to individual scientists. In no other country was there such bitter enmity between the armed services. As a famous Japanese scientist put it, "a general would rather lose the war than shake hands with an admiral."

Both their Army and their Navy developed systems, on different frequencies, for radar identification of friendly and hostile planes. As a result the Army equipment could not indicate the difference between a friendly Navy and a hostile plane, nor could the Navy distinguish between a Japanese Army plane and an American plane.

Both services distrusted the civilian scientist, especially if he had been educated in America, England, or even Germany. They consequently refused to give them sufficient information, and hampered research by security regulations pushed to the limits of fantasy. The civilian scientists thus groped in the dark on small-scale projects under individual contracts. In the fall of 1944 the Army and Navy set up a joint Technical Control Committee, with civilian representation, to co-ordinate research, but it came too late and accomplished little.

The Germans and Italians seem to have furnished the Japanese with much less scientific information than was to be expected. A notable exception was the field of underwater sound, in which the Germans gave help of great value in the development of both sonic and supersonic equipment. They also sent scientists to help the Japanese duplicate the Würzburg radar sets for the control of antiaircraft fire, though only three of these imitations were completed before the Japanese surrender. The Germans also furnished assistance on jet-propelled fighter planes and long-range rockets, but not in time to be of use.

By 1945 Japanese research on radar was three or four years behind British or American. The Japanese had, it is true, shown real originality in the design of magnetrons, produced independently by both Army and Navy scientists. Yet their product did not equal ours or the British. They did some systematic work on chemical warfare and on meteorology and developed a photoelectric proximity fuze for bombs, and a simple magnetic airborne detector for antisubmarine use, but in general their technical developments were little ahead of American and German prewar standards.

In short, if we had planned the Japanese system for research on new weapons, we could scarcely have devised one better calculated to promote our interests.

When the Germans attacked Poland in 1939, there were grave shortcomings in the organization of science for war in Great Britain and the United States. In both countries the Government had developed important service laboratories, such as the Naval Research Laboratory at Anacostia, D.C., founded in 1923. These institutions, however, were always in danger of being swamped as soon as war broke out by demands for routine testing, and thereby diverted from any fundamental research they might have under way. Few outstanding scientists, moreover, were attracted to government service in time of peace, for the conditions as to both pay and freedom are far less favorable than those of industry or the academic life.

The shadow under which Great Britain had lived for some years prior to 1939 had turned the thoughts of many scientists of the first order to problems of national defense. Her skies and her shores were so close to the German menace and were for so long an actual battle front that close and fruitful contacts developed early between her civilian scientists and her fighting services. The British, it is true, never created as simple an organization of science for war as that established in the United States in 1940 and 1941, but it is one of their qualities which have stood them in good stead that they can operate, under pressure, what seems to us an enormously complicated structure and get results which elsewhere could be hoped for only from simpler and better co-ordinated administrative machinery.

The organization of American science for war in 1939 was neither simple nor well co-ordinated. The services had not learned yet, as American industry had, that it is fatal to place a research organization under the production department.

Basically, research and procurement are incompatible. New developments are upsetting to procurement standards and procurement schedules. A procurement group is under the constant urge to regularize and standardize, particularly when funds are limited. Its primary function is to produce a sufficient supply of standard weapons for field use. Procurement units are judged, therefore, by production standards. Research, however, is the exploration of the unknown. It is speculative, uncertain. It cannot be standardized. It succeeds, moreover, in virtually direct proportion to its freedom from performance controls, production pressures and traditional approaches. . . . To be effective, new devices must be the responsibility of a group of enthusiasts whose attentions are undiluted by other and conflicting responsibilities.[2]

Human nature being what it is, the union of the research and procurement functions has another unfortunate consequence. A procurement unit that also is responsible for research tends to think all its geese are swans.

The result is to slow down the adoption of devices which first appear or are first suggested outside of the procurement unit. This may be particularly serious when we remember that modern weapons may either draw their components from or be, at least in part, the responsibility of several competing procurement units — each of which is in a position to retard or advance the progress of the other.[3]

What was required was the reorganization of the scientific establishments within the services which has thus far been only partially effected, and the creation of means to mobilize civilian science and link it effectively with the war effort. No existing organization was adequate for this

[2]Hearings before the Select Committee on Post-War Military Policy, 78th Congress, Second Session. Pursuant to House Resolution 465, pp. 244–245. Testimony of Dr. Vannevar Bush, January 26, 1945.
[3]Ibid.

task. The National Academy of Sciences had been created by Act of Congress in 1863 as a completely independent self-perpetuating body bound to give, without compensation, the best scientific advice of which its members were capable whenever requested by any department of Government. It has always operated through committees or boards, a majority of whose members have not been members of the Academy. President Wilson requested the President of the National Academy in 1916 to set up a National Research Council, which was perpetuated by the Executive Order of May 11, 1918, "to stimulate research in the mathematical, physical and biological sciences, and in the application of the sciences" alike to peace and war. Committees of the National Research Council were to render important service in the national war effort, but the Council lacked funds, was not a government agency supported by the Congress and reporting directly to the President, and the proceedings of its committees were often slow and cumbrous. They were set up to deal with every sort of problem in a large field of science, and were therefore not designed to focus attention on such relatively narrow portions of the field as those concerned with instrumentalities of war. To make the Academy and Council adequate to direct war research would have required drastic changes and a new Act of Congress.

A more effective organization, partly because it operated over a much narrower field, was the National Advisory Committee for Aeronautics, established by the Congress in 1915 "to supervise and direct the scientific study of the problems of flight." Generous Congressional appropriations had enabled the Committee to construct laboratories and wind tunnels, to develop a research staff under Civil Service, and to make a limited number of contracts with educational institutions for studies and reports. The results have been of incalculable importance in the development of civil aircraft, in which we are the acknowledged leaders of the world, and in the production of military and naval aircraft as well. The presence of the heads of the Army and Navy Air Forces on the Committee ensured close co-operation with the armed services. By order of the President in June 1939, the NACA was to become a consulting and research agency for the Joint Army and Navy Aeronautical Board at the outbreak of a national emergency.

For some years prior to the German attack on Poland the members of the NACA had been acutely conscious that they were living in a prewar, not in a postwar, period. It was quite natural that from the chief of this group should come the idea of providing as efficient an organization of American science for all other war purposes as had already been effected in the field of flight. Dr. Vannevar Bush, a Cape Cod Yankee of wide experience as Professor of Electrical Engineering, and an inventor with business experience, had been appointed to the NACA in 1938, and became its chairman a year later, not long after he had resigned the vice-presidency of the Massachusetts Institute of Technology to become President of the Carnegie Institution of Washington, the operating agency for the far-flung scientific activities financed by the late Andrew Carnegie. Bush was well known to scientists the country over for his contributions in applied mathematics and electrical engineering, especially for his extraordinary creation, the differential analyzer. The Army and Navy officers were familiar with his work in ballistics and in a more secret field.

After the outbreak of the war in Europe, Bush's thoughts turned more and more to the need for an over-all organization of science for war. He discussed this project with his former chief, President Karl T. Compton of the Massachusetts Institute of Technology, and with two groups who helped to catalyze his thinking, his colleagues at NACA and the members of a Committee on Scientific Aids to Learning, on which he was serving with President James B. Conant of Harvard and Frank B. Jewett, the President of the Bell Telephone Laboratories and of the National Academy of Sciences. It was John Victory, the Secretary of NACA, who proposed that the organization taking form in Bush's mind be named the National Defense Research Committee. At Bush's direction Victory prepared in May 1940 the draft of an Act of Congress setting up an organization

to co-ordinate, supervise, and conduct scientific research on the problems underlying the development, production, and use of mechanisms and devices of warfare, except scientific research on the problems of flight.

The National Defense Research Committee of not more than twelve members appointed by the President, and serving without compensation, was to include two members each from both the War and the Navy Department and from the National Academy of Sciences. It was to be authorized to contract with educational institutions, individuals, and industrial organizations for scientific studies and reports.

Dr. Vannevar Bush

Director of the Office of Scientific Research and Development

National Defense Research Committee

FRONT ROW (*left to right*): *F. B. Jewett, President of the National Academy of Sciences; Rear Admiral J. A. Furer, USN, Co-ordinator of Research and Development, Navy Department; J. B. Conant, President of Harvard University; R. C. Tolman, Dean of Graduate School, California Institute of Technology*

REAR ROW: *K. T. Compton, President of Massachusetts Institute of Technology; Roger Adams, Head of Chemistry Department, University of Illinois; C. P. Coe, U. S. Commissioner of Patents; Irvin Stewart, Executive Secretary of the Office of Scientific Research and Development*

Dr. Vannevar Bush

Director of the Office of Scientific Research and Development

National Defense Research Committee

FRONT ROW (left to right): F. B. Jewett, President of the National Academy of Sciences; Rear Admiral J. A. Furer, USN, Co-ordinator of Research and Development, Navy Department; J. B. Conant, President of Harvard University; R. C. Tolman, Dean of Graduate School, California Institute of Technology

REAR ROW: K. T. Compton, President of Massachusetts Institute of Technology; Roger Adams, Head of Chemistry Department, University of Illinois; C. P. Coe, U. S. Commissioner of Patents; Irvin Stewart, Executive Secretary of the Office of Scientific Research and Development

The sweep of the German armies across France precipitated American action. Bush saw President Roosevelt early in June, 1940, and convinced him that a new agency was needed. It was to be set up by executive action with funds of its own to be allocated from the substantial sum the Congress was about to place at the President's disposal. From the outset the President took a keen interest in the proposed Committee. As Bush outlined it, it was to be similar in form to NACA, but empowered

to correlate governmental and civil research in fields of military importance outside of aeronautics.

It should form a definite link between the military services and the National Academy. It should lean on the latter for broad scientific advice and guidance. It should supplement, and not replace, activities of the military services themselves, and it should exist primarily to aid these services. . . .

If it were welcomed and supported by the War and Navy Departments and by the National Academy of Sciences, it would

also be able to enlist the support of scientific and educational institutions and organizations, and of individual scientists and of engineers, throughout the country.

The President agreed to write to the Secretaries of War and the Navy and to the President of the National Academy of Sciences, requesting their support of the new agency.

In the next few days Bush talked the matter over in greater detail with Harry Hopkins at the White House and submitted to the President the names of Jewett, as President of the National Academy of Science, and Conway P. Coe, Commissioner of Patents, both to serve ex officio, Conant, Compton, and Richard C. Tolman of the California Institute of Technology. Tolman, who like Conant had been early convinced that the United States would soon be drawn into the war, had come to Washington in June 1940 to offer his services, and like the other civilian members had taken part in the discussions out of which the NDRC took shape. Things were moving so rapidly that Bush obtained on the telephone the consent of these men to serve. Conant asked only two questions: "Is it real?" and "Are you to head the committee?" Assurance on those points was enough. On June 15 the President signed the letters of appointment, naming Bush as chairman and indicating that the War and

Navy Departments would be represented by officers of distinction and would each detail a liaison officer to the chairman's office.

Bush had already called on General George C. Marshall and Admiral Harold Stark, who were both very cordial. In view of the prospect that their research establishments would soon be swamped with problems of immediate procurement, and that the Army would probably have more research allotments in the next fiscal year than it could use under the new situation, General Marshall expressed pleasure at the prospect that the National Defense Research Committee could take over some current Army research and his willingness to transfer funds for the purpose. General H. H. Arnold took Bush with him to Wright Field on June 17 to explore the possibility of transferring some of the research under way there, outside the field of NACA, to educational and scientific establishments under NDRC contracts.

Space, one of the most serious problems facing a new agency in a Capital already crowded, was easily obtained as Bush offered quarters in the Carnegie Institution of Washington building at 16th and P Streets, and Jewett made a similar offer of space in the National Academy of Sciences building on Constitution Avenue. It was soon decided to make the former building the headquarters. The latter eventually housed four NDRC divisions and the Committee on Medical Research. The four chemistry divisions of NDRC found quarters later in the museum wing at Dumbarton Oaks, thanks to the generosity of Harvard University.

Meanwhile Bush had made two ten-strikes in his first appointments to his staff. For executive secretary of NDRC he selected Irvin Stewart, a Texan long familiar with government procedures who had served from 1934 to 1937 as a member of the Federal Communications Commission and was now acting as Director of the Committee on Scientific Aids to Learning. The second appointee, who was to become Bush's alter ego, was Carroll L. Wilson, who had been Assistant to President Compton for five years before joining the staff of the Research Corporation.

The two immediate problems before the Committee were to find out what research the Army and Navy wished it to undertake and then to place contracts for research in the best possible hands. By June 20, a week before the agency came formally into existence, Brigadier General

George V. Strong, who was soon to become the Army member of the Committee, had furnished three lists of the research projects of the senior service; and Rear Admiral Harold G. Bowen, on becoming the Navy's representative, made similar information available.

Bush determined to leave his own hands free but to assign to each of his colleagues supervision of one class of problems he was especially qualified to handle. Tolman was to serve as chairman of Division A, dealing with armor and ordnance; Conant of Division B, bombs, fuels, gases, and chemical problems; Jewett of Division C, communications and transportation; Compton of Division D, detection, controls, and instruments; and Coe, Division E, patents and inventions. Each division was to have one or more vice-chairmen and was to consist of several sections, which it was assumed would be "the real working groups."

Compton's first assignment was to list the military research projects under way in government laboratories, especially those likely to be curtailed in favor of work on production, and also the projects not under way which the services considered desirable. It would then be possible to determine what programs the Committee wished to supplement. Meanwhile Jewett and Conant undertook to explore the possible assistance that might be had from the academic world. As President of the National Academy of Sciences Jewett wrote to the heads of 725 colleges and universities asking for information as to their facilities and their staff in the various fields of science. Conant followed this up with a letter to fifty academic institutions with extensive facilities for advanced research, explaining that the most immediate work of the NDRC would lie in the fields of physics and chemistry, civil, electrical, and mechanical engineering, and metallurgy. He asked that each of the institutions approached supply an outline of its special facilities and personnel for research in the fields within which NDRC would be working, "indicating only those in which your institution is exceptionally qualified," and that a description be included "of specific research projects in which your staff are now engaged which may have an application in devices or mechanisms of warfare." On the basis of the replies received by Jewett and Conant, Wilson compiled by early August a "Report on Research Facilities of Certain Educational and Scientific Institutions" which proved of much service, and was familiarly known as "the Bible."

Meanwhile the agency came formally into existence when the President approved on June 27 an order of the Council on National Defense establishing the National Defense Research Committee.[4] At the first regular meeting held on July 2, 1940, Tolman was elected vice-chairman and resolutions were adopted asking the co-operation of the National Academy of Sciences and the National Research Council.

In the normal pattern of Washington life at that time a new executive agency might be expected to obtain a broad grant of power, stretch that authority to the limit, and become involved in jurisdictional disputes with other agencies proceeding in similar fashion. From this type of controversy the lot of NDRC has been free. From the outset Bush preferred to stay in his own field, work as far as possible through existing agencies, and construe narrowly the terms "instrumentalities, methods and materials of war." Although it had first been intended to entrust NDRC with the heavy burden of evaluating the projects of inventors, he welcomed and indeed supported the movement which led to the establishment by the Secretary of Commerce of the National Inventors' Council as a separate agency on July 11. Procedures were developed to sift and bring to the attention of NDRC such inventors' projects as were of promise so that, if the Army or Navy wanted further research done on them, the Committee might arrange for it. The tie-in with the Inventors' Council was facilitated by the fact that the Commissioner of Patents was a member of both bodies. No friction developed between NDRC and NACA, not merely because of the clear definition of their respective fields, but because Bush retained his membership on the latter, while relinquishing the chairmanship, in June 1941, to Professor Jerome C. Hunsaker, of the Massachusetts Institute of Technology. The two agencies collaborated fruitfully in certain problems of jet propulsion.

Many proposals were soon received for research in borderline fields, especially with regard to strategic materials. An early ruling established the principle that no such work be undertaken without a specific request from the Advisory Commission. Bush's interpretation of the order under which he was operating ruled out, for example, research on steelmaking practice in general, synthetic rubber, and tung oil substitutes. Two members of this Committee, Conant and Compton, did serve with Bernard M. Baruch in the summer of 1942 in preparing the celebrated Rubber Report. But the standing policy of the Committee was to leave

[4] See Appendix A.

this type of research to other agencies, and Bush warmly supported the establishment of the Office of Production Research and Development under Dr. Harvey Davis in November 1942.

Money was never a limiting factor although at the outset the expectations were extremely modest. When Bush suggested at a breakfast conference in June 1940 that operations might reach $5,000,000 the first year, some thought the figure very high. By July 8, however, he was asking the Bureau of the Budget for an allocation of ten millions, of which he got six and a half. As the agency grew, Congress proved unfailingly generous. A temporary emergency developed in July 1941 when the passage of the annual appropriation acts was delayed, but this flurry was of short duration. The Executive Committee of the Trustees of the Massachusetts Institute of Technology agreed at that time to underwrite the salaries of the key men at the Radiation Laboratory to the extent of half a million dollars, and when it appeared that this sum might be insufficient, President Compton went to Mr. John D. Rockefeller, Jr., who agreed to underwrite personally a second half million. Congressional funds were, however, soon available, and thereafter were provided in ample measure.

Manpower, not money, constituted in the long run the limiting factor. The efforts of the NDRC to utilize to the full the resources of the academic world became therefore of prime importance. There was no disposition to slight industrial contractors or to minimize the immense contribution they could make to war research. But it was apparent from midsummer of 1940 that American industry was about to be called on for production of weapons in unprecedented amounts. Aware of the heavy load piling up on the shoulders of American business, the Committee determined not to make too heavy initial demands on scientists in industry but rather to obtain widespread support from the academic world.

The original idea was to decentralize research and leave the scientist free to work on his home grounds. This appealed to most of them and to university presidents who wished to keep their staff together. As late as December, 1941, Bush described the agency as one which conducted "research through cost-basis contracts with academic institutions and industrial companies which in most cases permit scientists to work in their own laboratories with the least disruption to other defense and training activities."

In mobilizing academic scientists the Chemistry Division got off the mark first. Its survey of Army and Navy needs and of the facilities available was pushed with such rapidity that the Committee approved on August 29, 1940, the placing of contracts with nineteen different institutions. As the latter were willing to proceed at once without waiting for contracts to be drawn, work was well under way on campuses from coast to coast by the beginning of the September term. At the University of Nebraska a contract was placed for the preparation of certain organic arsenicals needed in chemical warfare, the work to be undertaken by a member of its faculty who had done the most recent important American work in this field. Again, at a meeting of the Division held in Washington on October 3, it was pointed out that the Navy needed a portable instrument to be used on aviation oxygen-breathing equipment for measuring and indicating the partial pressure of oxygen in a mixture of gases. Linus Pauling, who came on from California to attend this meeting, thought about the problem for several days, put to himself the question, "What physical property of oxygen distinguishes it sharply from other common gases?" concluded that it was the magnetic susceptibility, and proceeded to devise an instrument which utilized this distinguishing property. This ingenious and successful device was promptly developed under a contract signed with the California Institute of Technology.

In the Chemistry Division a great effort was made for many months to avoid the development of central laboratories and leave the scientists at their home institutions. But as the volume of work increased it became more and more difficult to bring the workers together for consultation with sufficient frequency or to visit them often enough to keep them posted on advances in the same or adjacent fields. The benefits to be derived from teamwork of sizable groups were too great to be neglected. The organic chemist, for example, has mastered an art as well as a science. His knowledge and his techniques, no matter how eminent and versatile he may be, cover but a small portion of a vast and rapidly expanding science. When the organic chemist works in a central laboratory he is in constant contact with other men with special skills in other portions of the field, and out of the resultant pooling of knowledge and techniques great gains are derived. Sizable central establishments were therefore developed at the University of Illinois, Chicago, Northwestern, Carnegie Institute of Technology, and George Washington University.

The need of large central laboratories was immediately apparent when work was projected on radar and rockets. For both of these, ready access to airfields was indispensable. Rocket development required appropriate firing ranges and facilities for experimentation with explosives in considerable quantities. Out of such considerations grew the great rocket development at the California Institute of Technology.

There was great variety in the contracts with academic institutions. In some cases the contractor provided only space and management, as in the Johns Hopkins University contract to operate an important laboratory at Silver Spring, Maryland, later transferred to the Navy. More typical was the arrangement by which a university furnished space, management, and a portion of the scientific personnel. Sometimes these included the chief figures in the undertaking, sometimes not. The director of the Radio Research Laboratory at Harvard, Dr. F. E. Terman of Stanford University, had six hundred on his staff in 1945, of whom there were more from California institutions than from Harvard. At the giant Radiation Laboratory at Massachusetts Institute of Technology, of which Dr. Lee A. DuBridge of the University of Rochester was director and Dr. F. Wheeler Loomis of the University of Illinois associate director, only one M.I.T. professor was a member of the Steering Committee at the close of the war. By 1945 there were an extraordinary number of displaced persons in the academic world. These scientists worked full time on some sector of an NDRC contract, and had no other relation to the academic institution which now paid for their services. They were not receiving a grant-in-aid of pure research of the type now under discussion for the advancement of science in the postwar period. They were hired to hit an assigned target in an organized effort to create new instrumentalities of war. The government money which paid them was not expended to advance pure science or to aid the institutions from which they came or at which they worked, but to speed the day of victory.

Scores of institutions the country over released their scientists to work elsewhere on special projects. Harvard, Columbia, Princeton, and other institutions with research programs of their own released many of their men to work on other projects. Sixty-nine different academic institutions were represented on the staff of the Radiation Laboratory in 1945. For the scientists who moved to these large establishments it was an opportunity for rapid development, though often narrow and not usually in their chosen field. For the institutions which released them and then scoured the country for suitable replacements it represented real sacrifice.

California, Columbia, Harvard, and the Woods Hole Oceanographic Institute operated major laboratories for the study of underwater sound and underwater explosives. Princeton specialized in ballistics; the Franklin Institute of Philadelphia in airborne fire control; Penn State in hydraulic fluids.

The California Institute of Technology constructed and operated the longest known torpedo tube, while Harvard built for its studies in acoustics the quietest room in the world. Many academic institutions were called on to produce by "crash programs" some actual equipment for use in the field. The California Institute of Technology went much farther. Not only was it our chief center for rocket research, but the Institute found itself producing rocket motors by the thousand and special powders to propel them.

Some of the most interesting work was done by institutions which made few or no additions to their staff or facilities. This was true of Michigan in explosives and Rochester in optics. Other notable work was accomplished at Stanford, at the State Universitites of New Mexico, Texas, Iowa, and Florida, at Ohio State, Duke, and at Rensselaer Polytechnic Institute.

However versatile or broadly trained the academic scientists might be, most of them now found themselves working on problems of which they had previously known little or nothing. Psychologists developed methods of selecting and training the operators of countless new Army and Navy devices. Mathematicians and biologists mastered the intricacies of fire control and bombing techniques and staffed the operational analysis groups of the armed forces. Chemists made their contributions in chemical warfare or in research on penicillin, insecticides, and antimalarials. Werner Bachmann relates that when Conant and Roger Adams asked him to work on explosives his heart sank. Unfamiliar though he was with this type of work, he was destined within a year to develop in his laboratory at the University of Michigan a new process which saved the Government more than one hundred million dollars.

The college and university at war had their dormitories and classrooms filled with Army and Navy trainees and their laboratories turned over to war research of a secret character. This involved them, like the industrial contractors, in the complexities of a first-rate security system of which armed guards were the outward and visible sign and painstaking indoctrination the most important component. No one could start work for NDRC without a careful check by the Government's investigating authorities and until he had taken an oath and signed a statement that he had read the Espionage Act. From the outset the principle was established that no officer or employee of NDRC or of its contractors was entitled to any classified information whatever unless it was necessary for the performance of his duties. For instance, after Bush and Conant turned the contracts concerning atomic power over to the Corps of Engineers in May 1943, only they and one other member of their agency, Tolman, were cleared for this top secret project. If an OSRD employee were authorized to receive secret or confidential information, he was then furnished copies of the applicable Army or Navy regulations regarding classified matter. The record as to security has been admirable, proving that intelligent and patriotic civilians, carefully indoctrinated as to the importance of security, can maintain secrecy as effectively as members of the armed services. Had not this been true, decentralization of information and operations would have been as hazardous as an open flame in a powder magazine.

The task of the administrator in applying science to war was to find first-rate talent, assign it to the right jobs, and create the conditions under which the task could best be performed. Above all it was to save time. Irvin Stewart devised a streamlined system of processing contracts which enabled the ordinary ones to move rapidly along while the more difficult cases were receiving special handling. But the fact that NDRC could make contracts quicker than large government agencies was in the nature of things. The contracting officer, Bush or Stewart, was always available for a quick decision which in a large department might have taken a fortnight before all the necessary concurrences were obtained.

Streamlined contract procedures helped a great deal, but effective liaison with the armed services was still more important. The better the teamwork between the services, the academic contractors, and the industrial contractors, the more time could be saved. Great effort was required to get the scientists the information they needed with the minimum of delay; and to avoid the regimentation which so hampered the German effort. It is not an easy thing in wartime to afford full scope to inventiveness. Yet where scientific manpower and imagination are the limiting factors the creation of conditions favorable to prompt and original solutions is the crux of the problem.

It must not be imagined that the liaison established with the services was perfect or that it functioned without difficulty. In wartime the Army and Navy are immense and complex organizations in a constant state of flux. The first problem of the civilian scientist is to find the right people to work with. If his assignment has to do with aerial gunnery he may not know at the outset that though the Navy Bureau of Aeronautics is responsible for turrets the Bureau of Ordnance supplies the gunsights. When he has found the right people at the right level in the right bureaus his problem is not solved. The next time he calls, one of the men may have been ordered to sea duty and another to the European theater. In England it was much easier for the scientist to get in close contact with men just back from the front than it was in the United States. In both countries the scientist was sorely handicapped unless he could work closely both with his opposite numbers in the research and production branches of the various bureaus, and with operations officers as well. He also needed permission to use Army and Navy facilities for his experiments, which might require anything from airplanes and blimps to destroyers and submarines.

When the civilian scientists had demonstrated conclusively how good their work was and how well they could keep secrets, their liaison with the services became increasingly better, but it varied from bureau to bureau. The Army and Navy each had a representative on the National Defense Research Committee, and one or both services detailed at least one officer to each project. The success of these liaison officers varied in accordance with their knowledge of the work and the length of time they served before their transfer to other duties. Under Major General Clarence C. Williams, a former Chief of Ordnance, the War Department Liaison Office which had been set up to handle relations with NDRC became a very effective instrument. The Office of the Co-ordinator of Research and Development, under Dr. Jerome C. Hunsaker from July to December 1941, and Rear Admiral Julius A. Furer from that date until May 1945, worked wonders in handling NDRC liaison with the Navy Department. Fully posted on the needs of the Navy and alive to the possibilities of civilian contributions, these tactful and imaginative co-ordinators exerted a powerful influence over the whole field of Navy-OSRD collaboration. As later pages will show, they acted as catalysts in many developments of outstanding importance. "That your group would contribute brilliant ideas and achievements to the war effort was expected," wrote Admiral Furer to Bush, "but that you would be so versatile, and that the scientists and the Navy would find themselves so adaptable to each other's way of doing business, was unexpected by many."

CHAPTER II

SCIENCE AND STRATEGY

THE AXIS position in the early months of 1942 seemed unshakable. The Japanese, after neutralizing our Pacific Fleet by the surprise attack at Pearl Harbor, and sinking the *Prince of Wales* and *Repulse* two days later, had with great skill and astonishingly small losses made themselves masters of Hong Kong, Malaya, the Philippines, and the Dutch East Indies, and were threatening Australia. The Germans held Western Europe in great strength, and by their drive to the southeast and their brilliantly led campaign in North Africa, they threatened to cut Russia off from the oil of the Caucasus and wrest the Suez Canal from British hands.

There was a great difference between the Japanese and the German position. The wealth of the lands overrun by the Japanese was largely untapped. They lacked sufficient capital and skilled labor to exploit the conquered territory quickly. Above all they lacked merchant ships numerous enough to tie their scattered dominions together. The Germans possessed enormous resources in skilled labor and modern factory equipment and the most highly developed transportation network in the world. Since the United Nations were too weak in 1942 to mount major offensives against both Germany and Japan, they made their chief effort first against Germany.

Secretary of War Patterson has explained the reasons for that sequence in fighting.

One was to take advantage of the concentration of forces. Russia was fighting Germany, but not Japan. Another was the shorter distance to Germany; the shorter distance meant shorter time in getting into action. But the reason that seemed to me as compelling as any was the danger of the German scientists, the risk that they would come up with new weapons of devastating destructiveness. There was no time to lose in eliminating German science from the war. There was no comparable peril from Japanese science.[1]

[1]Address before the American Chemical Society, April 8, 1946.

From the standpoint of grand strategy the creation of the National Defense Research Committee as early as June 1940 stands out as one of the most important moves made by President Roosevelt in preparation for the eventuality of war. Not only were eighteen months of precious time gained before the sneak attack at Pearl Harbor, but the best system devised by any of the warring powers to mobilize science for the war was set in motion. This was soon followed by the establishment of full scientific interchange with Great Britain and Canada, giving us the enormous benefit of all that they had learned in preparation for war and in the long months since the German attack on Poland.

By the time of Pearl Harbor real progress had been made on an improved method to manufacture the potent explosive RDX, on the rocket, the proximity fuze, smokes, and incendiaries. The electromagnetic method had shown promise of separating in microscopic quantities the isotopes of uranium. No microwave radar sets had yet been delivered to the armed services, but within a few months they would be available for locating surfaced submarines, for night interception, and for many other purposes.

On the full use of the new weapons and equipment depended hundreds of thousands of lives, indeed, the possibility of victory itself. What use was it for the scientists to win the race against time unless the weapons they developed were exploited to the full against the enemy? If the new gear was in a warehouse or a rear area at the critical moment, the most brilliant conceptions of the chemist or physicist who brought it into being were less than dust in the scales of war.

The man in the street has long had the uneasy suspicion in peacetime that the military mind is preoccupied with planning not for the next war but for the last one. Now that the tempo of technological change has increased, the danger is greater than ever before. The staff planners of Great Britain and Germany during the First World War had made poor use of their chief new weapons, the tank and poison gas. Although the organization of science for the creation of new weapons had greatly improved in America since that day, was there any reason to assume that at the staff planning level men were better prepared to exploit new devices as revolutionary as radar?

From the standpoint of training it was dangerous for the rank and file to assume that they could not win without new weapons. They had to be indoctrinated with the will to win with whatever equipment might be at hand. In the counsels of the staff planners, on the other hand, it was necessary to be alert to the possibilities not only of the new weapons just coming into service use but of those still below the horizon. If one is planning for an operation twelve or eighteen months ahead one has to know not merely the possibilities of today but those of D-Day. Only the best men can exploit to the full the weapons with which they have been long familiar. Fewer yet have the imagination to grasp the potentialities of weapons not yet tested in combat.

How could one be sure that the men doing such planning were provided with the requisite information and the requisite predictions? The layman is prone to assume that if knowledge exists in one part of an army or navy, it will automatically come to the attention of all the authorities who need to know it. There are few greater illusions. At any given moment, in every large military organization, there will of necessity be intelligence reports that have not reached the commanders who need to see them or that have reached them and not been properly appreciated. The larger the organization the more often this is likely to happen. It is more likely to happen with scientific intelligence than with other types of information because a smaller proportion of men in all ranks are able to evaluate it.

Close collaboration between the armed services and civilian science had been provided for at the tactical level. Bush thought the new weapon too important in modern war for this to be sufficient.

At the level of strategy there needs to be a control of trends on new weapons, a determination of emphasis, and an insistence on progress on specific matters at the expense of other things, if the situation is to be complete. The planning of military strategy needs to be carried on with a full grasp of the implications of new weapons, and also of the probable future trends of development.[2]

A few days after Pearl Harbor, Conant, on his own initiative, went to Harry Hopkins and proposed a joint Army and Navy committee on new weapons, with Bush as chairman, reporting directly to the President.

The need for co-ordinating Army and Navy research was frequently discussed in the Advisory Council of OSRD, in which both services were

[2]Memorandum, April 26, 1942.

represented. The example of Great Britain, where the scientific effort was linked directly with the War Council, lent force to the views that our Army and Navy research programs were not thoroughly integrated, and that "the point of view of men whose entire lives have been devoted to the scientific effort needs to be brought into the picture" at the level of strategic planning.[3]

Harvey H. Bundy, the Army representative in OSRD's Advisory Council, submitted a memorandum to the Secretary of War on February 18, 1942, calling attention to the fact that "various modern inventions have been kept so secret and their development has been so rapid that important officers of the General Staff and especially those in the War Plans Division have not been and are not currently advised of their existence, functions and effect on strategy." He instanced airborne search radar as an additional defense for Panama, possible development in explosives and in the detection of submarines, and innovations under development such as the proximity fuze which might seriously limit the effectiveness of the bombing plane. As a solution he proposed the creation of a committee of three on new weapons and their effect on strategy, to consist of Bush as chairman, a general, and an admiral. They could, he argued, "make very valuable suggestions as to changes of strategy which can and should be made in the light of what they can see now and in prospect in the scientific world."

Bush suggested to the President on March 6 that, in view of the limited number of skilled scientists, it was time for a review on the strategic level of the work of OSRD on new weapons, "to determine emphasis and be sure that striking opportunities are not being overlooked or inadequately pushed." By the end of April, 1942, a solution was in sight in the form of a committee reporting not directly to the President but to the Joint Chiefs of Staff. The Joint Committee on New Weapons and Equipment, with Bush as chairman and Rear Admiral W. A. Lee, Jr., and Brigadier General R. G. Moses as the service members, held its first meeting on May 12, 1942. Its directive from the Joint Chiefs of Staff was to co-ordinate the effort of civilian research agencies and the armed services in the development and production of new weapons and equipment.

Between May 1942 and the close of hostilities, JNW, as the committee

[3]Minutes of Advisory Council, January 23, 30, March 20, 1942.

was called, held fifty-nine meetings. By way of JNW, Bush presented to the Joint Chiefs many studies prepared with great skill by himself or by members of the OSRD staff. In these masterly statements he not only brought out the possibilities of integrated use of the new weapons, but he proceeded on the assumption — the only safe one in discussions of such matters — that the enemy was as far advanced with new weapons as we were and hence was in a position to apply any devices which had reached the stage of possible application with us.

The JNW set up many panels, on which various members of OSRD represented civilian science, and after examination and comment passed their reports along to the Joint Chiefs of Staff for their consideration and for reference to the Joint Staff Planners.

Perhaps the most important of the *ad hoc* subcommittees of JNW was that on Radar Research and Development, which was set up in August 1942, with K. T. Compton as chairman.[4] Its functions were to prepare an American program of research and development in the field of radar and to define the responsibilities of various American groups and organizations in the prosecution of this program. It was to maintain close liaison with the Joint Communications Board, the War Production Board, the appropriate British planning committees, and the Combined Communications Board.

For a year and a half, if not longer, the Radar subcommittee of JNW was the top planning group in radar. They started by assuming a future military operation such as an expedition to North Africa, a landing there, or a campaign in Tunis, and then figured out what the needs for radar would be. DuBridge took the consensus of the fortnightly meetings back to the Steering Committee of the Radiation Laboratory, where the influence was immediate. The reports of the Radar subcommittee of JNW were approved by the Joint Chiefs of Staff and administered by the Joint Communications Board.

Close liaison between the British and American groups was promoted by visits from Sir Frank Smith of the Ministry of Aircraft Production to Washington in September 1942 and the return visit of Dr. Compton and other members of the subcommittee to England in April and May 1943

[4]The other original members were L. A. DuBridge, Rear Admiral J. A. Furer, Brigadier General H. N. McClelland, Colonel T. C. Rives, Colonel D. W. Hickey, Jr., Commander J. W. Dow, Lieutenant Commander F. R. Furth, and Lieutenant Commander L. V. Berkner.

as a "United States Special Mission on Radar."[5] This resulted in important Anglo-American agreements dividing the field of radar research, providing for closer collaboration, and effecting important economies in scientific manpower.

The Joint Committee on New Weapons and Equipment proved only a partial solution to the problem of bringing the civilian scientist in at the planning level. JNW never was brought in contact with the staff planners. The difficult problem of the relationships of scientists to the military at the strategic level still awaits a solution.

The armed services were more likely to ask OSRD for help in a field as new as microwave radar or the proximity fuze, than in the improvement of existing weapons such as rifles, machine guns, artillery, and hand grenades. When the history of the armored tank is finally written it will appear how little the Ordnance Department desired NDRC's assistance in its development, although the Committee on Medical Research was able later to do some effective work at Fort Knox in helping to adjust men to life in these uncomfortable and hazardous vehicles.

Tanks had less to fear from other tanks than from enemy artillery. Since the effect of a projectile on armor depends on its mass and the square of its velocity, NDRC stressed persistently the importance of high muzzle velocity. And with small encouragement they carried out important studies of gun erosion, an important limiting factor when one seeks to step up velocities. The successes of Rommel against British armor in the African desert depended largely on the high velocity of the German 88-mm. guns. By the end of the war Army Ordnance had in the field a 90-mm. gun of improved muzzle velocity. But by that time the Germans were out in front with antitank guns much superior in muzzle velocity to any of ours.

The failure to make the most of our possibilities in high-velocity ordnance reveals inadequate civilian influence upon strategic thinking. A similar instance was the delay of the Navy in making full offensive use of new airborne weapons and devices in the pursuit and destruction of the U-boats.

It was clear that for surfaced submarines the airplane had a much higher search rate than the surface vessel, say ten to one, and that it

[5]Dr. Compton's departure was delayed by pneumonia, but he left for London on May 2.

could carry long-wave radar for surface search and make even better use of the microwave sets of longer range when they became available in 1942. Most of the Navy's difficulties in protecting shipping that year in our coastal waters, and in the Gulf and Caribbean, were due to the shortage of ships and planes and to the heavy demands on those we had for troop convoys and other urgent services. Nonetheless it seems clear that full offensive use was not made of land-based air power in the early days of the crisis.

Through the Joint Committee on New Weapons Bush did his best to push the new airborne devices but for some time he made slower progress with the Navy than with the Army.

Deeply troubled by the success of the U-boats, and alarmed lest Germany increase not only the numbers of her submarines but their destructive power by means of new devices, Bush wrote to Admiral King. He expressed doubts whether "the full significance of the modern technical trends is being weighed in the councils where the strategic planning occurs."[6] In the interesting exchange of views which followed by letter and by personal conversation, Bush made it clear that he felt the relations of OSRD with the Navy in the development of weapons to be excellent, but that he believed "that planning at the top level in the absence of the scientific mind was an incomplete and hence dangerous procedure."[7] The upshot of these exchanges was that Admiral King asked Bush to suggest three NDRC scientists to serve as advisers to Admiral Low, the Chief of Staff of the newly created Tenth Fleet.[8] Bush named three Division Chiefs, John T. Tate, Hartley Rowe, and Alfred Loomis. From that time on the co-operation of the Navy and OSRD proved increasingly close and the teamwork in the development of antisubmarine weapons worked wonders.

It would be hard to exaggerate the role played by Secretary Stimson in ensuring effective co-operation between the civilian scientists and the huge organization over which he presided. No one in the War Department approached with keener zest the problem of extracting from scientific research the maximum contribution to the war effort. Again and again he provided the impetus which broke log jams and speeded major

[6]Bush to Admiral E. J. King, April 12, 1943.
[7]Bush's memorandum of April 19, 1943.
[8]See below, p. 40.

problems on their way to solution. When Harvey Bundy, a Boston lawyer who had served him earlier as Assistant Secretary of State, rejoined him in the War Department in 1941 as his special assistant, he gave him as a major assignment the task of following developments on the scientific front, especially as to the atomic bomb. Bundy served with distinction as a member of the Advisory Council of OSRD, helping with unfailing tact the smooth flow of information and advice between the civilian scientists and the top War Department echelons.

Secretary Stimson's interest in radar, first roused by his kinsman Alfred Loomis, the Chief of Section D-1 (later Division 14) of NDRC, never flagged. He made an early flight in a B-24 to see how airborne search radar actually functioned, and he threw his great influence unreservedly behind all those in the Army and in civilian ranks who were striving to make the greatest possible military use of radar and other important scientific developments. To further this end he appointed Dr. Edward L. Bowles of M.I.T., a pioneer in radar research, his special assistant in all matters concerning this new art. Bowles played a great role in bringing civilian science and the High Command, especially the Army Air Forces, closer together. Within the War Department he built up an extraordinarily able group of advisory specialists, and sent them or took them with him into the various theaters, to preach the scientific gospel and promote with enthusiasm, imagination, resourcefulness, and astonishing mastery of detail the full integrated use of new weapons and equipment.

Bush's ties with the Secretary's office remained close. As early as 1939 and 1940 he had suggested, through Army friends, the creation of a new weapons division in the General Staff, through whose agency might be resolved conflicts of opinion between the designing and the using branches of the Army. Nothing came of these suggestions at the time. But out of similar conversations with Secretary Stimson, General Marshall, and General McNarney in 1943 came a War Department directive establishing the New Developments Division of the War Department Special Staff, whose relations with OSRD under its successive Directors, Major General Stephen G. Henry and Brigadier General William A. Borden, were close and cordial.

One of the great achievements of scientists in the war lay in the anticipation of enemy moves and the devising of countermeasures against them. In October 1942, when the submarine threat to our lines of communications seemed — somewhat prematurely — to be gradually being brought under control, Bush pointed out that the trend might be reversed abruptly if the enemy attacked our convoys with homing torpedoes or homing aerial bombs.[9] NDRC was hard at work on countermeasures to the acoustic torpedo long before its introduction by the Germans in August 1943, and foxed them with great success.

But the most exciting story of anticipation of a new weapon was that of the celebrated V-1.

In August and September 1943 the Germans scored some successes with two guided missiles, FX and HS293, a high-angle and a glide bomb.[10] From fragments of these weapons recovered from damaged ships and from information gleaned from prisoners of war, Allied intelligence officers pieced together the story. At the request of the First Lord of the Admiralty the Minister of Aircraft Production set up a technical subcommittee to study the problem, on which NDRC was represented, and Allied scientists worked feverishly on countermeasures. The American countermeasures program centered in the Naval Research Laboratory and in the Airborne Instruments Laboratory of Division 15.

Close on the heels of this important development came secret intelligence that the Germans were engaged on a huge program for larger flying bombs. They had lost the ability to bomb Britain effectively from aircraft but they still had, in London, a target of great size and enormous importance and they now planned to strike at it by long-range flying bombs and rockets.

The story of how the secret intelligence concerning the German "reprisal weapons," V-1 and V-2, was obtained is one of the most interesting of the war, but it lies outside the scope of this study. In helping to piece it together and plan appropriate countermeasures NDRC played a leading role.[11] Long-range bombing missions were dispatched to pound Peenemünde, and other German rocket research centers. Photoreconnaissance indicated that the enemy had installed a hundred or more sites for launching flying bombs and perhaps half a dozen sites for a

---

[9]Bush to Brigadier General R. G. Moses, October 23, 1942. The Germans introduced both these weapons with some success in August 1943.

[10]See below, p. 194.

[11]It was well represented on the committee headed by Major General Stephen G. Henry, which co-ordinated these measures.

R.A.F. views of a V-2 experiment station at Peenemünde, June
1944, before and after heavy attack by R.A.F. Bomber Command

A — shows flak position; B — cradles; C — rockets

In the great Allied advance across Germany after crossing the Rhine,
the British captured this rocket bomb in a forest at Hahnenberg, north
of Rheine, Germany. Other V-2's near by had been destroyed by the
retreating German armies

larger type of rocket. The R.A.F. and the 8th Air Force bombed these sites with increasing fury and destroyed enough of them to slow down the German program and drive the Nazis to other methods of launching.

Meanwhile Allied scientists and intelligence officers racked their brains to determine what would be the pay load in these long-range missiles. Would it be gas, to drench London or the ports of embarkation in which Allied forces would assemble for the invasion of Normandy? Would it be some new incendiary or high explosive or a biological toxin? Might it not be that the Germans had solved the problem of the atomic bomb and were about to launch some of these missiles at long range against the British capital? By February the view in NDRC was that it would probably be a new high explosive, but there was no way of knowing for sure whether or not the missile would be radio-controlled, and therefore subject to jamming.

When the Germans first used the V-1 bombs against Britain on June 12, 1944, six days after the Allied landings in Normandy, the new missile did not lend itself to any countermeasure except direct interception by antiaircraft fire or machine-gun fire from an interceptor plane. A small fraction of the buzz-bombs carried radio transmitters so that radio direction-finding stations along the Channel coasts could plot their paths and figure out the wind conditions over England. The countermeasures experts who had hoped that V-1 would be a guided missile which they could jam were out of luck.

All that could be done was to shoot down the flying bombs, and fortunately for the Allies NDRC had provided them with three superlative new weapons which, combined together, turned the trick. The story of how the SCR-584 radar, the M-9 director, and the proximity fuze enabled British and American gunners to shoot down the flying bombs is told elsewhere in this volume.[12] Here should be noted the importance of the early warning given by Allied intelligence and the careful planning of countermeasures such as the release of the VT-fuze in which Bush and his associates took a leading role.

The V-1 flying bomb employed a pulse-jet engine in which air was forced into the combustion chamber by ram effect and mixed with fuel which was continuously injected into the inrushing air. As the pressure built up, shutters covering the air intakes were forced shut and the com-

[12]See pp. 234–236.

bustion gases were ejected at the rear. This created a suction at the completion of the combustion, causing the shutters to reopen and the cycle to repeat. The V-1 had to be launched at considerable speed before this motor developed sufficient thrust for flight, but once under way it produced speeds of 250 to 400 miles per hour. It was steered by a magnetic compass, kept at a given altitude by a barometric altimeter, and was enabled to turn and dive by an automatic pilot with gyro and clockwork devices.

The V-2's, which began to land in London on September 12, 1944, were long-range rockets weighing fourteen tons with a pay load of one ton of high explosive. The average error on a 200-mile shot was four miles, but London offered a huge target. They were immune to enemy jamming, and so fast that interception by fighter planes and destruction by antiaircraft fire were out of the question, for the missile traveled at 3400 miles per hour. Its maximum speed, attained at fifteen miles from the ground on descent, was 5300 feet per second. Its speed on impact was 3000 feet per second. No satisfactory means of defense was found, except capture of the area from which V-2's could be launched.

The planning of defenses against V-1 and V-2, and the introduction of the proximity fuze for antiaircraft and howitzer fire, brought the civilian scientists into strategic planning at the top level. When the Joint Chiefs decided late in 1944 to permit the ground forces to put the VT-fuze into use for military fire they sent Bush to General Eisenhower's headquarters to advise on how to get the maximum degree of surprise from the introduction of the new weapon, which contributed so greatly to our hard-won victory in the Battle of the Bulge.[13] The success of the operations in which civilian scientists were allowed to share in the staff planning, and the failure to make the most of our opportunities with respect to high-velocity guns throughout the war, show quite clearly what must be sought and what must be avoided in our postwar organization of science for war.

[13]See below, pp. 115–116.

CHAPTER III

THE SEESAW OF SUBMARINE WARFARE

T HE SIDE that loses a war usually writes the best history of it, in order to learn from its mistakes and make that knowledge the cornerstone of success the next time. The Germans, who knew that their submarines had brought them close to victory in 1917, produced far and away the best account of the U-boat war.[1] They noted its lessons, based on them sound tactical doctrine, and planned how to build more and better submarines and to man them better.

"I will show that the U-boat alone can win this war," boasted Grand Admiral Doenitz in 1940. "Nothing is impossible to us." He had almost every reason for confidence: more and better submarines than his predecessors had, and equally bold commanders. Had not Gunther Prien taken his U-boat into Scapa Flow itself on the night of October 13, 1939, and sunk the battleship *Royal Oak?*

When the war began, neither the Axis powers nor the Allies were prepared for intensive submarine warfare. The Germans had only about twenty 500-ton and ten 750-ton oceangoing U-boats. Whereas in 1918 Great Britain alone had 400 destroyers and her allies and associates brought the total close to 900, in 1939 the British went to war with only 180 destroyers. France had 59, but most of these were needed in the Mediterranean. The British had fitted their Asdic sound gear on 165 destroyers and 54 smaller craft. We had about 60 destroyers fitted with echo-ranging gear, and some of these were transferred to Great Britain in the exchange of bases for overage destroyers. The establishment of scientific interchange with Great Britain brought us information of much value concerning subsurface warfare. At the outset of the war, British antisubmarine craft carried no radar, no long-range aircraft were assigned to antisubmarine patrols, and the short-range aircraft carried 100-pound bombs quite unsuited to their task.

In the First World War the greatest advantage enjoyed by the British was their geographical position, which enabled them to block the exits

[1]Arno Spindler, *Der Handelskrieg mit U-Booten.*

from Germany to the Atlantic. Now General Geography had turned
traitor. The conquest of Norway, Holland, Belgium, and France gave
the Germans a broad ocean front of 2500 miles with ports outflanking
Great Britain from Bordeaux to Narvik. Operating from these longer
coastlines the U-boats steadily increased their kills. The Germans strove
to launch a score or more submarines a month and, as their losses were
very few, the number of U-boats at sea rose steadily. Shipping losses
were 515,000 tons in March 1941, 589,000 in April, 498,000 in May,
329,000 in June, when the nights were short. Then the British stopped
publishing monthly figures. As the British improved their antisubmarine
ordnance and the range of their patrol planes, the U-boats operated
further west and began to attack on the surface by night, diving deep
when hunted and varying their depth as a counter to the Asdics. During
the winter the British introduced radar into their surface craft and patrol
planes to spot U-boats on the surface. They thus greatly increased the
area covered by search and the number of sightings. When the U-boats
began to attack convoys at night in groups, they made considerable use
of wireless to direct and assemble the "wolf packs." This gave away their
position to the high-frequency direction finder, or "Huff-Duff."

Aircraft of Coastal Command, in the first two years of the war, es-
corted 4947 merchant convoys, made 587 attacks on U-boats, and flew
some 55,000,000 miles. In May 1941, they launched a vigorous offensive
in the transit areas through the Bay of Biscay and north of Scotland.
They did not get many kills,[2] but they drove the U-boats under. This fact
alone was of great importance. When a submarine submerged, her speed
dropped to two or three knots. She could, it is true, put on full submerged
speed, say six or seven knots, but if she kept it up she would exhaust her
batteries in less than an hour. Passage through the Bay of Biscay became
a long and risky business. The U-boat remained submerged by day, surfacing at night to recharge her batteries and ventilate. On the surface,
even though she maintained radio silence, she could be detected by radar.
Except in its gravity the submarine war was becoming more and more
unlike that of 1917. Then the U-boats worked as genuine "submarines,"
diving by day and attacking submerged, surfacing at night. They were
individualists with a free hand, working in the limited areas of coastal

---

[2]The Germans lost three leading submarine aces, Otto Kretschmer, Gunther Prien, and
Joachim Schepki, in March 1941, and a fourth, Fritz Julius Lemp, early in May.

waters and the close approaches to the British Isles. As 1941 wore on the U-boats were operating as submersibles, diving only when forced to do so, and attacking at night on the surface as torpedo boats. They reconnoitered and attacked in groups, under the orders of the admiral on shore, who controlled all their activities from the moment they sailed until their return to port.

When the United States entered the war the Germans found happy hunting ground on our Eastern seaboard. By that time they had about 200 oceangoing submarines and were commissioning about 20 a month. The transatlantic convoys were often hard nuts to crack,[3] but our Navy was too short of antisubmarine craft, both surface and air, to start coastal convoys until May 1942. The system was gradually extended to the Gulf of Mexico, the Caribbean, and the South American coast as vessels became available. As the coastal route was too long to cover adequately by patrol, the sinkings, especially of tankers and large ships, meanwhile reached catastrophic proportions. Six and a quarter million gross tons of shipping, over 40 per cent of the total loss to submarines during the war, were destroyed in the year 1942. Twenty-five ships were sunk off the mouths of the Mississippi, 25 more off the coast of Florida between Key West and Daytona Beach. Some of the German submarines were minelayers. These closed Chesapeake Bay to traffic for two days in June and three in September, and bottled up New York Harbor for three days, November 13 to 15, 1942.[4]

To beat the submarines and make the Atlantic safe for the ships carrying the troops and supplies needed to help breach Germany's European Fortress required prodigious efforts of Britain, Canada, and the United States. Huge programs of antisubmarine craft expanded the Royal Canadian Navy to close to 700 vessels, and gave the United States 306 of the new destroyer escorts between April and December, 1943. In merchant shipbuilding all three nations performed miracles. American yards turned out the hitherto unimaginable total of a million tons a month.

To direct this vast effort required the utmost in organization and administrative skill, and the utmost was forthcoming. While the Bureau of Ships, the Maritime Commission, and American shipbuilders com-

---

[3]Four U-boats were sunk in an attack on one convoy in December 1941.

[4]Other ports closed for brief periods in 1942 because of mines were Jacksonville, Charleston, and Wilmington.

bined to set all-time records, Admiral King reorganized the Navy command, creating under his direct command, in May 1943, that extraordinary organization the Tenth Fleet, with Rear Admiral Francis S. Low as its Chief of Staff.

The Tenth [says Admiral King] was a fleet without a ship. However, this highly specialized command co-ordinated and directed our naval forces in the Battle of the Atlantic, making available the latest intelligence to the Commander in Chief, U.S. Atlantic Fleet, and to other fleet and sea frontier commanders who directed the actual operations at sea, and supplying antisubmarine training and operating procedures to our forces afloat. The Tenth Fleet correlated the antisubmarine developments of the various technical bureaus of the Navy Department and the fleet training schools concerned with antisubmarine activities. In addition, it worked closely with the General Staff of the United States Army and with the British Admiralty and Canadian Naval Headquarters to avoid duplication and confusion, and to insure that maximum effort would be directed against the German underseas fleet.

When forced to cope with U-boats off our coast in 1942, our Navy was lamentably short of aircraft and surface vessels. The heavy requirements for troop convoys in the Atlantic and Pacific absorbed most of our available antisubmarine craft. We had turned over 50 old destroyers to the British in exchange for bases. To help us get coastal convoys started the British allocated 24 trawlers and 10 corvettes, and recast the system of transatlantic convoys to release other patrol craft. Wherever convoys could be introduced losses fell to modest proportions, as the U-boats promptly shifted to fields where the pickings were easier. Though convoying was of great value, it was still not enough. Army and Navy aircraft, assisted by the Civil Air Patrol, did the best they could to cover our coastal waters, but at first their numbers were inadequate and their kills were few. Heavy bombers might pound the factories where U-boats were built and the dock areas in the ports where they refitted, but the Nazis covered their submarine pens with concrete slabs thick enough to stop blockbusters. More ships and more planes of longer range were in part the answer, but both ships and planes needed new detection devices and new weapons for the kill.

At sea we seemed to be losing the war. During June 1942, an average of 48 U-boats operating at sea sank 143 ships.[5] Each U-boat was living

---

[5] So grave was the peril that some fanciful projects received respectful attention. On the Habakkuk project, originated by the British in September 1942, for an iceberg aircraft carrier of 2,000,000 tons, see the *New York Times*, March 1, 1946.

long enough to sink 20 ships. They remained at sea for long periods, obtaining food, fuel, and torpedoes from "cow" or supply U-boats, each of which took care of about 10 U-boats.

Subsurface warfare went through an extraordinary transformation from 1941 to 1945. The United States Navy, like the British, started the war with well-developed echo-ranging gear, but its ordnance, since the depth charge was practically the same as used in the First World War, was obsolete against a submerged submarine of modern construction. Operations research, still in its infancy, had been limited to some study of peacetime maneuvers. Operating personnel and methods had not yet been tested in the crucible of war. Training of specialists in operation and maintenance had been undertaken, but it was still far from satisfactory. Perhaps of even greater importance, definite knowledge as to the behavior of sound in the ocean was still lacking. Clearly the laws governing underwater sound required further study in order to formulate reliable operating procedures and to govern the design of sonar gear.

Fortunately our Navy had entered into a most effective and fruitful partnership with NDRC. It must be emphasized at once that the outcome was a Navy victory won with civilian help; and that considerable portions of the story remain shrouded in secrecy.

It may well be that the greatest contribution made by scientists to subsurface warfare lay in the application of statistical analysis to the records of operations and in the development of doctrine. Tactics had to be improved for old gear and devised for new. Much of the new antisubmarine equipment was relatively unfamiliar to naval officers, and in the hectic days of 1942 no headquarters staff had at its disposal an adequate number of persons sufficiently versed in modern mathematical techniques to derive from the statistics of past and current operations important tactical lessons.

On the basis of combat results and laboratory experiments the members of the Antisubmarine Warfare Operations Research Group (ASWORG) established the basic laws of visual and radar sightings and devised scientific search plans which made the most of the aircraft and surface ships available and increased the probability of sightings. To keep German submarines from bringing cargoes of tin and rubber from the Far East to Europe, barrier patrols were designed to close the gap between Africa and Brazil. Similar analytical studies were made the basis for radar and sonar search plans, for air-sea rescue, and for the use of the Magnetic Airborne Detector and the radio sonobuoy.

The operations analysts pointed out that the U-boats, when they heard our pings becoming louder and faster, estimated the moment of our attack and dove below the sonar beam. The remedy for this was the creeping attack carried out by two escort vessels, the first maintaining sound contact at a fixed range and ping interval while it coached the second attacker at very low speed over the U-boat by signals.

On their side the U-boats created disturbances by backing down, turning sharply, or ejecting chemicals that generated clouds of bubbles. These reflected strong echoes and thus simulated a second or third U-boat to confuse the attacker. The Allies broadcast to their patrol craft information about this trick and instructions to their sonar and Asdic operators on how to read through false targets. Futile attacks on clouds of bubbles ceased.

Because an aircraft equipped with radar has a search rate against surfaced submarines ten times that of surface craft equipped with radar, the importance of installing radar on our patrol planes was recognized early. Ten pre-production microwave sets were hastily assembled at the Radiation Laboratory early in 1942 and installed in B-18's commanded by the late Colonel William C. Dolan, AAF, which sank their first U-boats on April 1 and May 1. They formed part of the First Sea Search Attack Group activated in July 1942, under Colonel Dolan's command.

Fourteen more 10-cm. sets, designed for use in Liberators, were manufactured on a crash basis by the Research Construction Corporation and delivered to the British between August and December, 1942. These came just in time to play a useful part in the great battle raging in the Bay of Biscay.

In the first two and a half years of the war Doenitz's jibe that "an aircraft can no more kill a U-boat than a crow can kill a mole" had had some truth in it. Coastal Command damaged upwards of fifty enemy submarines but had been credited with very few sinkings. Radar had increased the number of sightings, but the attacks, though executed boldly, lacked a knockout punch. This was provided in May 1942, by equipping Wellington bombers with searchlights for night attacks and depth charges filled with Torpex, a mixture of RDX, TNT, and aluminum — superior in destructive power to the previous depth charges by about 50 per cent.

The number of long-range aircraft operating in the Bay steadily rose and the sightings and kills of U-boats mounted.

What the Germans needed was warning of the patrol plane's approach. They got it by equipping their submarines with search receivers which indicated whenever the vessels were "floodlit" by radar, long before the submarine could be detected on the radar screen.[6] This gave the U-boat warning in plenty of time to submerge before the airplane or surface vessel came within attacking range. As soon as the search receivers got into use in September 1942, the number of radar sightings rapidly dwindled. Unless the British could find an answer, their splendid counter-offensive seemed doomed to failure.

The answer was 10-cm. radar installed in aircraft and surface vessels, for the search receivers designed to pick up transmissions at 200 mega-cycles could do nothing with microwaves. The Nazis, formerly so confident, grew panicky as the patrol planes, equipped with the new 10-cm. sets, dove on the U-boats unannounced. The Nazis could not for a long while figure out the reason, and, believing the British had switched to infrared detection, made frantic efforts to counter that. They were disappointed at their failure to do more damage to the huge armada of over a thousand vessels which moved from United States and British ports to the coasts of North Africa. Although some 40 U-boats were lying in wait, they sank only 23 ships during November. The Germans had concentrated their U-boats on both sides of Gibraltar, mustering every submarine that could reach the area within ten days. "Defense in these African waters," Doenitz gloomily reported, "was very effective and U-boat losses were correspondingly high." Heads fell. Doenitz succeeded Grand Admiral Raeder as Commander in Chief at the end of January, and announced a fight to the finish. "The entire German Navy," he declared, "will henceforth be put into the service of inexorable U-boat warfare."

The campaign launched by the Nazis early in 1943 was indeed menacing. Desperate efforts were made to regain the ascendancy which the U-boats had enjoyed in November 1942, when nearly a million tons of shipping were sunk. The mole fought back against the crow. Running submerged at night along the transit routes through the Bay or north of Scotland, the U-boats surfaced by day to speed their passage, and, if attacked by patrol planes, put up a stiff battle with their flak guns.

[6]Search receivers outrange radar systems.

As the weeks passed punctuated by staccato bursts of fighting, the numbers of U-boats operating in the Atlantic mounted steadily. In general half the submarines available were in port and half at sea. Of those at sea half were in the combat zone and half in transit. In the winter of 1942–1943 as many as 70 to 80 submarines were operating simultaneously in the combat area, chiefly in wolf packs in the 600-mile gap in mid-Atlantic, out of reach of shore-based aircraft. Allied shipping losses reached three quarters of a million tons in the first three weeks of March 1943. Defending one convoy the British destroyer *Harvester* rammed a U-boat but was herself disabled and sunk by two torpedoes from another craft. The Free French corvette *Aconit*, in company, finished off the first of the U-boats, picked up the survivors of the *Harvester*, and rammed and sank the second submarine, which had dealt the British destroyer her deathblow.

At the end of March the tide turned against the U-boats. First among the factors was the closing of the gap in the mid-Atlantic. Liberators equipped with extra gas tanks and microwave radar, and navigating in part at least by Loran, enabled the British, American, and Canadian Air Forces to establish a shuttle service between the United Kingdom, Iceland, and Newfoundland. These squadrons of Very Long Range (VLR) aircraft burst in on the wolf packs unheralded, warned and diverted our convoys, protected them like an umbrella, and soon made it impracticable for the U-boats to refuel in midocean, as they had been doing with impunity. These VLR patrol planes were soon reinforced by aircraft from the new escort carriers, the first of which vessels entered the fray in March and scored its first success in April. The magnificent exploits of U.S.S. *Bogue* and U.S.S. *Card* won for these escort carriers the coveted Presidential Unit Citation. Support groups organized around these and similar vessels took the offensive in hunting out the U-boats and harried them relentlessly.

At the same time the number of escort vessels steadily increased and their equipment improved. Admiral Cochrane's superbly executed destroyer escort program paid big dividends. The DE's swarmed on the convoy routes admirably equipped with centimeter radar, with sound gear for close-in detection, and with the spigot mortar for "Hedgehog" attacks with forward-thrown, faster-sinking Torpex depth charges.

Smaller surface craft made good use of the Mousetrap. By June 1943, the U-boats had largely withdrawn from the North Atlantic. Speaking at the Guildhall on June 30, Prime Minister Churchill proudly boasted that hardly a single Allied ship was sunk in the North Atlantic between May 17 and the end of June.[7]

When U-boats used their wireless to assemble a wolf pack the location could be plotted by British and American Huff-Duff stations. Land-based and carrier-based aircraft equipped with radar soon scoured the area. If the U-boat submerged, the planes parachuted several expendable radio sonobuoys whose hydrophones could detect U-boat noises. These activated the radio transmitter which summoned near-by planes or surface escorts to close in and start their search with sonar or Asdic.

It was clear, however, from intelligence reports, that the battle was not over. The Germans were fitting their U-boats with radar to detect approaching aircraft and with greatly increased antiaircraft armament. They had also instructed their submarine commanders to make less use of their radio to prevent location by the Huff-Duff. When they appeared on the transit routes the *Luftwaffe* contributed long-range fighter patrols in the Bay which the British countered with Beaufighters and Mosquitoes. The battle raged in the skies as well as on and under the surface. In August the Germans startled the world with the first successful guided missile, the glider bomb HS293, and followed it almost immediately by the Gnat acoustic homing torpedo. This formidable weapon might have taken a far heavier toll had its introduction not been anticipated by Allied scientists.

A great improvement in the coverage in mid-Atlantic came when Coastal Command, at the end of October, 1943, began operating Very Long Range aircraft from Terceira in the Azores. By this time the U-boats were beginning to adopt more cautious tactics, for their losses had been staggering. In the last four months of 1939 they had lost nine submarines; in 1940, 22; in 1941, 35; and in 1942, 85. All these losses were more than offset by new construction. In the single month of May, 1943, 42 were sunk, a net loss of 22 as only 20 new craft were completed. For the whole year 1943, the total of German losses reached 237. In such a struggle, moreover, the more daring commanders were likely to be the first to be lost, for they pressed home their attacks more boldly.

[7] The U-boats returned to the North Atlantic routes in September wthout much success.

Aircraft had played the foremost role as submarine killers, thanks to their high search rate, their admirable microwave radar, and the new weapons they carried. They had used Magnetic Airborne Detection effectively to cork the Strait of Gibraltar, had employed with success the radio sonobuoy and other secret airborne devices, and had found the rocket an excellent antisubmarine weapon.

"For some months past," wrote Grand Admiral Doenitz on December 14, 1943, "the enemy has rendered the U-boat war ineffective. He has achieved this object, not through superior tactics or strategy, but through his superiority in the field of science; this finds its expression in the modern battle weapon — detection. By this means he has torn our sole offensive weapon in the war against the Anglo-Saxons from our hands. It is essential to victory that we make good our scientific disparity and thereby restore to the U-boat its fighting qualities."[8]

Despite this note of gloom, and the heavy losses in submarines during 1943, the Germans opened the campaign of 1944 with more U-boats than ever. They had equipped them not only with radar, to detect approaching airplanes, but with heavy AA armament to shoot them down, and with the Naxos search receiver designed to pick up 10-cm. radar transmissions. This device fortunately did not prove nearly so effective as they hoped, but the vigor of Germany's counteroffensive on the scientific front is attested by the fact that they had made good progress with a search receiver for 3-cm. radar.

In the early months of 1944 it was clear that Doenitz was husbanding his U-boats in the hope that they might play a decisive part in repelling the impending invasion of Europe. In the meanwhile he fitted a considerable number of them with *Schnörkel*, a retractable air intake and exhaust pipe which could be raised or lowered from inside the boat, and which enabled the U-boats to run on their diesels at periscope depth, charging their batteries while submerged. Elaborate precautions were taken to coat the top of the *Schnörkel* with a camouflage which it was hoped would not reflect a radar echo. This pipe, projecting above water a little lower than the periscope, was a difficult target for aircraft to detect and attack. Although its use increased the discomfort of the crew,

---

[8]To Dr. Karl Keupfmueller, charging him with the formation of a German Naval Scientific Directional Staff.

Depth charge spells doom for a U–boat

The end of a U–boat

they managed in the closing months of the war to operate without surfacing for weeks at a time, providing personnel on board with vitamin
pills and daily sun-lamp treatments to preserve their health.

On their side the Allies greatly increased their patrol vessels and aircraft, drilled their sound men so they would not be duped by German
sonic decoys, and installed airborne search receivers for intercepting and
homing on enemy radar transmissions. Much attention was also given to
the co-ordination of air and surface attacks.

In May, Coastal Command, reinforced by the American Air Force
and Navy squadrons, opened a brilliant offensive in Norwegian waters
against U-boats leaving to join the forces of the *Kriegsmarine* in the Bay
of Biscay for a joint attack on our invasion forces in the English Channel. The pursuit ranged widely over the Eastern Atlantic and into Arctic
waters and few U-boats got through. Those who did joined up with
U-boats based on French ports for a bitter struggle in the Channel and
the eastern portion of the Bay of Biscay, fighting back desperately with
their antiaircraft guns against increased attacks from the air. Taking
heavy losses, they were unable to interfere with the greatest of amphibious operations, and it was ten days after the landings in Normandy
before the first U-boat was operating on *Schnörkel* in the combat zone.

After June 8 few U-boats were caught on the surface and Allied patrol
craft resigned themselves to endless searching for periscopes, *Schnörkel*,
and oil slicks. In this wearisome hunt microwave radar of high resolution
proved its value again and again, and the radio sonobuoys gave the fliers
extra ears that could stand watch under water. Few U-boats got through
to our shipping lanes and many paid for the attempt with their lives.
As an historian of the Coastal Command well said, "The weapon which
was to cut our communications in the Atlantic had failed even to cut
them in the Channel."

As the advance of the Allied Expeditionary Forces made it clear to
the Germans that they would soon lose the use of the French coast,
they began to send the U-boats northward, producing a new flock of
hard-fought actions. A few, by using *Schnörkel*, penetrated into the
Channel, but only nine ships were sunk by U-boats of the thousands
operating there.

In the last phase of the European war the Germans tried to complete
for duty two new types of submarine — a heavy cruiser of 1500 tons

with high underwater speed, and a smaller craft of 300 tons. By this
time the steady pounding from the 8th Air Force and the R.A.F. had
hamstrung German industry and the war ended before these new craft
could be tested in action. In the last month of the European war the
U-boats made a determined effort to break through to our Eastern seaboard in considerable strength, but they lost five submarines in the
attempt and were not successful in reaching their goal until, after V-E
Day, they came in peacefully to surrender.

After Doenitz's tribute to the part played by Allied scientists in the
defeat of the U-boat it is almost superfluous to say more. The figures of
German losses in submarines and Allied losses and gains in merchant
shipping must be tabulated.

| Year | German Subs Sunk (number) | Allied Ship-ping Sunk | New Construction | | | Net Gains or Losses |
| | | | U.S. | British | Total | |
			(in thousands of tons)			
1939 (4 mos.)	9	810	101	231	332	−478
1940	22	4,407	439	780	1,219	−3,188
1941	35	4,398	1,169	815	1,984	−2,414
1942	85	8,245	5,339	1,843	7,182	−1,063
1943	237	3,611	12,384	2,201	14,585	+10,974
1944	241	1,422	11,639	1,710	13,349	+11,927
1945 (4 mos.)	153	458	3,551	283	3,834	+3,376
TOTALS	782	23,351	34,622	7,863	42,485	+19,134

The pattern of subsurface warfare in the Pacific was very different
from that in the Atlantic. The Germans, regarding the submarine as
their best weapon against Britain and the United States, concentrated
their naval effort on the use of the U-boat as a commerce destroyer, and
almost won the war with it. Although convoys proved a countermeasure
of the utmost importance their use resulted in a great slowing down of
shipping. The fastest ships, relying on their speed, could in general sail
independently. A convoy has to sail at the speed of the slowest vessel,
over routes which are generally longer than normal.

The great danger from the U-boats made Allied operations in the
Atlantic down to the landings in Normandy largely a defensive operation, though the R.A.F. and Royal Navy took a heavy toll of German
shipping through bombing, mining, and surface attacks. The Allied task
primarily was to put more and more pressure on the U-boats until a
point was reached at which they could stand it no longer and quit until

they could develop new tactics. So severe was our counteroffensive that the German submarine forces took losses two or three times as heavy as those they used to consider excessive in the First World War. But still the U-boats kept coming out and their crews did not mutiny.

The Japanese had at one time about 70 oceangoing submarines, whose speed of 22 knots on the surface and eight knots submerged compared favorably with submarines of other nations. They could not safely dive as deep as German or American craft, but they fought to the limit. Our antisubmarine craft pursued them with equal vigor, and one of them, U.S.S. *England*, set a war record by destroying six submerged Japanese submarines in a period of eleven days with the help of sonar gear.

The Japanese used their submarines for two primary purposes: as adjuncts to their fleet and for supply to cut-off bases. The latter, as events showed, had no great effect on the course of the war, but the Japanese submarines inflicted heavy losses on our naval vessels. They sank the *Yorktown* and the destroyer *Hammann* at Midway, the *Wasp* on September 15, 1942, and torpedoed the *Saratoga* twice during the first year of the war. They damaged the heavy cruiser *Chester* and many other craft, sank the antiaircraft cruiser *Juneau* November 13, 1942, the escort carrier *Liscome Bay* in November 1943, the destroyer escort *Shelton* in September 1944, and the heavy cruiser *Indianapolis* on July 30, 1945. Against our own submarines they proved Japan's most effective weapon.

Their losses were heavy: three in 1941, 22 in 1942, 21 in 1943, 35 in 1944, and 24 in 1945. Of these 105 submarines sunk or captured at sea, 23 were credited in Admiral King's reports to United States submarines, and two to British submarines.

Although the protection of our task forces against submarines remained a problem requiring destroyer escort and combat air patrols, and affording an opportunity of using some of the advanced techniques developed in the Atlantic, the protection of merchant ships from underwater attack was not a major task for us in the Pacific. Small, special convoys operated between San Francisco and Pearl Harbor, San Francisco and the South Sea Islands, Seattle and Alaska, and Seattle and the Aleutians, but practically all of our shipping in the Pacific was able to operate independently.

It was we who made commerce destroying by submarines a major part of our Pacific offensive. The lack of sufficient shipping to tie together effectively her sprawling empire was Japan's Achilles' heel, and we attacked it relentlessly, by every means at our disposal. Here our submarines proved our best weapon. "At a conservative estimate," declared Admiral King, "they sank, in addition to many combatant ships, nearly two thirds of the merchant shipping which Japan lost during the war. They made it more difficult for the enemy to consolidate his forward positions, to reinforce his threatened areas, and to pile up in Japan an adequate reserve of fuel oil, rubber, and other loot from his newly conquered territory."

Including only enemy merchant ships of 1000 tons or over, our submarines destroyed by gunfire and torpedoes over 1000 vessels, of so much tonnage that by the end of the war the Japanese merchant marine had virtually ceased to exist.

	Ships Sunk	Total Tonnage
1942	134	580,390
1943	284	1,341,968
1944	492	2,387,780
1945	132	469,872
	1,042	4,780,010[9]

Our submarines took the offensive from the beginning of the war in the Pacific. Admiral King credited them with one battleship, the *Kongo;* the carriers *Soryu, Shinano, Shokaku,* and *Unryu;* the escort carriers *Chuyo, Jinyo, Otaka,* and *Unyo;* the heavy cruisers *Atago, Kako,* and *Maya;* 9 light cruisers; 43 destroyers; and 189 smaller vessels. They also performed reconnaissance, rescue, supply, and lifeguard duties, evacuated personnel from Corregidor, and delivered supplies and equipment to guerillas in the Philippines. They rescued more than 500 aviators and provided intelligence of the utmost importance. The advance information they furnished our surface and air forces prior to the Battle of Leyte Gulf played a large part in that victory.

Considerations of security preclude a detailed analysis of the many contributions of NDRC to the effectiveness of our submarines. The radar they carried was not of Division 14 origin but their radar search

[9]Our submarines sank or destroyed, chiefly by gunfire, large numbers of smaller craft not included in these figures, especially in the latter part of the war, when few large enemy merchant ships remained afloat.

receivers had been developed by Division 15. Many of the devices Division 6 produced for antisubmarine use were installed on our submarines, sometimes in modified form, to great advantage. The careful studies of underwater conditions made by that division and the maps based on them enabled submarine commanders to hide at times over rocky bottoms in tropical waters where snapping shrimp made such a noise that it masked the sound of the submarine.[10]

Temperature gradients were not likely to affect Asdic ranges seriously around the British Isles, but they were troublesome for the stalker of submarines in the Mediterranean and worse yet in Japanese waters. The Bathythermograph became standard equipment on submarines, which by means of this instrument could seek out a suitable temperature gradient, or thermocline, and hide there with less risk of detection.

The war cost the Allies 4773 merchant ships of 23,000,000 gross tons sunk by enemy action. A total of 996 Axis submarines were sunk, and 221 large and scores of midget submarines fell into Allied hands after V-E and V-J Days. The British and Canadians received credit for sinking 70 per cent of the enemy submarines and the United States credit for 30 per cent.

These figures give but an imperfect idea of the stakes of the game. The defeat of the U-boats made it possible to keep supplies flowing to Great Britain and Russia and to transport to North Africa, Italy, and France the armies which forced Germany to surrender. In the Pacific the Japanese submarines failed in the long run to interfere with the freedom of Allied naval forces to operate where and when they chose. Allied submarines, on the offensive from the outset, destroyed the maritime communications which were the weakest link in the Japanese Co-Prosperity Sphere. Once they were gone, it fell apart like a house of cards, leaving the main islands exposed to attacks by sea and air that reduced Japan's cities to ashes.

When the war in Europe ended, the Germans were about to send to sea submarines which could operate for weeks without surfacing and could make such high speed under water as to upset the whole Allied defense system. Even without atomic power and atomic missiles the

[10]Many other fish, including croakers and drummers, contributed to the bedlam of noise in shallow waters.

submarine remains a most dangerous weapon. With them, it might prove more formidable than the long-range bomber. If we make mistakes enough in postwar years, a revived Germany or some other European power might think that it could win dominion of the world as Germany twice so nearly did by subsurface warfare. Batters have been known to hit a home run with two strikes against them.

CHAPTER IV

NAVAL WARFARE ON AND ABOVE THE SURFACE

IN THE early years of World War II there was a widespread tendency to underrate sea power. The extravagant assertions of the champions of air power had made a deep impression on the public mind, reinforced by the success of the brilliantly conceived German conquest of Norway and the hammering administered to the British naval forces when the Nazis captured Crete. Although Malta stood fast under repeated bombings, the Axis had cut the British line of communications from Gibraltar to Suez, and forced the ships supplying the fleet in the Eastern Mediterranean and the army in Egypt to take the long route around the Cape. With the submarines taking a heavy toll of merchant shipping, this loss of the Mediterranean route was a punishing blow. It is 11,393 nautical miles to Suez from Plymouth, and 12,200 from New York, by the routes around the Cape of Good Hope.

It was a terrific assignment that had fallen to the Royal Navy when the British fought on alone after the fall of France. Before the successful Japanese air attack on the *Prince of Wales* and *Repulse* on December 10, 1941, the Royal Navy had lost the battle cruiser *Hood*, the battleships *Royal Oak* and *Barham*, and three of the six aircraft carriers with which it started the war. The *Courageous* had been torpedoed by a U-boat off the Western Approaches a fortnight after the war began. The *Glorious* encountered nearly the entire German surface fleet off Norway on June 8, 1940, and went down under the gunfire of the battleships *Scharnhorst* and *Gneisenau*. The *Ark Royal*, which had survived repeated sinkings in the German press, fell at last to a U-boat east of Gibraltar on November 14, 1941.[1]

The failure of the *Luftwaffe*, which it is true had been conceived as an auxiliary to ground troops rather than as a strategic bombing force, to reduce Britain to surrender had led some champions of air power to

[1] The carrier *Hermes* was sunk on April 9, 1942, by Japanese aircraft off Ceylon, and the *Eagle* on August 11, 1942, by a U-boat in the Mediterranean.

moderate their language. The British Navy continued to operate two fleets in the Mediterranean, with distinguished success. One of its admirals pointed out that the lesson of the war in that inland sea was that "you can go anywhere with ships under your own umbrella of aircraft, but you can't go anywhere if you have no umbrella and the other fellow has the aircraft."

The task of sea power is to deny one's enemies the use of the sea and to ensure its safe use by one's own nation and its allies. The more important the use of the sea in a given war, the higher are the stakes for which the two sides are playing. Never have the stakes been as high as in the Second World War. The British Isles were the base both for the invasion of the continent and for the strategic bombing of Germany. The Germans could have crossed the Channel with ease after Dunkirk had it not been for the ships that stood between them and the dominion of the world. On the free flow of supplies to the British, American, and Canadian ground and air forces building up in Britain depended all our chances of success in establishing a front in France.

Among the gravest of the logistic problems was the supply of Russia, to keep the pressure of her enormous armies on the *Wehrmacht* and make it certain that when D-Day came the bulk of the German forces would be pinned on the Eastern Front. Some supplies could be sent to Vladivostok, some via the Persian Gulf, despite inadequate port facilities and rail and road transport. But the best route was that to the Murmansk coast and against it the Germans massed submarines, long-range bombers, and strong surface forces, based in northern Norway. For a time, which seemed an age to the hard-pressed Russians, sailings were interrupted on this vital artery. Yet in February 1945 the British Admiralty could proudly boast: —

During the past forty-two months our Russian ally has safely received no less than 91.6 per cent of the vast amount of war supplies shipped by the northern route, the great proportion of which have been convoyed under British escort.

In the Pacific, sea power worked even greater miracles. The size of that vast ocean is difficult to grasp, unless one has had to fight in it. It "occupies more space than all the land on the globe. It would hold two Atlantics and still have room for a few Mediterraneans. Better than half of all the world's water is in the Pacific. Its greatest north-south dimension is 9,300 miles and its greatest width, 10,300." The defensive strength of Japan was so great that even if she had not succeeded in sinking four of our battleships at Pearl Harbor and damaging four more, we should not have sent this battle force to save the Philippines. A large part of naval opinion the world over agreed with the view expressed by Captain Taketomi of the Imperial Japanese Navy: —

The line connecting the Bonins, Marianas Islands and Palau is the country's southern defense line. When this line is protected Japan will be able perfectly to control the North Pacific.

While we hold this control no economic blockade is possible. Furthermore this line cuts in two the line of the United States footholds in the Pacific running from San Francisco to Hawaii, Guam, the Philippines and China.[2]

Probably the wisest strategy for the Japanese, once they had decided on war, would have been to leave both Hawaii and the Philippines alone, and to concentrate their first attacks on the British and Dutch, in the hope that the Congress of the United States might wrangle for months over a declaration of war. This would give Japan a chance to move in on Australia before our forces could interpose. Instead the Japanese sent six carriers against Pearl Harbor, in an attack resembling Admiral St. George Lyster's brilliant victory at Taranto. It proved even more successful. No landing had been planned, for the object of the sneak raid had been simply to neutralize our forces, and gain complete freedom for the drives to the southward against Malaya, the Philippines, and the Dutch East Indies. These were carried out with great skill and astonishing speed and economy of force. Firmly established on the Melanesian Shield with the priceless advantage of the "unsinkable aircraft carriers," the islands of the Caroline, Marianas, and Palau archipelagos, the Japanese proceeded to move south against our hastily reinforced lines of communications with Australia and New Zealand.

Naval history entered a new phase in May and June 1942 when in two successive naval actions neither surface fleet came within sight or gun range of the other. In the first of these great carrier actions, the Battle of the Coral Sea, we traded the *Lexington* for the small *Shoho*, damaged

---

[2]Willard Price, *Japan's Islands of Mystery*, John Day Co., New York, 1944, pp. 13, 14.
The *Nevada*, which had been beached to prevent sinking, the *California* and *West Virginia*, which had been sunk, and the *Pennsylvania*, *Tennessee*, and *Maryland*, much less severely damaged, were all restored to fight again.

the *Ryukaku*, and turned back a Japanese force directed against southern
New Guinea. In the second, aided by knowledge of the Japanese dispo-
sitions, we sank four of the six carriers which had attacked Pearl Harbor.[3]
This magnificent victory at Midway, though it cost us the *Yorktown*,
not only turned back a major Japanese offensive, it greatly weakened the
resistance they could offer to the offensive-defensive campaign which we
opened in August in the Solomons. Before that grueling series of land
and sea actions was over, we had lost the *Wasp* to a Japanese submarine
on September 15, and the *Hornet* to a brilliantly co-ordinated air attack
in the hard-fought action off Santa Cruz on October 26.[4] By this time
we had only one carrier operational in the Pacific, the damaged but un-
beatable *Enterprise*.

It was a far cry from these closely matched carrier duels of 1942 to
the great sweeps of our Pacific forces deep into enemy waters in 1944
and 1945. This huge armada, known as the Fifth Fleet when it was under
Admiral Spruance's command and as the Third Fleet when under Admiral Halsey's, was something new in naval warfare, in its ability both
to maintain itself so long at sea and to cope with land-based air power and
submarines while thousands of miles from home and close to enemy bases.
In part the difference was caused by sheer weight of numbers, due to
our ability to turn out one after another the huge carriers of the *Essex*
class, the lighter carriers built on cruiser hulls of the *Independence* class,
and the fast battleships and smaller craft that screened them. Some
might argue that their numbers made them irresistible, that in the creation of a fleet as well as of an atomic bomb there is a critical size which,
once exceeded, unleashes an irresistible force. But in the case of the Fleet
mere size is not enough. If our naval building and the evolution of logistics had enabled us to send Admiral Spruance's huge force to Okinawa
in 1942 instead of 1945, without the new weapons and devices scientists
had made available meanwhile, the Japanese might have rubbed their
hands and said: "The bigger they come, the harder they fall."

The first requisite for such deep sweeps into enemy waters was protection against air and underwater attack. The marvelous development

[3]*Kaga, Akagi, Hiryu,* and *Soryu.* Of the two others, the *Shokaku,* damaged at Coral Sea
and Santa Cruz, was finally sunk in the Battle of the Philippine Sea, June 19, 1944. The
Zuikaku was at last sunk by our carrier aircraft on October 25, 1944.
[4]Planes from the *Saratoga* sank the *Ryujo* on August 24, 1942, in the Battle of the Eastern Solomons.

of radar had extended the eyes of the Fleet, scanning the ocean for surfaced submarines and the skies for bogeys, to more than a hundred and fifty miles at all times of day or night regardless of weather. The Fleet was screened against submarines not only by destroyers and destroyer escorts with their sonar gear and their greatly improved antisubmarine ordnance, but by the planes of the antisubmarine patrol equipped with radar, rockets, and better depth charges.

The primary defense of a task force on the move was a combat air patrol. This could be bigger, with four carriers operating in company, taking their turns at the duty. And thanks to radar it could be much better handled. The controller got information of the appearance of hostile planes long enough in advance to vector out his fighters to intercept them, giving the task force not a passive outer rampart of protection but a blazing, whirling, diving fury which sent 402 Japanese aircraft hurtling down in flames in the famous Marianas turkey shoot of June 19, 1944, from which Japanese naval aviation never fully recovered.

The protection of a task force under way at night was a more complicated business. The radar gave as good coverage as by day but the handling of fighters was a different matter. If a report came in of planes a hundred miles away which the IFF detector could not identify as friendly, it was necessary to catapult some specially equipped night fighters, vector them out in the desired direction, coaching them on to their target by Very High Frequency voice transmission. Each of these night fighters was equipped with aircraft interception radar, not of the old types evolved in 1941 but specially designed for single-seat fighters whose pilot must be navigator, radar man, and gunner as well. Relying on this "cat's-eye" to enable him to see and fight in the dark, the fighter pilot would shoot down his foe and home on his carrier, unless he received instructions vectoring him towards another enemy plane.

Early in the war it had been seen that the information reaching a ship by means of radar, Loran, sonar, Huff-Duff, and friendly voice and radio communication was of a volume and complexity hard to handle with dispatch. The result was a remarkable development of the brain of the ship. Originally it was called Radar Plot, the place where the controller and his assistants marked on the plotting board the movement of planes and ships tracked by the various radars and directed his own fighters to intercept hostile air strikes. At the same time radar was locating surfaced submarines and sonar submerged ones. Soon it was realized that all information of enemy movements, from lookouts, from sonar, from friendly ships as well as one's own, ought to be handled in the same place. The result was the Combat Information Center, or CIC, as fascinating a setup for the student of naval warfare as the central nervous system is for the student of anatomy.

On carriers, the CIC specializes in defense — fighter direction and antiaircraft fire — though it is of course concerned with the control of its bombing and torpedo squadrons when they are launched against the enemy. In battleships, cruisers, and destroyers, it is primarily concerned with fire control, of guns or torpedoes, and secondly with the control of AA fire.

Sea power ran the interference and took out the tacklers. On two occasions the Japanese threw in their main surface forces to check our advance. The first was at Saipan where Admiral Spruance not only carried out his primary mission of defending our landing forces engaged ashore in a crucial struggle, but also, thanks to the planes of Task Force 58, dealt an irreparable blow to Japanese naval aviation and heavy damage to their surface forces. The second occasion on which the Japanese threw in their fleet led to the three separate actions we lump together as the Battle of Leyte Gulf.

Here the Navy not only won a great victory at sea, it also played an important part in General MacArthur's brilliant victory ashore. Bad weather delayed the establishment of airfields on Leyte and left the Army dependent for a time for air support on carrier aircraft of the Seventh and Third Fleets. Throughout the whole Philippines campaign the role of naval air power was of enormous importance. Analyzing this campaign a great British seaman, Admiral of the Fleet Lord Keyes (Retired), pointed out: —

The success of the battle for the Philippines was only made possible because the United States Navy had been free to develop its own naval Aviation. It has been done with an amazing skill and enterprise and on a gigantic scale. Furthermore, it has shown that in the complex business of waging war on the seas, it cannot be set down as a maxim that any one factor can be exclusively decisive.

The handling of a large task force, cruising at high speed in close formation and zigzagging in a blackout, makes station keeping a fine art.

A collision between two capital ships might so weaken the force as to leave it inferior to the approaching enemy. Radar has made the problem relatively simple, for the duty officer, watching the Plan Position Indicator screen, knows at all times his exact position in relation to the other ships in company. The admiral has a similar picture of the whole force under his command, and of the enemy forces.

To the layman it looks too easy. Given our superiority in force and such a complete display of information, why did any Japanese ships get away in the Battle of Leyte Gulf? Why was our Fleet so roughly handled by the Japanese off Okinawa?

The answer is that the enemy, too, had resources at his disposal, and though inferior in numbers, he could choose a time and a method for striking designed to give him the advantage of surprise. In the kamikaze ("divine wind") pilots he found a weapon of great value. In earlier years American naval officers had questioned whether a man could execute with perfection a mission from which he had no chance whatever to return. The Japanese proved again and again that this could be done. It is said they did not select their best pilots for kamikazes, but the men they did pick, who took off after two months' indoctrination with only gasoline enough for a one-way trip, proved formidable foes.

From the time we first entered Leyte Gulf in October 1944 the Japanese land-based planes sought to find every weak spot in our radar coverage. They knew that as we approached those rugged shores the radar echoes from their planes might be overlaid, on our scopes, by echoes from mountains and cliffs along the shore. Sometimes the Japanese pilot came in low, hoping that "sea-return," the clutter on the radar scope caused by the ocean waves, might cover up the telltale pip that would give our ships his location. Sometimes he tagged along behind some of our planes he saw returning to their carrier, hoping that he might not be spotted by our IFF and might be able to get within distance to strike. If he dove on a ship he tried to dive out of the sun, to improve his chances against flak. Many of the kamikaze pilots were shot down by the combat air patrol, but some got through.

A task force on the move was relatively immune from high-altitude heavy-bomber attacks, for it was not much of a trick to dodge the falling missiles. The kamikaze pilot intent on a death ride was another matter altogether. He laid heavy burdens on our AA defense.

The early American raids in the Pacific in 1942 had revealed one glaring weakness, the ineffectiveness of our antiaircraft fire. Now our ships bristled with 5-inch dual-purpose guns and with 20- and 40-mm. automatic weapons. Their fire had increased in volume and at the same time in accuracy thanks to the Sperry-Draper sight, which served the *South Dakota* so well in screening the *Enterprise* at Santa Cruz, and to the proximity fuze first used by the *Helena* on January 5, 1943. The latter device increased the effectiveness of our 5-inch shells at least threefold and they proved even more deadly after the introduction of the Mark 57 director.[5] But suicide attacks from airfields on the main islands of Japan, so numerous that we could not interdict them all by our own air strikes, remained a serious danger.

By June 21, when organized resistance had ceased at Okinawa, says Admiral King, "about 250 vessels of all classes, from battleships and carriers down to destroyers and landing ships, had been hit by air attack, by far the greatest proportion of them in suicide crashes. Some 34 destroyers or smaller craft were sunk." Radar picket vessels which took heavy losses but saved bigger ships proved the most valuable countermeasure.

Radar and Loran guided ships and planes on their way, gave marvelous precision to their gunfire and a reasonable degree of accuracy to bombing, even at night and through the overcast. Indeed we were able on occasion to take advantage of the superiority of our radar to strike where the Japanese could not strike back.

The shortest route from San Francisco to Yokohama is the great circle route which passes in sight of the islands of the Aleutian chain. "Sometimes in sight" would be more accurate, for this locality suffers from close to the worst weather in the world, and fog a mile deep often blankets the area, where the Japanese Current meets the chill waters of the Bering Sea. In May and September what the British call "bright intervals" are less infrequent, but the region, with its treacherous currents, fog banks, and sudden furious gales, was a terror to navigators by sea or air. To make matters worse the Japanese had seized Attu, Kiska, and other islands on the western end of the chain, and as the weather brewed in the west, their meteorologists could figure out its vagaries before ours could.

Radar helped to offset this disadvantage and to make sea and air

[5]See below, p. 237.

navigation less hazardous. Too many planes crashed as it was against the jagged peaks studding the fog, but hundreds of our aircrews owe their lives to the outline maps on their radar screen.

After we recaptured Attu and Kiska in 1943, we developed air bases at the western end of the Aleutian chain and struck by air and on the surface against the Japanese bases in the northern Kuriles. The fact that the industrial strength of Japan lay so far to the south precluded our making this our main line of attack, but it was a useful one for diversionary raids to force her to worry about her northern flank, and keep more of her strength in men and planes on these inhospitable northern islands.

In June 1944, at the time of the critical offensive against the Marianas, a task force under the command of Rear Admiral Ernest G. Small struck twice at the northern Kuriles, bombarding Matsuwa Island and Kurabu Zaki, an important air base on the southeast tip of Paramushiru, on June 13 and 26. In the days before radar no attack would have been risked in such waters except in some rare interval of good weather. Now we waited for bad weather of which there was plenty. Approaching a fog-bound coast by the help of radar, and using it to keep station in our tight formation, the force pounded the Japanese shore installations with radar-controlled gunfire, and sped away, with the Japanese planes, which had risen like angry hornets, droning above the overcast, unable to locate our vessels.

From the start of the war it had been clear that he who wished to command the sea must first command the air over the sea. By 1945 carriers constituted the largest single portion of our Navy's combat tonnage, and more than 30,000 naval aircraft were in combat status. The planes launched by our carriers owed much to the scientists of the Army and Navy, NACA and OSRD. They were better built, equipped, and armed, and their crews were better selected and trained. The combat aircrewman who fired his guns in too prolonged bursts earlier in the war often paid for it with his life as the barrels heated and drooped, and the guns ceased to shoot true. Now the liners developed by Division 1 of NDRC were so resistant to heat and erosion that they often outlasted the guns themselves. The planes carried better bombs, loaded with explosives of higher power, and dropped with reasonable accuracy by night or through the overcast. The Low Altitude Bombsights helped Army and Navy planes to take a heavy toll of enemy shipping.

The Allied world had shuddered when the guns of the escaping *Scharn-horst*, *Gneisenau*, and *Prince Eugen* shot down every plane of the British squadron of torpedo bombers who attacked them in the Channel in January 1942, and when the Japanese gunners made a clean sweep of the planes of Torpedo Squadron Eight in the following June off Mid-way. What was needed was a torpedo which could be launched from a higher altitude at high speeds and still run hot, straight, and true. Di-vision 6 found the answer to the launching problem and Section T gave our torpedoes an influence exploder which had been sorely needed. The NDRC scientists in collaboration with the Bureau of Ordnance im-proved the aerodynamic qualities of the torpedo during its air flight so that it entered the water clean without making a "belly whopper." Further improvements in design improved its underwater performance. These successes not only reduced the risk to the crews of torpedo bomb-ers and increased the chances of hitting, they made it possible to launch torpedoes into much shallower water. This was a factor of much impor-tance, for the enemy vessels often hid in shallow anchorages.

By 1944 the Navy was ordering rockets at the rate of $100,000,000 a month, for they had proved themselves an ideal airborne weapon. British tests and those subsequently made by NDRC scientists at Mor-ris Dam had shown them to have an excellent underwater trajectory and they did good service in the antisubmarine campaign. They proved a destructive weapon against shipping, a good support for landing forces, and a knockout against pillboxes and shelters of cocoanut logs, whose location often protected them from the trajectories of naval or field guns. The 5-inch high-velocity aircraft rocket, known as the "Holy Moses," bored through one and a half inches of armor and nearly four feet of high-quality reinforced concrete. Savage as were these blows they were but the jabs of a middleweight compared with the tremendous force of the "Tiny Tims," rockets more than ten feet long and 11.75 inches in diameter, which hit the target with almost 1250 pounds of steel and explosive. A single fighter plane equipped with 5-inch rockets can fire a salvo equal in many respects to that of a destroyer; and a squadron of Grumman Hellcats carrying Tiny Tims packs a punch com-parable to a broadside from a division of heavy cruisers.

In the closing days of the war our carrier planes struck savagely at the battered remnants of the Japanese battle fleet. They sank the redoubtable *Yamato* on April 7, 1945, off Kyushu, heavily damaged the *Nagato* at Yokosuka on July 18, and ten days later, at Kure, finished off the battleships *Haruna*, *Hyuga*, and *Ise*, and the heavy cruisers *Aoba* and *Tone*.

If the surface ships came to grips at all it was usually at night. The Japanese had prepared for such actions methodically, made good use of star shell, and proved highly skillful in the use of the torpedo. Off Savo Island, on the night of August 9–10, 1942, they won one of the most clean-cut victories on record, sinking one Australian and three American heavy cruisers and severely damaging the U.S.S. *Chicago*. In subsequent night actions better radar gave us the edge, as when the guns of the *Salt Lake City* sank a heavy cruiser off Cape Esperance, and the *Washington* and the *South Dakota* sank the *Kirishima* off Savo Island.

The classic night action of the war came on October 25, 1944, when a Japanese force composed of the battleships *Fuso* and *Yamashiro*, a heavy cruiser, and four destroyers tried to pass through the Surigao Straits to strike at our transports bunched in Leyte Gulf. Their way was blocked by PT boats, destroyers, cruisers, and five old American battleships under Rear Admiral Jesse B. Oldendorf, the *West Virginia*, *Maryland*, *Tennessee*, *California*, and *Pennsylvania*, all survivors of Pearl Harbor, and now modernized and more powerful than ever. It was the first action in history where one fleet blinded the eyes of another by radar countermeasures and sank it in the dark by use of its own radar.

The defeat of the Japanese naval forces opened the way to our reconquest of the Philippines. Their liberation gave us air bases from which we could complete the destruction of Japanese shipping in the South China Sea, but it put us no nearer to Japan itself than we were already in the Marianas. "American forces were already on Okinawa, nearly a thousand miles nearer to Japan, before the Philippines had been completely regained."[6]

The road to Japan ran northward from the Marianas. On Saipan, Tinian, and Guam we built the bases from which our B-29's could reach the cities of Japan and pour down the incendiaries that ate their hearts out. But to make the most of these bases we needed Iwo Jima as well. Japanese planes based there could deliver sneak attacks on our bases in the Marianas and the radar on Iwo gave the Japanese at home warning of the B-29's in time to get their fighters in the air. If we took Iwo we

[6]Robert Sherrod, *On to Westward*, p. 4.

could base long-range fighters there to escort our B-29's to Japan and to harry the patrol craft which maintained a lookout about latitude 30°. Once we had an airstrip on Iwo, moreover, our long-range bombers could carry less gasoline and more bombs. Before the end of the war more than 2000 B-29's had pulled up at Iwo on the way back from Japan, and from this rocky island, taken by our Marines after such a desperate struggle, rescue planes could fly to pick up downed pilots all the way to the coast of Japan.

When we took Iwo the Japanese Navy had no strong surface forces available to throw into the fray. The next move, against Okinawa, was quite another matter, for this large island was not only defended by over 100,000 troops, it was within range of at least 100 Japanese airfields. The logistic problems were fantastic, for Okinawa, only 330 miles from the Japanese home islands, was 1200 from Saipan or Ulithi and 6200 from San Francisco.

Shortly before and shortly after the landings at Iwo Admiral Spruance had sent the fast carrier task force to the coast of Japan to strike at the Japanese aircraft industry. To those who had pondered over the "lessons" of Norway and Crete, these raids of a thousand carrier planes on cities of the Japanese mainland seemed almost beyond belief.

It was one thing to hit the Japanese aircraft industry and another to knock it out, in bad weather. The Japanese had plenty of planes left and their kamikazes made the long campaign of Okinawa a grim and costly one. Their suicide attacks took a heavy toll of the great Fleet without whose support the campaign could not have been launched, and whose withdrawal would have forced its abandonment. As the Japanese did not defend the beaches the landings proved surprisingly easy, but the fighting ashore was long and costly and the battle of the Fifth Fleet against the kamikazes was the hardest fought in our naval annals.

Victory gave us air bases close to Japan, dominating her sea routes to China and Korea. At last we had our foot in the door of the Japanese Empire. While our staff planners busied themselves with preparations for landings on Kyushu and Honshu the strategic importance of the Marianas received a final demonstration.

It was from Tinian that the B-29's carried to Hiroshima and Nagasaki the atomic bombs which at last enabled the Japanese, with less loss of face, to admit that they had been already beaten.

A B–25 opens up on a Jap destroyer near Amoy, China, on April 6, 1945

The result

Navy AA gunners hit a bull's-eye: a Jap kamikaze explodes in mid-air

Let us not for one moment underestimate this contribution, for it saved hundreds of thousands of lives both Japanese and American. It may be true, as has been so often stated, that the Confederates were really beaten by July 1863, after Gettysburg and Vicksburg. If they were, they did not know it and they fought on for nearly two years longer. The Japanese, though beaten, were preparing a savage welcome for those who planned to land on their shores. Thanks to the atomic bombs the surrender on the *Missouri* had no prelude on the beaches of Kyushu and Honshu.

Sea power, underrated by many at the start of the war, enjoyed ample recognition at its close. It had enabled us to knock out all our foes, and to do so thousands of miles from our home bases. In a war marked by great devastation, we were fortunate in being able to fight the enemy on his home ground, not on our threshold.

On his arrival at Tokyo Bay to take part in the ceremonies of the surrender, Admiral Nimitz voiced his reflections: —

We have seen an island empire, its Army almost intact, well-equipped and with a large air force — but no Navy — brought to surrender before any invasion assaults had taken place. That was brought about by sea power, spearheaded by carrier-borne aircraft and aided by the excellent work of our submarine force. This sea power has made possible . . . the movement of Army and Marine troops, the seizure of bases for land and air power, and bases for the fleet itself. It is the same sea power that made possible the use of the atomic bomb by seizure of bases from which our planes, using weapons of that type, could operate. Without our sea power we could not have advanced at all. What has been accomplished is the result of teamwork of the very highest order . . . in emphasizing sea power I am not detracting from other branches of the service. But it must be obvious to everyone that no matter how much Army and air power we have, we can't get started without bases in the direction of the enemy; these must be taken and protected by naval vessels.

Our victory at sea was due not to numbers alone but to the quality of our men, our ships, and our weapons. The Bureau of Ships had lived up to the tradition established in Washington's time when Joshua Humphreys built the *Constitution:* always to turn out the best ship in every type of vessel. To do so today is a far harder task than in the days of sail, for the tempo of scientific change has been enormously accelerated. It puts tremendous pressure on both the naval constructor and his ally, the civilian scientist. Both must be alert not merely to the lessons of the last war but to what still lies below the horizon. On their dispassionate evaluation, and their increasingly close co-operation in a setup which enables each to create freely, depends our safety. No longer, in the modern game, does any player pick up a pat hand. He may be looking at what appears to be a straight flush ace high, and the next moment be blasted into eternity.

CHAPTER V

AMPHIBIOUS WARFARE

IN THE amphibious maneuvers in the Chesapeake shortly before Germany plunged Europe into war, a battalion of United States Marines climbed over the side of a battleship down cargo nets to 50-foot motor launches. In 1944–1945 task forces lifting three to six divisions put whole armies ashore in Normandy, Southern France, and the Pacific. In the space of five years what Admiral King has called "the most difficult of all operations in modern warfare" had been entirely transformed, by an amazing series of developments in most of which scientists played an important role.

The concept of utilizing one's control of the sea to launch an overseas expedition of wide strategic possibilities is a very old one.[1] But the technological developments of the nineteenth and early twentieth centuries had strengthened the defense to such a degree that by 1939 opposed landings on hostile shores seemed too hazardous for contemplation. The mine, the submarine torpedo, heavy ordnance, and land-based aircraft were generally assumed to have made the great land powers immune from overseas attack.

It was not sufficiently realized that one man's poison may be another man's meat: that the submarine, customarily regarded as par excellence a defensive weapon, could play an important role in an amphibious attack. Nor was it foreseen that an umbrella of aircraft could control the air and help control the surface, as an amphibious force approached its target, and that the development of communications would permit it to team up with surface vessels in placing so heavy a fire on hostile shores as to make possible the establishment of a beachhead and the interdiction or at the least the curtailment of counterattacks by enemy air and ground forces during the initial period of the build-up.

In the prewar discussions at the Army or Navy War College or in the

[1]The student of grand strategy will still find much food for thought in the British use of such expeditions in the Seven Years' War and the Wars of the French Revolution and Empire.

War Plans Divisions of the two services an officer would have been regarded as an impractical dreamer if he had suggested that the classic theories of step-by-step advance across the Pacific should be scrapped, and that an American task force, of a size and kind hitherto undreamed of, could by-pass important enemy bases in the Carolines, including Truk, then believed to be a sort of Japanese Gibraltar, and seize bases in the Marianas and Ryukyus from which long-range bombers could burn and blast the cities of Japan.

The armchair strategist who talks glibly about bold advances usually fights shy of what Mr. Churchill is said to have referred to as "that horrid American word 'logistics.' " If he neglects the all-important factor of supply, he will be committing as grave an error as the inventor who talks about perpetual motion with no concern for friction. The historians of World War II who write a century from now, with a long view of the development of naval strategy, will probably be less impressed with the great developments of communications and fire power than with our ability to maintain huge naval forces for months in active operations so far from our shores. In World War I the main fleets were tethered to home bases by a line not over 450 or 500 sea miles long. In the Pacific in 1944–1945 such a distance might seem to a supply officer just a good long spit. It is easier to understand radar or the atomic bomb than to grasp how we were able to maintain our huge fleet for months off the shores of Okinawa.

Unlike the armchair strategist the war plans officer has a thorough grounding in logistics. Both of them no doubt laughed at the story of the GI "down under" who received a letter from his American sweetheart asking, "What has that Australian girl got that I haven't got?" and replied, "Nothing, but she's got it here." The war plans officer's job requires him to know what it takes to get it there.

Because of the comprehensive nature of amphibious warfare the larger part of the new developments sponsored by OSRD influenced its transformations. Some new weapons and equipment played much the same role in the landings in Sicily or France as they did at Saipan or Lingayen. Others had more importance in either the European or the Pacific theater than they did in the other. The amphibious operations in the Mediterranean and Europe involved essentially short oversea movements, employing an endless amphibian chain-belt to move and supply armies carried from the United States and Great Britain to Africa, Sicily, Italy, and France. In the Central Pacific, possibly the "most amphibious" theater, the great distances, and the fewer bases available, resulted in longer lines of supply.

Amphibious operations in the South and Southwest Pacific theaters combined the features of those in the Central Pacific, Atlantic, and Mediterranean with special features of their own—a large land mass, less initial opposition, but little land maneuver because of the jungle. Our potential in amphibious and land-based air power in these theaters permitted brilliant "end run" landings and enabled us to achieve much with little in the way of troops, landing craft, bombardment, and striking forces.

Navigation from ship to shore was a minor problem in the great landings of the Central Pacific, which were "power plays" carried out in broad daylight. Here there was little or no concern about surprise, but it was an important factor in some pre-dawn landings in the South and Southwest Pacific and in the landings in Africa, Sicily, Italy, and France. On the way to his objective the officer commanding an amphibious force had Loran in his command ship as a navigation aid. The VHF (Very High Frequencies) tended to get tied up with tactical traffic but NDRC had provided an excellent alternative for night signaling in convoy.

In these night landings it was not easy to hit the right beach at the right time. To do this required accurate navigation, first from the transport area to the line of departure, where the attack was launched, thence to the hostile shore. To grapple with this problem the Chairman of NDRC, at Admiral Furer's request, set up a committee in April 1942 to study navigational aids to landing operations. The Committee's problem was to devise means of finding a beach within 200 yards of a target point and within one minute of H-Hour from a position five to ten miles off the coast, in the dark of the night and without compromising the security of the whole operation.

With the co-operation of the Navy the Naloc committee began testing radar and landing craft at Norfolk. Their program called for navigational tools and doctrine, for training, and for redesigning and procuring LCC's (Landing Craft Control) to lead other craft to the beaches.

During the summer tests went ahead at Fisher's Island and at Woods Hole on radar and radio sonobuoys, fathometers, odographs, and gyro compasses. The SG radar could furnish tangents and ranges but the NDRC scientists came up with another device, the Virtual PPI Reflectoscope, something like a Disney animated chart, which enabled a navigator to determine the position of his ship by superimposing on his Plan Position Indicator the image of an actual chart. A refinement known as the Navigational Microfilm Projector replaced the paper chart by a system of lenses to project the image of a small film on a screen. These devices were tested successfully on cruises along the Maine coast and in the Caribbean.[2]

By October 1943 LCC's designed to carry this gear were coming from the production line at the rate of one a week and trained crews were ready to man them. The craft had excellent compasses, fathometers, and communications equipment but were too uncomfortable for the necessary prolonged use by their crew. They proved too large for ready handling overside from an assault transport and too small to go any distance under their own power in heavy weather. They were generally replaced as primary control craft by the PC's (submarine chasers), but they did good service in numerous operations as secondary and tertiary control craft.

In the former role on D-Day in Normandy, for example, they accompanied the PC's to a line three to four thousand yards off the beach, where tank landing craft unloaded their amphibious tanks. Then the LCC's led the tanks to within 400 yards of the shore, returning to the line of departure to help control smaller craft. On D-Day they assembled and dispatched 25 assault waves from the transport area. As tertiary control craft they put over the buoys for the Mulberry and Gooseberry docks.

In anticipation of amphibious attacks the Germans and Japanese expended considerable effort and ingenuity on underwater defenses. A steel rail with one end sharpened to a point and the other imbedded in a large block of concrete was a likely device to skewer a landing craft and a difficult item to blow up or move away. Mines were interspersed

[2]Before the end of the war Radar Center, established at Pearl Harbor, had trained more than a thousand men in the use of the Virtual PPI Reflectoscope, and the equipment had become a standard supplementary installation for inshore piloting on various types of vessels, including battleships, cruisers, and destroyers.

among the various obstacles in such profusion that an invader who timed his arrival for low tide would have a hard time clearing a lane on the beach before the tide rose enough to complicate his operations. The Japanese made effective use of coconut logs in bolstering the already formidable protective screen of natural coral reef at Tarawa before our attack in November 1943.

Two months earlier a Joint Army and Navy Board on the Demolition of Underwater Obstacles had been established at Fort Pierce, Florida, and at Navy request, NDRC had set up a committee, later known as DOLOC, to collaborate in the work. It was clear that demolition of underwater obstacles by hand-placed charges would be costly under enemy fire, and that mechanical aids were much to be desired before the Normandy and Pacific landings of 1944. The deadline set for the gear to be on the dock for shipment, February 1, left too little time for satisfactory solutions, and showed up the limitations of forced-draft research. Such research may work in developing a specific piece of apparatus, but even good men will often fail to solve a highly complex problem against an early deadline.

Within the time limits set it was clear to the members of the NDRC committee that they could not develop satisfactory new weapons. The best they could do was to take existing weapons, make hasty improvements, demonstrate their possibilities, and make suggestions for their tactical use. It was also clear that no single device would be able to demolish the variety of obstacles likely to be met: deep-water mines, shallow-water mines, water obstacles, wire, dragon teeth, traps, and beach walls. The brilliant successes of the Navy underwater demolition teams and the comparable Engineer units were due to their training, their courage, and their leadership, rather than to anything the scientists could do to help them.

The two chief problems of amphibious assaults were the control of traffic from the transport area to and from the beaches and the massing of fire power to cover the landings. Both were the subject of constant study, resulting in a long evolution of tactical doctrine as our new weapons and equipment came into use and the enemy introduced weapons of his own and methods of countering ours. Both problems laid tremendous burdens on communications, and led to the introduction of special command ships with every variety of communications channels and a wealth

of radar and sonar information. A parallel development was the installation of Combat Information Centers in destroyers and headquarters
ships for the tactical control of aircraft over the targets in the Pacific
theaters.

The use of deception in amphibious operations varied greatly with the
theaters. In the great landings in Normandy and in Southern France it
was carried to the peak of perfection. On D-Day the Germans were convinced that the operations in the Bay of the Seine were a feint, or at best
a secondary operation, and that the main attack was coming in the Pas
de Calais. Tactical surprise saved thousands of lives, at the very least, if
not the success of the whole operation. Here the radar countermeasures
experts gave full rein to their imagination and turned loose a bewildering
array of jammers and deception devices. They blinded the eyes of enemy
radars to conceal the true direction of the Allied attack and filled the
German scopes in the Pas-de-Calais area repeatedly with the fanciest
imaginable assortment of simulated echoes. A ghostly procession of nonexistent battleships, cruisers, destroyers, transports, landing craft, and
air squadrons swam into the Germans' ken, thanks to the most sophisti-
cated faking in the history of man.

This was what one might call a single-wing offensive in the field of
deception. We faked a play straight through the center of the line, and
smashed off right tackle. To ensure the success of the landings in Southern
France on August 15, 1944, we resorted to a double-wing offensive. We
created the illusion of sweeps around both ends, and smashed straight
ashore through the center. The illusion we created was so perfect that
the Germans expected a landing in the Bay of Genoa to the east and
another far to the west of our actual landings.

Hot debate has raged as to the use of smoke as a screen for an amphibious landing. There has been no dispute as to its indispensability in
screening the transport area whenever necessary between dusk and daylight against enemy air attack. For that purpose it was as necessary as
radar or sonar. Between the landings on Leyte, when the Japanese first
countered with kamikazes, and those on Okinawa, there was a tremendous growth in the use and application of the smoke tactics developed
for the Marianas operations. Smoke became a major concern in logistics.
One shudders to think what would have happened to our fleet off Leyte,
Lingayen, or Okinawa if smoke had not been available to shroud it.

Supplies pour over the beaches of Normandy for invading Allied armies

A Dukw takes off from an LST for Iwo's battle beach

When an airplane approaches a transport area veiled in smoke the bombardier has little time in which to make his decisions. He must make them long before he is directly over the target and must consequently look through a thickness of screen considerably greater than its perpendicular depth from top to bottom. Because of this, and the fact that he has flak and his instruments on his mind, a smoke screen may be much more effective against him that it would be against an unhurried observer.

If smoke was used in daylight hours it often blinded our own anti-aircraft gunners, and if whipped along the surface of the water in a strong breeze, it sometimes broke into eddying patches which only partly concealed our ships.

The offensive use of smoke to cover the assault waves was another story. In theory, if the wind was on shore, you could send a cloud of smoke ahead of the first wave to blind the eyes of the enemy. But what if the wind changed and the smoke rolled back over your coughing, choking men, throwing the landing craft into confusion? Theoretically, smoke could be used on the leeward flank of a landing force to screen it against enfilading fire. Here again there was a risk of a change of wind. Where everything depended on accurate timing and the perfect control of the ship-to-shore movement, was it wise to take chances? Admiral Turner did not think so.[3]

His classic landings in the Central Pacific were "power plays," with little or no need for deception. The airfields from which enemy air attack might come had been carefully neutralized by sweeps of carrier groups and bombardment by cruiser divisions. A striking force of fast battleships and carriers was at hand to dispose of the enemy fleet if the Japanese cared to risk it as they did at the time of the landings on Saipan and Leyte. And fire power so heavy that the figures fail to give any adequate idea of it was massed on the enemy targets — fire power better controlled than ever before, and applied after careful study of the effects of previous land bombardment.

"How are you feeling?" asked Vice-Admiral Harry Hill of a wounded Marine who had just been brought back to his ship off Saipan. "Fine, thank you, sir," replied the wounded man. "I was in the thirteenth wave today. Next time I hope to be in the first or second." There spoke an

[3]Smoke from the explosion of our shells ashore caused plenty of trouble as it was.

old hand who knew the paralyzing effect on the defenders of a preliminary (pre-assault) barrage laid down by surface vessels when combined with bombing and artillery fire from land-based artillery.

In the attack on Munda in 1943 pains had been taken to secure advanced bases from which field pieces could be brought to bear on the main enemy positions. In defending an atoll as extensive as Kwajalein in 1944 the Japanese did not have men and guns enough to defend all the low islands surrounding the great lagoon. By means of A-frames the superb Dukws landed on an unoccupied island four batteries of 105-mm. guns which poured 75,000 rounds on the defenses of Kwajalein Island. Here we were profiting from the lessons of Tarawa as well as the experience of Munda.

When to end the barrage is one of the most critical decisions in an amphibious operation. If it is lifted too late it will mow down the men of our own first wave. If it lifts too soon, the enemy — or the part of the enemy that has not been killed, stunned, or badly wounded by the bombing and shelling — will leap to any guns still capable of action and sweep the beach with them. Was there any means of keeping the enemy fire down in the critical period between the time when the barrage had lifted and the first waves hit the beach?

Because of its recoilless feature, and light construction which permitted the installation of launchers on landing craft and gave them fire power equal to that of much larger vessels, the barrage rocket proved to be the answer. NDRC distinguished itself in the development of rockets and rocket launchers. Its expenditures for research on these weapons stood second only to those for radar. The successes of Division 3, recounted in a later chapter, did much to shape the development of amphibious warfare. Rockets fired from support boats — LCS(S) — helped to cover our landings in Sicily in July 1943. United States forces took their first islands in the Pacific without them, but at Arawe, in December 1943, two Dukws and two subchasers, each equipped with rocket launchers, helped to break down the beach defenses prior to the assault landings.

Their fire offered such a good solution to the problem of keeping the Japanese down when the barrage lifted and the troops hit the beach that the use of rockets spread rapidly in the South and Southwest Pacific theaters. The LCI's (landing craft infantry) could fire to cover a broad front, not merely straight ahead. LCT(R)'s, LCVP's (landing craft vehicles personnel), and LCM's also carried rockets. An officer of the 2nd Engineer Special Brigade stated that as an instrument of morale they were extremely valuable.

It is much easier for troops to make an initial landing on a beachhead which they know has been well covered by rocket fire in advance of their landing. Second, as an antipersonnel weapon, the rocket is by far our most important weapon used in amphibious assault operations.

The landings in Normandy were a halfway point in the development of rocket tactics. At Omaha Beach rocket craft took a position in close formation in line abreast, about 2700 yards astern of the leading wave of landing craft. They were to proceed in and deliver rocket fire when the landing wave was about 300 yards offshore. Their commanders, after the operation, pronounced rocket craft the most valuable of close-fire support weapons.

Leyte and Lingayen were big rocket shows, but Admiral Turner did not make much use of beach barrage rockets until the Okinawa landings. This may have been due in part to the enormous fire power at his disposal. He made great use of the airborne rocket both as a pre-H-Hour weapon and in direct support of troops. Here the role of the rocket was a big one.

It was at Okinawa that rocket tactics reached their culmination. There the "Interim" LSM(R)'s (landing ship medium rockets) fulfilled a variety of needs. They bombarded the beaches just before H-Hour, harassed isolated strong points, patrolled against enemy suicide boats, and upon call supplied fire support to advancing troops. A single LSM(R) could hit a beach with 100 rockets a minute. With fifteen craft loosing a barrage against a single beach — 7500 rockets in five minutes — a beach must have been almost as hot as an exploding ammunition ship. In another instance a rocket bombardment before landing completely disrupted about 200 yards of a highway and of a small railway between Naha and the southern beaches, and thus effectively denied the enemy their use of reinforcements.

In affording call fire support at Okinawa LSM(R)'s came definitely into their own. Four LSM(R)'s, two on the east side of the island and two on the west, fired an average of two deckloads of rockets each, daily for ten days, in support of our troops pushing south. Rockets which arched over protecting ridges just inland from the landing beaches inflicted heavy casualties on retreating Japanese forces. At the same time our commanders used air spot of rocket fire for the first time. Successful as its introduction was, it would doubtless have been even more valuable with "Ultimate" LSM(R)'s equipped with improved launchers.

In all uses to which the Interim LSM(R) was put, performance was impaired by the limited range of rockets — 4000–5000 yards — the time required for reloading, and inaccurate fire. Nevertheless it performed yeoman service. The varied ways in which rockets and rocket ships were now employed showed how the conception of their tactical uses had grown since their initial employment.

Of all the devices specially designed by NDRC for amphibious warfare the Dukw was the most successful. Its versatility made it of use in all the amphibious theaters. When the staff planners were racking their brains as to how to land supplies on the coast of Sicily despite the shallow beach gradient, this seagoing $2\frac{1}{2}$-ton Army truck came as an answer to prayer. The driver, able to adjust tire pressure without leaving his seat, could change the pressure to what would give him traction in soft sand, and the trick would be turned.

At first thought, it seemed preposterous to use rubber tires on jagged coral which tore the steel tracks off other amphibians. But exhaustive tests on the Florida Keys showed that rubber tires with the right pressure — 30 pounds — could take the beating and still hold up. As a result of these tests Division 12 of NDRC evolved the doctrine of a particular tire pressure for a particular terrain — 10 pounds pressure for soft sand, 30 pounds for coral, and 40 pounds for hard roads. This was only part of the job. The Army and Navy had to be convinced, too.

The Dukw was conceived primarily as a means of expediting discharge of cargo from ships, through surf if need be, to shore dumps. It made good in this role, though as things turned out there were a number of other things it could do even better than serve as a general cargo handler.

The first Transportation Corps Amphibian Truck Company to be activated, the 451st, reached New Caledonia in March 1943, the same month in which the Dukws first arrived in North Africa. But it was in Sicily that they scored their first great combat success. General Patton

Official Photo U. S. Navy

Beach barrage rockets screaming toward Okinawa

Dukws landing ammunition and supplies for our forces on Saipan

had been much impressed by a demonstration of these amphibians at Arzeu in April and had immediately requested increased numbers of them for the forthcoming invasion.

In the Sicilian landings of July 10, 1943, the British on the east coast had about 300 Dukws, divided between two companies and a temporary group (which left England after only four days of Dukw training and came directly into Sicily). The Americans used about 700 Dukws.

The British Dukws landed without difficulty and surf conditions in the British sector remained mild. But the American landings took place in heavy weather. Several transports smashed up boats trying to get them over the side. On one transport a twenty-ton LCM swung back and forth over the deck like a charm on a watch chain. Two thirds of the LCVP's and LCM's broached in the surf, but the Dukws kept rolling. General Eisenhower declared the new amphibian to be invaluable. "It greatly facilitates flow of supplies over beaches and on one beach was used as assault craft. Mechanism should be kept secret as long as possible. We should be delighted to get some more of them."

In the Ellice Island operations in 1943 pre-loaded Dukws swam out of the LST's to the amazement of those who saw them for the first time. To see ships well offshore opening their bows, letting down ramps, and disgorging Dukws was an incongruous picture. It resembled nothing so much as a novel and grotesque manifestation of the age-old business of birth. In fact, it was just that — birth of a tactic which became Standard Operating Procedure.

The Dukw was not used at Tarawa, but by the time of the landings at Kwajalein Atoll on January 31, 1944, it was on the first team. It had found a new role, which some regard as the most important it played in the Pacific. This was to carry a pre-loaded artillery piece and initial ammunition ashore, unload by means of an A-frame, mounted on a fellow Dukw, return to the parent LST, and shuttle ammunition and supplies till all were ashore. A well-trained crew could rig the A-frame, unload the piece, and hitch it to the Dukw pintle hook in seventy-five seconds. A battery could be set up in firing position within seven minutes of landing.

The Dukw had many advantages, which steadily increased its circle of friends. It could be carried on transports, usually on deck in place of LCVP's or in small areas in between the LCVP skids. In action the

Dukws' wonderful bilge pump kept many of them afloat even if they
had been severely holed.

As with all new equipment, mistakes in use of the Dukw were inevitable. Ranking officers of both Army and Navy were often ignorant of
the capabilities and limitations of the Dukw. Because of their slow
speed afloat — about five knots — it was inefficient, unless unavoidable,
to have Dukws make a water-carry of much over a mile from ship to
shore. Ships to be unloaded sometimes moored too far offshore. Dumps
were sometimes too far inland. Because of their high speed ashore, there
was constant temptation to take Dukws from their primary assignment
for purposes of land transportation. At times Dukws were overloaded
or badly loaded. There was consequently a high loss both in vehicles and
in tonnage hauled. Crews were sometimes green. Teamwork with crews
of ships on the one hand and with crews at dumps on the other was
sometimes ragged. Technical officers and men were often hopelessly inadequate in number to provide satisfactory maintenance. There seemed
never to be enough spare parts.

The most crucial amphibious operation in history was Operation Overlord, the landing in Normandy; and circumstances conspired to make
the Dukw virtually indispensable to the success of the operation.

The first companies landed on D-Day — with the 1st Engineer Special Brigade on Utah Beach, and with the 5th and 6th Brigades on
Omaha Beach. Loaded with high-priority engineering equipment, artillery pieces, and ammunition, these Dukws pushed through passages
only partly cleared of underwater obstacles and mines. On the beaches,
they encountered heavy enemy fire as well as land mines. In contrast
to the driver of a land truck, a driver of a Dukw rarely became a casualty if his vehicle detonated a mine. The front wheels and engine com-
partment well in front of the driver absorbed the shock of the explosion.
Still casualties ran high.

On D+3 the first of the Negro Dukw companies arrived on the beach
in LST's and LCT's. To make land runs by Dukws as short as possible,
transfer points were set up in the dunes close to the beaches. Though
the beaches were of firm sand, the Dukws encountered other operating
difficulties. The small North Sea coasters were used for cargo vessels
because they are a difficult target and are able to operate close to shore.
But they rolled violently in the rough Channel waters, and they had

heavy side guard rails which caused much damage to Dukw hulls and headlights.

Sea conditions were bad much of the time, particularly at Omaha, which was partly open to prevailing northwest winds. Surf was high, and tides ran as fast as three knots. The shore was cluttered with wreckage and spilled cargo. There was consequently a high mortality to Dukw propellers and rudders. Maintenance became a nightmare but the Dukw met the test.

The first three weeks of the assault on France demonstrated beyond question the usefulness and dependability of the Dukw in the hands of an experienced operator. Not only did it move cargo from ship to shore, as other ferry craft could, but it could and did transport that cargo overland to a dump. This ability, possessed by the Dukw alone of all the ferry craft used in Operation Neptune, went far to solve the problem posed by a shortage of trucks and cranes during the first days on Omaha Beach. Again, following the storm of 19 – 22 June, it was the Dukw that enabled immediate resumption of the movement of large quantities of cargo. While the hulls of other types of ferry craft were being battered on the beach, the Dukws were safely ashore in their parks, waiting to begin work when the storm abated. Undoubtedly, the present model of the Dukw is susceptible of modification and improvement to give it greater sturdiness, but, with all its imperfections, it converted this beach operation from what might have been a random piling of supplies on the beach to an orderly movement from ship to dump.[4]

The Germans had been sure that even if the Allies succeeded in landing, they could not bring enough supplies across the open beaches of Normandy to support a major offensive. The *Wehrmacht* had only to gather strength and drive the Allies back into the sea. With the breakwater gone the very survival of the Allied field armies depended more than ever on the Dukw.

In spite of all difficulties, the Normandy beaches continued to serve as major ports into the late fall, with Dukws bringing ashore 40 per cent of all supplies landed between June 6 and September 1. They sustained General Eisenhower's report on their high value in the Sicilian landings. Altogether approximately 2000 Dukws were operating on the coast of Normandy by D+60. Even so Operation Overlord hardly represents the culmination of Dukw tactics in themselves.

[4]Report of the Engineer Special Brigade Group.

In the Pacific the going was often heartbreaking. At Iwo, for instance, beaches were so steep that front wheels would bury in the soft volcanic ash before the rear wheels could obtain proper traction. Hit by heavy surf, a vehicle would be swung broadside and swamped — if not towed out without delay by tractors. A few spots were found where with tires deflated as low as five pounds the Dukws could climb out themselves. They were under mortar and small-arms fire much of the time and their hulls were often punctured in many places. Shore conditions were so critical for a time that Dukws had to put back to sea regardless of seaworthiness, and several LST's were designated as repair ships.

Though losses in Dukws during the first five days of the Iwo operation were 50 per cent, casualties among Dukw drivers were light — each company of approximately 184 men averaged about three killed or missing and ten wounded. General Holland M. Smith, Commanding General of Fleet Marine Forces, commended the Army Negro drivers for their courage and skill. Their performance led the Marines to request training for their Dukw companies in the Dukw school at Oahu under supervision of OSRD personnel.

At Iwo Jima, Dukws took on another major role for which their ability to swim in and out of an LST ideally qualified them. This was transporting casualties directly from field stations to hospital ships. Otherwise it was necessary to carry casualties back to the beach by truck, then by litter through surf to landing craft. Gravely wounded men could hardly withstand so much handling. But by carrying thousands of casualties untouched from field stations to hospital LST's, Dukws unquestionably saved many lives.

In the Central Pacific landings, LVT's (amphtracks) were used more extensively than Dukws for cargo transfer because there were more of them, and the Dukws available were in high demand for specialized tasks. Their role in transferring cargo, however, was important, as at Saipan, Guam, Peleliu, and Angaur, especially in the early stages of a landing when channels for LCVP's, LCM's, LCT's, and LST's had not yet been blasted through the reef.

As one control officer described the operation: —

We would load LCVP's, LCM's, LCT's and pontoon barges with high-priority cargo (and in the early stages with reserve troops) and send them in to a "transfer area" off the reef. Empty LVT's and Dukws would come off the beach, cross the reef, transfer cargo from the boats (under the direction of primary and secondary control officers in PC's and LCC's at the Transfer area) and take the cargo back across the reef to the beach dumps. Refinements included: (1) landing LCT's and LST's on the reef, where LVT's and Dukws could drive into them for loading; (2) anchoring pontoon barges off the reef to make it easier for LVT's and Dukws to come alongside for loading; (3) loading the pontoon barges with gasoline drums to provide offshore filling stations for LVT's and Dukws, when the opposition was too tough or the beach too rugged to land the drums and establish fuel dumps ashore.

American resourcefulness turned the Dukw to many other uses. Dukws were landing artillery pieces during early phases of an assault — as in the surprising "end runs" up the Italian coast at night to turn Kesselring's flank. They were mounting rockets and artillery. They were evacuating wounded from shore to hospital ship. They were laying communications wire across water channels. They were landing troops over reefs and sandbars which hampered the usual craft for carrying personnel. Ashore they were towing vehicles and transporting both men and supplies. They were useful in underwater salvage work. And on occasion — as at Saipan where a freighter was hung on a coral reef with solid seas breaking over her and washing men off her decks — Dukws rescued shipwrecked crews. By the end of the war, over 21,000 Dukws had been procured besides nearly 7000 more whose production had been authorized. Enough companies had been trained to man 5000 to 6000 vehicles.

Years from now, under different conditions as to secrecy, when the archives of all the combatants are equally accessible, an historian of amphibious warfare may be able to trace in minute detail the evolution of the Standard Operating Procedures of friend and foe, and show with precision influences of each new weapon and each countermeasure in the evolution of tactics. Even now the main lines are clear. Because naval power, air power, and land power merge in amphibious operations, the greater part of the contributions made by the scientists who came to the aid of the Army, the Navy, and the Air Forces, helped to increase our amphibious might. It is well that they did, for in no earlier war had leaders even dreamed of amphibious attacks on such a scale. Nothing but the immense stakes and the lack of a satisfactory alternative would have justified taking the risks involved in the Normandy invasion. The great contributions of the scientists lent confidence to the chiefs who shouldered this terrible responsibility, to the planners who conceived the complicated procedures, and the brave men who carried them out. The new weapons and equipment saved thousands of Allied lives in forcing open the European and Pacific fortresses. Indeed without them it is hard to believe that the invasions could even have been attempted.

CHAPTER VI

AIR WARFARE

I N THE six years which followed the German attack on Poland air warfare developed from the "infancy" of World War I to "a stage of full adolescence."[1] The scientists contributed greatly to this rapid evolution, shifting the basis of air warfare from hunches to statistics, enabling the Tactical Air Forces to support ground troops much more effectively, and enormously enhancing the power of strategic bombing.

In 1939 no air force had adequate scientific data on the effects of bombing. Strong opinions were held as to the merits of small explosive bombs but the methods of measuring what they might do were crude. As Britain was a battle front, the Regional Technical Intelligence Officers of the Ministry of Home Security had abundant material for their studies of bomb damage. The British scientists discovered what types of structures best resisted air attack and laid the basis for a better selection both of enemy targets and of the missiles best suited to destroy them.

NDRC scientists studied what happens when a projectile strikes a target protected by earth, concrete, steel, or plastic armor. They introduced vastly improved techniques of measuring the effects of explosives in air and water and greatly developed the theory of shock waves. Members of Division 2 convinced the Army Air Forces of the importance of the British studies of bomb damage as a guide to our bombing policy.[2] They served as scientific advisers to General Arnold, General Spaatz, and the Joint Target Group. The Division furnished our services and the British with an invaluable loose-leaf book, *Effects of Impact and Explosion*, containing data sheets on the effects of high-explosive projectiles and bombs, incendiaries, rockets, mines and demolition charges on various targets, and compact descriptions of particular bombings, showing all the types of damage that occurred.

[1] U. S. Strategic Bombing Survey, *Overall Report (European War)*, p. 1.
[2] This division grew out of a Committee on Passive Protection against Bombing, which Dr. Frank B. Jewett, as President of the National Academy of Sciences, appointed in July 1940 to advise the Chief of Engineers. Gradually NDRC absorbed the Committee, which was eventually dissolved in July 1944.

E. Bright Wilson, Jr., who relieved John E. Burchard as Chief of this
Division in June 1944,[3] vigorously advocated the idea of "controlled attacks." He urged that at least some raids should be confined to bombs of
a single type, to give the operational analysts more accurate data as to
the effectiveness of a given missile. Without such information the study
of bomb damage is far removed from the reproducible experiment on
which scientific advance is based. With it air operations can rest not on
hunches but on judgments based on quantitative measurements.[4]

The ever-recurring questions were: How much will it take? What size
bomb causes the most destruction? What kind of burst, air or surface?
Are incendiaries more devastating than high explosives?

The Applied Mathematics Panel of NDRC developed for the Army
Air Forces a bombardier's calculator, which would so determine the
spacing of bombs in a train of bombs released from a single aircraft as
to maximize the chances of hitting a given target. Mathematical investigation showed that the spacing depended upon various factors such as
aiming errors of the bombardier, dispersion of the bombs in the train
from their theoretical positions, number of bombs in the train, dimensions of target, and angle of attack. Many calculations were made in
order to find out the effect of these factors on the total result. On
the basis of these computations the Panel developed a bomb-spacing
calculator.

The Army Air Forces' request for this device implied that the bombardier of each bomber would aim his bombs at the target. Normally,
however, against German targets, the AAF used formations of six to
eighteen planes which dropped their load of bombs simultaneously on
signal from a single lead bombardier. The bombers had to band themselves together to increase their defensive fire power against attacking
fighters, and by this method the best bombardiers could control the aiming operation. Although the bombardier's calculator was of no use in
formation bombing of Germany, the Navy made some use of it, because
most of its air operations against shipping, warships, and shore installations depended on individually aimed bomb releases.

Work on this device brought the Applied Mathematics Panel into
touch with numerous Army and Navy agencies which made increasing

---

[3]When the latter became Assistant Chief of the Office of Field Service.

[4]It is much easier to apply statistical analysis to strategic bombing than to the operations
of aircraft supporting ground troops.

demands on its services. The AAF repeatedly called for estimates of the percentages of bombs of a given size which might be expected to fall within 500, 1000, or 2000 feet of an aiming point, and for estimates of bomb requirements for the achievement of at least one hit with a reasonably high degree of probability on bridges, submarine pens, V-1 launching installations, and gun emplacements. The Chemical Warfare Service wanted to know how many toxic gas bombs of a given kind must be used to cover a given area, so that a specified proportion of that area would have minimum concentration of gas within a certain number of minutes. The Joint Army-Navy Experimental Testing Board asked for estimates of the number of bombs of a given type required for clearing paths through land and beach minefields.

The assumptions made by the Air Forces in the early days of the war as to the amount of bombing necessary to render an airfield unusable now seem naïve. After learning to their cost how quickly the enemy could resume operations from an airfield pasted by bombers, the Air Forces relied increasingly on their operational analysts and the Applied Mathematics Panel for estimates of the amount of bombing of an airfield necessary to make it practically certain that no portion large enough for a fighter plane strip would remain undamaged. In similar fashion the mathematicians calculated the bomb loads necessary to destroy given fractions of the target in area bombing of cities.

The German dive bombers astonished the world in 1939–1940 by their effective support of ground troops. New weapons and equipment enabled British and American Air Forces to give even better support to ground attacks.

Air-ground co-operation raises some of the most difficult problems in the art of war. The mission of a Tactical Air Force is first to gain the necessary degree of air superiority in the theater of operations; second, to prevent the movement of enemy troops and supplies into or within the theater; and thirdly, to take part in a combined effort of the ground and air forces in the battle area. The tragic death of General McNair, Chief of our Army Ground Forces, killed by one of our own bombs, reminds us of the dangers of close air support. Yet the new devices of World War II eventually permitted great advances in the tactical use of aircraft. And the scientist who followed the new equipment into the field aided and abetted the most progressive officers in the Air Forces to squeeze from the new devices the last drop of offensive power.

The landings in Normandy illustrate well the new devices in action. One of the first problems was to deny the enemy the use of his radar and to ensure the safe use of our own. Along the coast the Allies found no less than fifty air warning and coast watching sites with an average of one radar every mile and a half. These radars were of twelve separate and distinct types. Their sites were bombed shortly before D-Day, all along the coast, to avoid giving away the beaches selected for landings.

Five separate "spoof" raids were executed by the R.A.F. and the Royal Navy on the night of June 5–6. Eighteen small naval vessels faked an attack north of the Bay of the Seine, accompanied by an R.A.F. squadron dropping the metallic strips called Chaff or Window to give the impression of a large convoy moving slowly across the Channel. The Navy ships towed balloons, each of which simulated a big ship on the enemy radar screens. A similar force of sixteen ships, magnified by another spoofing squadron of planes, feinted at Boulogne. Between these two forces 29 Lancasters carrying 82 jamming transmitters posed as top cover for a landing in the Pas-de-Calais. Meanwhile in the Channel 20 British planes and four Flying Fortresses maintained a jamming barrage which covered the enemy's coastal radar frequencies and screened the Allied squadrons which were forming over England and approaching the Continent. As diversion for the paratroop landings in the Cherbourg Peninsula two dummy airborne invasions were staged, one halfway down the peninsula, the other east of Fécamp. Dummy paratroopers floated to earth at both points accompanied by enough Window to give the impression of a twenty times greater vertical envelopment. The Germans sent night fighters against the force feinting at the Pas-de-Calais, and the approach of the actual invasion forces was not opposed by air or sea.[5]

At H-Hour minus 30 minutes, landing forces were scheduled to be about a mile offshore; at H-Hour minus 5, about 500 yards. Up to take-off time — from 0230 to 0300 — the 8th Air Force had hoped to be able to bomb the beachhead visually. Then clouds closed in, requiring bombardment through the overcast, by squadrons led by Pathfinder planes equipped with the radar bombsight H_2X. Rather than chance hitting our advanced boat waves the center of impact was shifted inland.

[5]"Greatest Hoax in Military History," *London Calling*, December 13, 1945, p. 3.

Our Air Forces achieved a great success in disrupting German communications, destroying bridges, and interdicting the approach of German reinforcements to the battle area in the critical period of the build-up.

Personnel of the British Branch of the Radiation Laboratory had also proved of great assistance to the Troop Carrier Command in the use of radar aids for the landing of paratroopers. On D-Day the Gee and SCR-717 equipments provided complete navigational information to the dropping points for the first Pathfinder drops and the main force homed on the radar beacons dropped by the lead planes, all of which beacons operated perfectly. The operations executed at night or through the overcast were in marked contrast to those in Sicily, where the troop carriers had great difficulty in locating the landing areas and dropped troops in widely scattered positions and even in the sea.

The Microwave Early Warning set on Start Point in Devon did a marvelous job in guiding fighter and bomber sweeps into and around the invasion area. Although there had been some doubts as to whether the huge traffic could be adequately handled by the MEW, the "Big Bertha" of radar, the fears proved ungrounded. The large glass plotting screen to which information was transmitted by the Plan Position Indicator scopes gave at all times a complete picture of the operations.

As the armies advanced, Major General E. R. Quesada, Commanding the 9th Tactical Air Command, got a MEW in the field, mounted in Ordnance vans.

We move it around with relative ease [he reported], and it has made a great contribution to the attainment of air superiority. We are using it to control Night Fighters, and it is much more effective than any GCI (ground control of interception) that we have used in the past. I am particularly proud of the MEW as so many tried to discourage our efforts by saying that it could not be made mobile. We keep it up front at all times. . . .

The MEW was in large measure responsible for the high ratio of kills to losses achieved by our fighter aircraft. General Orville Anderson declared, "Within the range of MEW every one of my fighters is worth two outside its range."

The MEW and the SCR-584 did a good job in navigational control of fighter bombers. The man at the controls of the latter set could automatically release the bombs of the planes in his charge from straight and level flight as he saw them reach the right spot in their bombing run. Ground control of bombing could also be carried out by the admirable Shoran, or by the use of double-base interrogator-responder systems which determined the aircraft's position by triangulation from accurate range measurement.

The development of the rocket provided the Air Forces with a new weapon of great power for strafing. Our squadrons flying from England and Italy had been using the Army 4.5-inch rockets against industrial centers and transportation for several months before D-Day. When provided with the High Velocity Aircraft Rocket (HVAR) developed by NDRC for the Navy, they were able to deal more punishing blows. The 9th Air Force first used this weapon against the railroad yards of Paris. Soon after D-Day some Thunderbolt fighter planes were equipped with eight HVAR's apiece. They were especially effective in supporting the breakthrough at St. Lô and combating the German counteroffensive at Vire and Mortain in August. One or two Thunderbolts hovered constantly over the advancing tanks of the Third Army, attacking the heavy German tanks and the formidable 88-mm. antitank guns when they threatened to hold up the American advance.

On July 17 twelve aircraft, carrying four rockets apiece, attacked the railroad yard at Tiger-Quail. They hit and silenced a flak tower on their first run, then damaged 25 locomotives, three repair shops, and a round-house. On the following day twelve planes launched 37 rockets at the airfields at Coulommiers, hitting one large and four small hangars and a fuel dump. Later they riddled two staff cars and destroyed a bridge.

Sixty-four rocket sorties were flown on July 24 and 25, destroying 12 tanks, damaging 13, and hitting many other vehicles. Major General B. E. Meyers declared that the development of the HVAR had "resulted in providing the Army Air Forces with the best antitank weapon of the war."

In the landing operations in Southern France, the Navy provided the invasion troops with air support by carrier-based F6F's. These planes fired 693 rockets during the period August 15–29, and played a large part in the demoralization of German transport. As the Allied use of airborne rockets increased, the reports became more numerous of German ground forces which on the approach of rocket-firing aircraft left their vehicles and guns in headlong flight to seek cover.

In the Pacific theaters air-ground co-operation went through a similar evolution. The development of Combat Information Centers gave the Navy new techniques for the control of fighters, night fighters, and bombers, not merely for the defense of task forces and attacks on enemy ships, but for the support of our Marines and soldiers ashore.

Aircraft rockets were first fired from American planes in combat by the Army Air Force in Burma early in 1944. But it was the Navy that used them most. A Marine squadron, VMTB-134, flying Grumman torpedo bombers, had the distinction of firing the first Navy aircraft rockets at the Japanese. With only three days' training with the new weapons they put them to good use in a strike on Rabaul, February 15, 1944. Grumman and Martin torpedo bombers fired them in the Marshalls, Palau, New Guinea, Carolines, and Marcus-Wake actions. In the Marianas, from June 11 to August 1, Navy planes fired nearly 5000 rockets against the enemy. Rocket-firing F6F's took part in this first large-scale demonstration of the use of the rocket for close support.

When our forces landed on Saipan, Guam, Tinian, Iwo Jima, and Okinawa, they found the Japanese in caves, blockhouses, and pillboxes, artfully camouflaged and so well protected that only direct hits were effective. Aircraft rockets proved superior to bombs against such targets. Wave after wave of Navy planes flew in at low altitudes to blast the refuges from which the Japanese were taking such a toll of our advancing ground forces.

Aircraft introduced another effective method of knocking out Japanese gun positions when they began, during the landings on Tinian and Guam, to drop auxiliary fuel tanks on them filled with NDRC's famous thickened fuel, Napalm. With this new weapon direct hits were not necessary for the mixture spread over an area larger than that affected by the burst of a high-explosive bomb. The flaming gel burned off the natural growing cover, penetrated the slits in pillboxes, and suffocated and cooked the gunner. So intense was the effect of these incendiary attacks that enemy dead were sometimes found in the open air without a sign of a burn, but smothered to death by lack of oxygen.

The Allied Air Forces won control of the air over Germany by destroying in combat or on the ground more than 57,000 German planes at a cost of 18,000 American and 22,000 British planes lost or damaged beyond repair. Strategic bombing failed until the last few months of the war to lessen the *Luftwaffe's* strength in planes. Indeed 1944 was Germany's greatest year for aircraft production. But bombing finally curtailed Germany's supplies of oil and gasoline, and the combats in the skies killed off the best of her pilots and forced the *Luftwaffe* to rely on less bold and less skilled personnel.

Allied scientists contributed to this victory in the air through the selection, training, and equipment of superior pilots, and design and equipment of better planes, improved armament, and better fire control. Gun liners lengthened the life of our airborne machine-gun barrels, and of the gunner who used them. Improved sights and better training in gunnery, due in part to the frangible bullet, made our fighter pilots formidable antagonists.

Quite early in aerial combat it became essential to devise some means of warning a fighter pilot that an enemy plane was approaching from behind. The Radiation Laboratory solved this problem of tail warning with a radar set standardized as the AN/APS-13. This ingenious equipment indicated the presence of an enemy plane by ringing a bell and by lighting an indicator light in the cockpit. It was not until December 1944 that the first of these sets became operational in Europe, where they were installed immediately in the day and night reconnaissance planes of the 9th Tactical Air Force. Operationally the set was quite effective, although pilots considered the maximum range inadequate, especially against German jet-propelled craft which could overtake them at the rate of 100 yards per second.

Airborne gunnery was greatly improved by sights developed by Division 7 and by radar range finders developed by Division 14, such as the Falcon for the fixed 75-mm. cannon and fixed .50-caliber machine guns in the nose of the B-25 H plane; or the comparable aids to flexible gunnery, AN/APG-5 for turret gunners and AN/APG-15 for tail gunners of heavy bombers. Tests conducted by NDRC showed that a turret gunner's tracking ability increased fourfold when he was freed by radar of the job of estimating range. The APG-15's installed in the B-29 plane produced a three- to fourfold increase in hits. Both the Applied Mathematics Panel and the Applied Psychology Panel made important contributions to the effectiveness of the B-29.

The Royal Air Force, after suffering heavy losses in day bombing, soon came to rely on night bombing for its strategic offensive. The American Air Forces, on the other hand, relied on day bombers, which would fight their way to the target, if need be relying on the massed strength of their guns as the planes supported one another in tight formations. Both great air forces learned to their cost that they had to deal with a resourceful foe.

Ground-controlled night interception is probably the most complex form of aerial combat. A control officer on the ground or on a ship directs the fighter pilot towards his foe by means of radar, and coaches him by voice transmission to a point where the fighter pilot picks up the enemy plane on his own radar screen and closes in for the kill. The British had first introduced this tactic during the Battle of Britain, but the Germans later used it with great effect, inflicting a loss of 100 bombers on the R.A.F. during the attack on Nuremberg on the night of March 30–31, 1944. For a time there was some question as to whether or not the R.A.F. could continue its night attacks.

To keep the enemy guessing as to the real target for the night, the British resorted to diversionary and "spoof" raids accompanied by jamming of the Germans' air defense communications system. Improvements in Allied radar for night fighters were pushed vigorously, both for the famous Black Widows and for the deadly F6F-5(N)'s. The greater range of the new systems made possible intruder missions over enemy airfields to disrupt the foe's night operations. These improved sets permitted the use of the F6F-5(N) against ground and ship targets at night and to escort radar-equipped torpedo and dive bombers in pre-dawn attacks.

The American theory that bombers could fight their way to the target without fighter escort was demolished by German rocket-firing planes in the space of a few minutes. Our tight formations offered a tempting target for rocket fire and the Germans chose their weapons well, introducing an 8.27-inch spin-stabilized rocket of great hitting power.[6] When 228 heavy bombers set out to attack the ball-bearing plants at Schweinfurt on October 14, 1943, the Germans waited till the American formations had left their fighter escorts behind, and attacked

[6]They also experimented during this period with air-to-air bombing, and used captured Flying Fortresses against our formations. If they had succeeded in their attempt to develop a proximity fuze for rockets, the results would have been serious.

savagely in waves from the German frontier to Schweinfurt and back. Our bombers dropped more than 450 tons of high explosives and incendiaries, inflicting heavy damage on the target, though production was soon restored to normal. Out of the 228 bombers that set out for Schweinfurt 62 were lost and 138 damaged, some beyond repair. We lost 599 men killed and 40 wounded. This ended our deep penetrations of Germany without escort, but the advent of the long-range P-51 fighter plane known as the Mustang, in December 1943, enabled us to provide fighter cover for bombing squadrons all the way to the target.

The German flak remained the best in the world until NDRC uncovered its triple threat, the SCR-584 radar, the M-9 director, and the proximity fuze, to shoot down the buzz-bombs in the summer of 1944. Flak inflicted such severe losses on the 8th Air Force in 1943 that day bombing might have had to be suspended if we had not found a way to blind the eyes of the German fire-control radars.

The first step in jamming an enemy's radar or communications system is to find out the location of his stations and the frequencies on which he is operating. Just as a bombardment or an assault must be preceded by aerial photography and careful study of the resulting pictures, a jamming maneuver must be preceded by mapping and analyses of the enemy's radar resources and of his communications network. The specialized planes carrying a series of search receivers were called Ferrets. The first American Ferret set out in January 1943 to find a Japanese radar installation on Kiska, whose suspected presence had been suggested by photoreconnaissance. Two second lieutenants fresh out of radar school made the initial flight, found the signal, homed on it, and confirmed the photographic report. They logged the station's frequency, power, and pulse repetition frequency and provided the data necessary for indicating its coverage.

The information they brought back proved of much value to Major General Butler in planning the coming air offensive of his 11th Air Force. The Ferret pilots showed the bombers how to approach the radar station with the least risk of detection and where bomb hits on it would be likely to do the most damage. The success of this pioneering effort got ferreting off to a good start.

Shortly after the first Ferret mission in the Aleutians, three B-17's equipped as Ferrets undertook a far more ambitious series of missions in the Mediterranean. Their problem was to locate and investigate all enemy radar along the Mediterranean coast from Spain to Crete. It was a demanding assignment since they found a radar site every thirty miles along that coast. Adopted by the 16th Reconnaissance Wing, they maintained an up-to-date record which laid the basis for an effective countermeasure program in the Mediterranean theater.

A Ferret plane might contain twenty or more antennae, a variety of receivers, pulse analyzers, jammers, compasses, and odographs, as well as Loran for navigational purposes. The operator's duties might run round the clock. After a mission of eight or ten hours he would report his observations to the intelligence officers and then go into a huddle with the photointelligence officers to co-ordinate their findings. From maps which they drew up, they plotted out the paths of approach to circumvent enemy radar coverage and determine specific countermeasures.

As the Pacific war neared its end and we moved closer to the main Japanese islands, five specially equipped B-24 Ferrets of a new design were operating over Japan. They supplemented the information as to Japanese radar coverage supplied by the search receivers in our submarines. And they often co-operated with the Heckler teams, composed of fighter planes and torpedo bombers, whose task it was to neutralize Japanese airfields in the vicinity of carrier operations. All Superfortresses carried Window and Rope, which was believed to be particularly effective against the Japanese low-frequency radars, and at least one electronic jammer as well.[7]

The losses of the 8th Air Force at one period in 1943 became so heavy that, if continued at the same rate, they would have required the replacement of that Force's air strength two and a half times per year. Something had to be done and done quickly about the small Würzburgs which controlled the German flak so accurately. The British used Window for the first time over Hamburg on the night of July 24–25, 1943, and the *Luftwaffe* and the 8th Air Force soon followed suit. The Radio Research Laboratory of Division 15 developed narrower and more economical types of Chaff and a high-speed cutter which solved the problem of mass production of this invaluable material. As the little slips

[7]See below, pp. 163–164.

fluttered slowly earthward they returned echoes which cluttered the
scopes of German radars and made them as impotent as a long-distance
movie camera in a blizzard. Chaff lent itself to deception, or "spoof"
tactics, as well as to the protection of bomber formations.

Instead of shifting to microwave radar, as they might have done had
they not thrown away two years of research time on Hitler's orders, the
Germans strove feverishly to render their existing sets jam-proof. To
make their task more difficult the 8th Air Force introduced in October
the electronic jammer known as Carpet, which proved a most telling
countermeasure. On the first raid against Bremen the planes equipped
with Carpet suffered 50 per cent fewer losses than those without it.

While the Germans struggled to find countermeasures against Carpet
and Window, the Allies crossed them up by combining the two in the
same operation. The beauty of this was that anti-jamming measures
taken to circumvent Window rendered the Würzburgs more vulnerable
to Carpet, and vice versa. The combination of the two types of jamming
thus proved to be far more effective than either type alone.

One of the great crises of the war was thus surmounted. The R.A.F.
and the AAF were able not only to continue their pressure on German
industry but vastly to increase it. Unless the Germans could shift their
radar to a shorter wave length than those we could jam, or develop jet-
propelled fighters or a proximity fuze, they could no longer hope to
blast the Allied bombers from their skies.

It is unfortunate that the use of such phrases as "pin point" and
"pickle barrel" bombing gave the public erroneous notions of the accuracy attainable from high altitudes under normal operating conditions.
What the Air Forces designated as "the target area" was a circle having
a radius of 1000 feet around the aiming point of attack. The over-all
figures of the United States Strategic Bombing Survey show that only
about one bomb in five of those aimed at precision targets fell within
the target area as so defined.[8]

The low-altitude radar bombsight (LAB) proved a great aid to both
Army and Navy planes in the destruction of Japanese shipping. The
13th Air Force pioneered with LAB in the Solomons area, and the 5th,
late in 1943, extended its use westward into the Bismarck Sea, then
farther north and west to Mindanao. In 233 missions conducted in a

[8]A peak of accuracy of 70 per cent was attained during February 1945.

period of six months, mostly in daylight, the 5th claimed to have sunk 122,050 tons and damaged 65,650.

It was Major General Claire Chennault's 14th Air Force that really brought LAB into its own during the summer of 1944 on night missions over the China Sea. During June, July, and August the 14th sank 113,400 tons of cargo shipping, damaged 54,300 more, and claimed a bag of seven warships. In the single month of September they sank 110,000 tons, or 1700 tons per sortie. These losses help to explain the motives of the Japanese in seizing Chennault's forward bases in the fall of 1944.

By developing radar, Gee, and Loran[9] the scientists made it possible for planes to locate the target by night and through the overcast, so that a much greater and steadier pressure of bombing could be maintained. The British took the lead in the development of these navigational aids, of which the Gee receiver was the most generally installed. This enabled the air navigator to determine his position by measuring the relative time of arrival of radio pulses emitted from three ground stations. Before the end of the war 80 per cent of the 8th Air Force was flying with it, and the 9th, 12th, and 15th were using it as well.

NDRC personnel collaborated with the British in the development of Oboe, which like Gee is both a navigational and a blind-bombing aid. Instead of a one-way signal, like those of Gee and Loran, Oboe employs an interrogator-responder system related to IFF. It was used extensively by British Pathfinders for night attacks on France and saw service with both the 8th and the 9th U.S. Air Forces.

Until the autumn of 1943, the 8th Air Force had been practically grounded during the winter, during which its planes could not operate more than one or two days a month. Having used the British H2S, they were looking for something better. The Radiation Laboratory provided this on a wave length of three centimeters in the guise of H_2X, the celebrated "Mickey," and built twenty sets on a crash basis while Philco engineers sweated over the production design and procurement.

On November 3, 1943, nine B-17 Pathfinder planes, equipped with Mickey, took off in solid overcast, each leading a combat wing of 60 planes. Their target was the dock area of Wilhelmshaven, which eight previous visual raids had missed. Through overcast extending to 20,000

[9]See below, pp. 150–152.

feet they found their way to the target, dropped their markers, and bombed it by radar. In the following two months planes equipped with H₂X guided fifteen large-scale bombing missions to their targets, which included Münster, Bremen, Kiel, Hamburg, and Solingen.

From this time on air forces in every theater relied increasingly on Mickey, though it was not as accurate as visual bombing. During February 1944, H₂X led the way to Hitler's aircraft and ball-bearing industries. In March, 191 aircraft equipped with Mickey took off and of these 181 reached their designated target. So lively was the demand that a training school for Mickey operators, established in England, turned out 75 graduates a month.

The intricate pattern of air attack on D-Day depended heavily on H₂X for navigational as well as bombing purposes. A few weeks later in the invasion of Southern France Pathfinder planes equipped with H₂X again solved the problem of navigation. After a night take-off, the lead Pathfinder operator guided the lead ship of the second bombing group to the assembly position. After assembly the bombers depended entirely upon Pathfinder planes to determine winds and drift and to bring the formation to the beach targets at precisely the proper time. As in Normandy, perfect timing was vital to the success of the mission and to the safety of our own troops in the area. Without the aid of H₂X it is doubtful whether it would have been possible to achieve such a precise feat of navigation.

In the Pacific the 20th, and later the 21st, Bomber Commands were equally dependent upon H₂X (APQ-13, the equivalent in B-29's of APS-15 in B-24's and B-17's). Its debut came in what amounted to little more than a shakedown raid over Bangkok in the spring of 1944. Not until the middle of June, when the 20th Bomber Command first hit the Japanese home land, did the equipment have a real operational test. It got the planes there and back through the night over unknown territory. Much of the navigational success of this equipment came from the full emphasis which the Bomber Command gave to training personnel in the capacities and limitations of radar navigation, in which briefing itself played a very important part.

While Loran stations were spreading round the world and the Radio Corporation of America's excellent navigational and blind-bombing aid, Shoran, was proving its worth, the Radiation Laboratory perfected its high-resolution navigational aid and radar bombsight known as Eagle. This had been installed in a few bombers rushed to the 8th and 15th Air Forces but not in time to see service in Europe. In the closing phase of the Pacific war, Eagle won golden opinions, beginning with the strike against the Maruzen Oil Refinery at Shimotsu on July 6–7, 1945. General LeMay described it as the best radar bombing device yet seen in his command.

Bringing a plane down to a friendly base through overcast and fog is no less important than finding a target. This could be achieved by various systems, such as continuous signals from radio beams transmitted by the base, or by installing radar beacons at the base and a radar set in the plane. By still another system operators on the ground got a continuous radar picture of planes within a radius of thirty miles and could give a pilot accurate information as to his azimuth, elevation, and range from a distance of ten miles so that they could place him within fifty feet of the center of a runway.

Throughout the latter half of 1944 OSRD scientists had been giving much thought to the possibilities of large-scale use of incendiary bombs against Japanese cities. On October 12 one of them sent to Bush a memorandum which he transmitted to the Army Air Forces, containing a remarkable prediction of events to come: —

Advance estimates of force required and the damage to Japanese war potential expected from incendiary bombing of Japanese cities indicate that this mode of attack may be the golden opportunity of strategic bombardment in this war — and possibly one of the outstanding opportunities in all history to do the greatest damage to the enemy for a minimum of effort. Estimates of economic damage expected indicate that incendiary attack of Japanese cities may be at least five times as effective, ton for ton, as precision bombing of selected strategic targets as practiced in the European Theater. However, the dry economic statistics, impressive as they may be, still do not take account of the further and unpredictable effect on the Japanese war effort of a national catastrophe of such magnitude — entirely unprecedented in history.[10]

On March 9, 1945, Major General LeMay launched an all-out low-level incendiary attack on Tokyo at night by unarmed B-29's. It took courage to risk 300 unarmed aircraft on a new type of attack utterly

[10]R. H. Ewell to Bush, October 12, 1944.

opposed to the traditional doctrine of high-altitude precision bombing for which the B-29's had been expressly designed.

Probably no previous mission except the first historic one against Tokyo was sweated out with more anxiety. Two hundred seventy-nine B-29's loosed on urban Tokyo 1900 tons of incendiary bombs, with the M-69 predominating. The bombing took place at night, both visually and by radar, from altitudes of 5000 to 9000 feet.

On the afternoon of March 10, when one by one the B-29's came straggling back to the Marianas, the results began to unfold. Japanese defenses had been confused, and fighter opposition had been slight. We lost only three aircraft to enemy action and fourteen to all causes. Pilots reported how Tokyo had "caught fire like a forest of pine trees," with smoke towering to 18,000 feet and fire visible for 150 miles. Subsequent photographic coverage revealed almost sixteen square miles of the heart of Tokyo burned out in what was probably the most devastating air attack in history. Radio Tokyo reported: "It was worse than anything in Germany."

The B-29's carried a mixed load comprising M-69 aimable clusters and M-47 Napalm-filled bombs, but the major damage was attributed to the M-69.

Never before or since [runs a report of the 20th Air Force] has so much destruction resulted from any single bombardment mission regardless of the number of airplanes involved or the type of bombs employed. This mission was not only important in the air war against Japan because of the tremendous damage achieved, but it was also important in that it pointed the way to revolutionary new tactics for the employment of bombardment aircraft.

The Tokyo attack was followed by devastating night incendiary attacks on Nagoya, Kobe, and Osaka in quick succession. Indeed if the supply of incendiaries at the bases in the Marianas had not run short the 21st Bomber Command might possibly have brought Japan to surrender before the August raids on Hiroshima and Nagasaki. The preceding destructive incendiary raids had so weakened the morale of the Japanese people and demonstrated to their leaders the force of our air power that a very limited use of atomic bombs was necessary to bring the war to an end. These two historic missions carried out by B-29's from Tinian were in a sense the culmination of the air war. They did

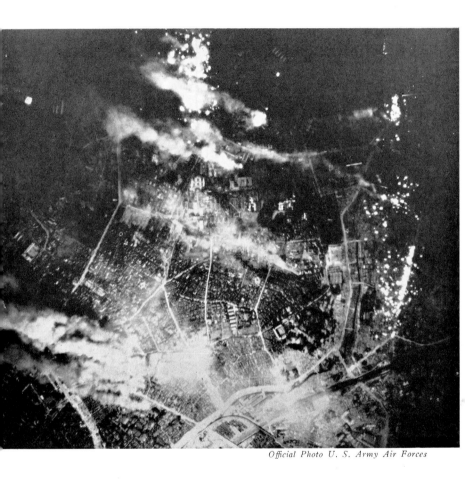

Official Photo U. S. Army Air Forces

A night incendiary raid on Tokyo, May 26, 1945

Life *Photo by George Sue*

How our incendiaries brought Japan to her knees: Tokyo at the end
of the war

less damage to life and property than the great incendiary raid of March 9–10 on Tokyo, but their effect on Japanese morale was decisive.

In all the incendiary attacks over 100,000 tons of bombs were dropped in the course of more than 15,000 sorties, against 66 Japanese cities ranging in population from Tokyo, with its teeming millions, to the fish-processing city of Tsuruga, with a population of 31,000. Nearly 169 square miles were destroyed or damaged in the 60 cities for which photographic reconnaissance was available, with more than 100 square miles burned out in the five major cities attacked. The destruction, including that caused by the two atomic bombs, mounted to over 42 per cent of the urban industrial areas involved. The 68 Japanese cities attacked with incendiaries and atomic bombs had in 1940 a total population of over 21,000,000, almost exactly equal to that of our twelve largest American cities. We can imagine the effect on our capacity to continue the war if the tables had been turned, and Japanese airmen had destroyed nearly half of any group of our industrial cities having a population of 21,000,000.

Premier Prince Naruhiko Hagashi-Kuni admitted that by June 1945, when all of the major cities of Japan had been attacked with incendiaries, Japan's ability to carry on modern warfare was "disastrously undermined," and that the destruction of the medium and small cities in rapid succession thereafter had "calamitous consequences." In addition to the destruction of industrial installations, the casualties caused had significant effect in the dislocation of industrial manpower and on enemy morale. The Japanese have stated that air attacks killed 260,000, injured 412,000, left 9,200,000 homeless, and demolished or burned down 2,210,000 houses.

The corresponding figures for Germany compiled by the United States Strategic Bombing Survey indicate that the Allied Air Forces destroyed or heavily damaged 3,600,000 dwelling units and rendered 7,500,000 persons homeless. These figures placed the total deaths at 305,000 and the wounded at 780,000. If these are the figures for air warfare in its "stage of full adolescence" the time to stop all warfare is now, before air power reaches its full maturity.

CHAPTER VII

LAND WARFARE

IT IS much easier for a scientist to devise new equipment for a ship or an airplane than for an infantryman who has to carry his weapons into battle. When GI's discuss the war's most useful novelties they are less likely to mention gear of their own than the jeep or the C-47, or, if they are engineers, the Bailey Bridge and the bulldozer.

One thing they passionately desired was a good land-mine detector. The War Department assigned it top priority. The Germans and Italians had a fine collection of mines, and they used them lavishly, and with great ingenuity. As a means of slowing up the enemy's advance they got results economically. Mines did so well in the Libyan Desert that they were used more widely in Italy, where belts and patches of anti-personnel mines protected forward positions, especially machine-gun emplacements, and antitank minefields were thrown in for good measure. Some mines would take a man's foot off just above the ankle, some would take off his leg. Others could put a tank out of action.

The approaches to Cassino, for example, along the valley and on the lower mountain slopes, were sowed with antitank and anti-personnel mines. As the minefields were covered by machine-gun and artillery fire, most clearing operations had to be done at night.

The surest method of dealing with mines reduced itself finally to a man crawling on his knees and probing carefully into the ground ahead of him with a bayonet or a pointed steel rod. With a longer probe and if the conditions of visibility and fire permitted, the work could be done standing up with some increased risk from trip wires. It was ticklish business, for a downward pressure of six to eight pounds would detonate a Schu mine. The procedure, once a suspicious object was located, was to dig away the earth from around it carefully, checking anxiously for anti-lifting devices if it was a mine. If the lifting did not have to be done silently, as was most often the case, the safest procedure was to dig the dirt away from the handle only, tie on a length of telephone wire, retire to a safe distance, and pull. A large percentage of mines the Germans laid had anti-lifting devices of one kind or another, some of them fiendish in conception, which made all such work extremely risky. Once the mine was out of the ground it had to be carefully disarmed by removing the detonator, and could then be considered safe.

Frequently the mines had trip wires connected to them which increased the danger area. They might run in any direction through grass or brush, at any height from ground level to about three or four feet high. They were exceedingly difficult to locate without setting off the mine; once again the surest method was a careful barehanded combing of the grass and brush ahead.

After the Germans had made such good use of mines in North Africa, the British and Americans pushed work on magnetic detectors. Under an NDRC contract the Hazeltine Service Company of New York developed a device so promising that the Army standardized it as the SCR-625 and bought over 100,000.[1] This was the major item used by the ground troops in mine detection, and the operators did not often miss a mine of the type for which it was designed, namely one with a large metallic content either in the mine itself or in the case. In the hands of a highly skilled operator the SCR-625 would sometimes detect mines with wood or plastic covers if they had as many as four or six nails in their construction or had metal parts in the detonator. Its effectiveness was limited by the quantities of shrapnel which covered the ground and by the fact that in certain areas of Italy the volcanic soil is highly magnetic.

A vehicular antitank-mine detector was developed by the Engineer Board and after a year of service tests was standardized as the AN/VRS-1. Approximately five a week were delivered beginning with July 15, 1944. This device consisted of a detector unit, carried on a hinged boom mounted in front of a jeep, and the necessary controls and electronic equipment. The boom was partially supported by a coil-spring tension so that the supporting wheels, which served to keep the detector at a uniform height over uneven ground, each carried a load of only twenty-five pounds. This unit swept a path six feet wide and could detect one of our M1A1 metallic mines buried to a depth of six inches. It could be driven at a speed of five miles per hour and would automatically stop short of a mine picked up by the detector, or a good-sized piece of shrapnel.

[1] This was the only American magnetic mine detector which was used in combat areas.

After this stop, the driver could back up, set the controls for individual operation of the four detector coils, and locate the mine by maneuvering the vehicle; or he could have recourse to a portable SCR-625.

The trouble with these devices was that the Germans, too, had thought of a magnetic mine detector, and had provided themselves with mines cased in wood or plastic, like the famous Schu mine, a wooden box with a hinged lid.

The detection of nonmagnetic mines was a large order. An Englishman proposed that dogs be used to locate them by scent, and hush-hush training programs were promptly instituted. The dogs did well in some field tests, but their performance in Italy was not as satisfactory.

Various sorts of mechanical devices were tried, with limited success. In one theater a large platform to carry troops over a minefield was constructed on sled runners, spaced to conform with the tracks of tanks. The tanks pulled the platform along, exploding the mines ahead of the sled. The British developed vehicles known as crabs and scorpions, equipped with flails to detonate mines in front of advancing troops. The Applied Mathematics Panel of NDRC made a careful analysis of the problem and recommended a roto-flail with chains striking the ground at right angles to a cylinder which was pushed ahead of a tank. A model was built incorporating this idea but did not meet with favor. A large mechanical mine-clearer, of American manufacture, was described by one irate division commander as the most effective roadblock his troops encountered in Europe. The tank bulldozer could be used to plow mines out of the ground and detonate the more sensitive types, but the Germans made this method more risky by planting occasional charges of several hundred pounds of explosives arranged to go off when an anti-tank mine was detonated. The explosion of a mine under the blade of a tank dozer usually would result in damaging the dozer blade to such an extent that it could not be used further.

Another approach to the problem was to construct a flexible tube called a snake, fill it with explosives, usually Bangalore torpedoes laid in side by side, and project it across a minefield to clear a narrow passage on detonation. The snake cleared a wide gap sufficient for the safe passage of foot soldiers but it was not certain for the full width of a tank. The explosion sometimes made buried Tellermines which were not exploded so "tender" that they would go off at the slightest touch. The

Engineer Board worked hard on this method which was used to good purpose at the time of the breakthrough from the Anzio beachhead.

Research on methods of breaching minefields was carried on by all echelons down to the squad. Most of them were field expedients and very rough but were occasionally successful. Usually they were confined to projecting primacord or a grapnel across a field by means of a mortar shell or bazooka rocket. Detonated primacord would cut trip wires but tended to hang too high in the grass to be effective on mines. If you threw a grapnel across a minefield and pulled it back it would catch on trip wires and detonate the mines attached to them.

NDRC's contributions to the field of mine clearance lay almost entirely in the field of detection. The SCR-625 did a good job on mines containing metal. For those that did not, another approach was required.

The Radio Corporation of America, under an NDRC contract, developed an electronic detection device which was standardized as the AN/PRS-1. It was, unfortunately, a rather complicated piece of apparatus. It is not easy to describe an arc just three inches above the ground, swinging like a scythe a nineteen-pound object. Rocks, roots, and holes gave false indications which the operator had to learn to distinguish from those given by a live mine. When the Germans sowed numerous anti-personnel mines of dimensions smaller than those the AN/PRS-1 had been designed to cope with, the device was naturally the scapegoat for men who had had a foot or leg blown off.

The Japanese mines were larger and less sensitive than German mines. At one point in the Okinawa campaign an American division was held up over a week by extensive minefields planted by the retreating Japanese, who used wooden-box and terracotta, or flowerpot, mines. The commanding general promptly launched an intensive training program in the use of the AN/PRS-1.

The difficulty of locating our own nonmetallic mines once they were laid resulted in a definite curtailment in their use by our forces in the field. To solve this problem of detection by friendly troops, NDRC, in co-operation with the Engineer Board, developed individual mine markers and a special detector.

The markers were pebble-like baked ceramics, of inconspicuous shapes and colors, impregnated with a radioactive substance. They were mixed into the dirt covering buried mines. The detector, carried on a soldier's back, consisted of a gamma-ray counter thirteen times as sensitive as the most efficient counter known before the war. When the detector approached a marker, the radiation was indicated by a change of tone in the operator's headset. This device was simple, rapid, and efficient and was not affected by proximity to metal or by volcanic soils of magnetic content. It could be used at night by patrols to get through our own minefields or through enemy fields after lanes had been cleared and marked.

The development of a waterproofed magnetic detector for the use of underwater demolition teams was still another problem. NDRC took a magnetic device which had been contrived by the Department of Terrestrial Magnetism of the Carnegie Institution of Washington and adapted it for this purpose. It was standardized as the AN/PSS-1, and was procured in small quantities by the Engineer Board.

Despite the large amount of research expended on new devices for land-mine detection and clearance, the soldier on his hands and knees with a probe accounted for more enemy mines than did all the various detectors. The best of the lot was the SCR-625. But the scientists were not able to give the GI a sense of security in dealing with this most difficult problem.

It would be hard to overstate, on the other hand, the beneficial effects on morale of the remarkable advances made in the treatment of wounded. It was the first war in history in which a soldier could say to himself that if he were not killed outright he was reasonably certain to recover.

American Army casualties in all theaters totaled 943,222, including 201,367 killed, 570,783 wounded, 114,205 prisoners, 56,867 missing.[2] Although the infantry comprised only one fifth of our Army strength overseas it took 70 per cent of the total casualties. But the amazing improvements of surgery and medical care "reduced the rate of death from wounds to less than one-half the rate in World War I, and permitted more than 58.8 per cent of men wounded in this war to return to duty in the theaters of operations."[3] Ninety-seven per cent of the casualties survived if they lived to reach front-line dressing stations.

[2]Of the total wounded, prisoners, or missing more than 633,200 returned to duty or were evacuated to the United States. The battle deaths were greater than the combined Union and Confederate losses in the Civil War. *Biennial Report of the Chief of Staff of the United States Army. July 1, 1943, to June 30, 1945*, p. 107.

[3]*Ibid.*, p. 108.

Minefield detection: sweeping an area near Venafro, Italy

American paratroopers knock out a Nazi tank with bazooka fire

The American soldier was a healthier and better fed fighting man than the world had hitherto seen. Medical scientists had increased his chances of survival, diminished his risk of infection, and speeded the rapidity of his recovery from wounds and disease. To lessen the incidence of combat fatigue, psychiatrists not only made exhaustive case studies but set up greatly improved procedures for handling the many casualties of this sort which occur in modern warfare.

As World War II mounted in intensity, psychiatric cases became increasingly a problem. Psychoneurotic casualties not only affected available manpower but severely taxed the medical resources of the Army. If tuberculosis accounted for the highest percentage of medical casualties in the First World War, psychiatric problems proved to be the largest single category of disability discharges in the Second. Roughly speaking, for every five men wounded, one was killed and one became psychiatrically disabled.

A notable commission, sent to the European theater in April 1945 under the joint auspices of the Office of Field Service, OSRD, and the New Developments Division, War Department Special Staff, concluded that the picture of psychological disorganization known as "combat fatigue" did not correspond either in its moderate or in its extreme form to any recognized or established psychiatric syndrome. It had elements of excitement, of inhibition, of terror, of panic, of depression, of anxiety, and of dissociation. It was not merely a state of "exhaustion," nor a neurosis in the ordinary sense.

No other branch of medicine or surgery probably conserved manpower for the armed forces more effectively than psychiatry. Of all neuropsychiatric casualties occurring in the Army Ground Forces in the European theater 80 per cent were returned to duty, though probably not more than 30 per cent to combat.

The blood program had much to do with the marked reduction of mortality among battle casualties for it enabled quick succor in cases involving hemorrhage, burns, and shock. Success was due on the one hand to a vast national effort in which blood donors, the American Red Cross, and the Air Transport Command teamed up to save tens of thousands of lives; on the other hand to new discoveries by medical scientists, such as the work of Dr. Edwin Cohn and his associates on fractionization of blood albumin.

The net result was to increase enormously the chances of survival and the morale of our fighting men, and to add to our armed strength the equivalent of several divisions. One of the major surgical discoveries of the war was that wounded men suffered from rapid destruction of proteins and red blood cells and consequently needed a diet rich in proteins supplemented by transfusions of whole blood.

At the same time that mortality from wounds and disease was greatly reduced, the health of the Army was maintained at a higher level than that of any civilian population. Here again the contribution to the effective strength of the armed forces was enormous. Penicillin alone was worth more than an Army corps in speeding recoveries from syphilis, gonorrhea, and pneumonia.

In no previous war had so large a proportion of the armed forces fought under the extreme conditions of high altitude or northern latitudes, deserts, and tropical jungles. OSRD aided the Quartermaster Corps to provide clothing and equipment suited to these varied environments. A study of methods of treating leather to retain pliability at low temperatures resulted in one procedure which permitted the leather to remain pliable at thirty degrees below zero Fahrenheit. Many tests were made of the strength, waterproofing, and flameproofing of materials, and various substitutes were found for materials in short supply.

The Committee on Medical Research conducted studies on the need of the human body for water which afforded a firm basis from which to attack the problems of desert warfare and air-sea rescue. It had been widely believed that troops destined for desert warfare could be trained in such a way as materially to lessen their water requirement. Exhaustive investigation showed that this was no more possible than for a man by taking thought to add a cubit to his stature.

One of the awkward features of operations in tropical jungles is that high humidity, excessive rainfall, and high temperature affect the performance of equipment and material. The prevention of fungus attack on fabrics and optical instruments becomes a major problem. An OSRD Committee on Tropical Deterioration studied methods of packaging, lacquering, and spraying instruments and materials destined for the tropics, and effected important savings.

In tropical climates clothing is of enormous importance to health and morale. Scientists tested cloth for durability; coolness as affected by air temperature, humidity, and radiation; warmth on men sleeping out at night; speed of drying, and ease of cleaning. The importance of clothing in preventing mosquito bites ranks second only to the use of atabrine in malaria control, for most combat troops spend their nights without the protection of mosquito nets. It was found that mosquitoes bit readily through herringbone twill, Army twill, and cellular weave, the fabrics which had been in general use for jungle uniforms, but that other fabrics gave better protection. The color of clothing, moreover, is important not merely from the standpoint of camouflage, but because it affects the amount of radiation absorbed.

CMR scientists made important studies of the relation of clothing to fatigue in the tropics, and found that trained men can run long distances faster when wearing poplin than when wearing herringbone twill suits. Poplin was also warmer on cool nights, probably because it dries more quickly.

Care of the combat soldiers' feet is one of the major problems of tropical, as it is of mountain and arctic, warfare. No completely satisfactory combat boot for all-round use in the jungle was developed, but progress was made toward a lighter boot, which was important because it requires four times as much energy for a soldier to carry a pound of weight on his feet as in his pack. The scientists studied socks as well as boots, and urged that each soldier be provided with two extra pairs of socks. Skin trouble, so common in Burma, India, and the Pacific, was the subject of careful investigation. Other studies dealt with the problem of glare in desert areas, which is so intense that men often, on first arrival, cannot adapt to it within minutes or even within a period of hours.

As the war progressed, some three million soldiers moved into highly infected malarial regions in North Africa, the China-Burma-India theater, and the South Pacific. In the absence of successful preventive measures, half of these men would have become malarial casualties in the first mosquito season. This disease caused many more casualties to our troops in the hard-fought Buna-Gona campaign than did Japanese bullets. In the early days on New Guinea the malaria rate was running at 4000 per 1000 per year. Before the fighting was over the rate in several New Guinea areas stood lower than that in Louisiana.

Part of the story is the successful quest for a substitute for quinine, resulting — after the testing of thousands of compounds — in the discovery of one drug far more effective than anything hitherto known as a suppressive of malaria. Part of the story lay in mosquito control, for here, as in so many other phases of warfare, it was necessary to take the offensive.

A small bomb of DDT effected total destruction of mosquitoes and other flying insects in rooms or tents, and even in caves and foxholes. The persistent effects of a DDT spray, moreover, suggested that with infrequent spraying of larval breeding places it might be possible to abolish all mosquito-borne diseases from large portions of the world. The malaria rate in Sardinia and Corsica had seemed to the Germans and Italians too high to permit their full utilization as air bases. We cleaned them up with DDT and used them as bases not only for air squadrons, but for the invasion of Southern France. DDT proved so successful as a louse killer that it nipped in the bud a serious outbreak of typhus in Naples.

The men of the Red Arrow Division who crossed the Owen Stanley Range on foot or by plane got within three miles of Buna Village on November 19, 1942, and for days were stopped in their tracks. By that time most of them had malaria, many had been killed or wounded, and some of them had never seen the foe who raised death against them from cleverly concealed positions in the New Guinea jungle. Dogged heroism, timely reinforcements, and some sorely needed tanks and artillery brought along the north coast by sea enabled them to take Buna and Gona. Their hardships and their losses focused attention on new gear for jungle fighting.

One great contribution of NDRC to the infantrymen in the jungle was the improvement of the portable flame thrower. The Japanese pill-boxes and camouflaged strongpoints protected by coconut logs were hard to detect from a bombing plane, or to blast with any weapon men could carry. The flame thrower of World War I was a fearsome weapon, but its range was short, its aim uncertain, and only about 10 per cent of the flame reached its destination. The introduction of thickened fuels enabled the man with the flame thrower to project a rod of flame to greatly increased ranges with sufficient accuracy to find the slits in the Japanese defenses. He could put 80 per cent or more of the flame where he wanted it. By this means a single determined man could rout the Japanese from strongpoints that had held up a company.

The road back — the toll of combat

Eighteenth Field Artillery launches rocket barrage in Hurtgen Forest,
November 26, 1944

Pack flame throwers played an important part in the capture of Munda Airfield and in the island battles in the Central Pacific. The naval bombardment of Kwajalein, supplemented by artillery fire from a near-by island, amounted to about five times the pre-invasion shelling of Tarawa. But there were enough Japanese left alive in their pillboxes to make the going rugged for the men of the 7th Infantry Division. They threw hand grenades to drive the enemy back from the entrances to their shelters and then tossed white phosphorus grenades in among them.

Riflemen covered the advance of Private Charles R. Craig, a soldier of slight stature, carrying a pack flame thrower which gave him a load of seventy pounds.

He was getting only about ten seconds of fire out of each fuel load and would usually exhaust it in one burst. Then he would jog back to the dump, 400 yards away, and come up with a fresh load. Twice his weapon broke and he had to hike back for a new one. Although he attacked upwards of a dozen shelters, necessitating that many trips back and forth, he did not tire. In his own words, "Excitement kept me going."[4]

West of Eniwetok Americans had to fight, not on low-lying atolls, but on rugged islands honeycombed with caves and studded with fortifications cleverly camouflaged and tucked away in hillsides. These were far less vulnerable to shell fire, rockets, and aerial bombing than the defenses of Tarawa or Kwajalein. The Japanese had an amazing capacity for making the most of the ground, and a fanatical readiness to die that made them hard to budge. They made effective use of mortars and inflicted heavy casualties.

Their strong defensive positions could be destroyed by demolition charges and by flame throwers, but to get close enough with these weapons was a costly business. The mechanized flame thrower, whose development had been hindered by events related in a later chapter, here proved itself useful.

One flame-throwing tank on Guam approached a cave on Azan Point while covered by the fire of another tank, blew half of a charge into the cave, and killed seventeen Japanese. On the approach of a second flame-throwing tank, three snipers fled from another cave and were shot by infantry. Others began to scream when three short bursts penetrated a

[4]Lt. Col. S. L. A. Marshall, *Island Victory, Infantry Journal,* Washington, D. C., 1944, p. 90.

third cave, and hastily surrendered. Similar successes were scored during the heavy fighting on Saipan, Peleliu, and Okinawa.[5]

Nowhere did the Japanese put up grimmer resistance than on the volcanic island of Iwo. Close to 40,000 tons of shells and bombs fell on its eight square miles, while its determined defenders made the most of their strong defensive positions.

Pfc. Robert Fransko was a flame thrower operator. On D plus 7 a company of the 9th [Marines] First Battalion was held up by an emplacement on a ridge which had contained a dual-purpose gun, but now contained mortars and machine guns. Fransko ran across a field of fire 40 yards wide, let go several bursts into the main entrance of the cave, frying the Japs there. He walked through the main tunnel, spraying his flame into other openings. He picked up a bazooka, fired nearly a dozen rounds at an approaching Jap tank, one of the few mobile tanks the Japs had (most of their tanks were buried deep into the earth, and used as armored pillboxes). After he knocked out the tank, Fransko was wounded in the right arm. Ordered to the rear, he carried an empty flame thrower for refilling; it might be needed.[6]

The problem of the foot soldier facing a tank was even graver than that of the jungle fighter versus the pillbox, for the tank had mobility plus a heavy weapon. One line of approach advocated by NDRC was the development of antitank artillery with unusually high muzzle velocities, applying the familiar formula that the hitting power of a projectile varies with its mass and with the square of its velocity. We fought most of the war without as effective a weapon as the German 88, and by the time our fine 90-mm. dual-purpose gun got into action the Germans had proved what Division 1 of NDRC had long been preaching, the possibility of developing field pieces of still higher muzzle velocities.

The combination of a rocket, with its lack of recoil, and a shaped-charge war head gave the foot soldier a portable weapon that would knock a hole in a tank or pillbox.[7] The first model of the bazooka, despite recognized technical imperfections, was rushed through production in 1942 and demonstrated its effectiveness in November of that year in the Allied landings in North Africa. At Salerno, in Sep-

[5]Before the end of the war the Canadians had used flame throwers in more than 3000 operations.

[6]Robert Sherrod, *On to Westward,* 1945, p. 206. Reprinted by permission of the publishers, Duell, Sloan & Pearce, Inc.

[7]On shaped charges, see below, p. 259; on the bazooka, p. 204.

tember of 1943, bazookas destroyed seven enemy tanks in one day.

In spite of its short range — it was most effective within 200 yards — the bazooka dealt crippling blows to enemy armor and gave a great lift to the morale of the GI.

We had been hard hit [recalls a private who won the Bronze Star], and all of our bazooka men had become casualties. This Mark VI tank was really giving us a going over, and something had to be done about it. Although I had never used a bazooka before, I knew how to handle it. So one of my buddies loaded the weapon for me, and I crawled up a ditch until I was close to the German tank [he was within 40 yards]. I couldn't miss, and let them have it. That one round really did the trick.

As a German Tiger tank, spearheading a counterattack on an American position, lumbered forward, a sergeant who had never fired such a rocket, dropped by a wounded bazookaman, seized his weapon and fired at the track, 75 yards away. The tank's machine gun and supporting German riflemen opened up on him. He reloaded and sent a second rocket crashing home, immobilizing the tank, whose crew abandoned it. Our riflemen smashed what was left of the counterattack, and the sergeant won the Silver Star.

Bazookamen found that their improved weapon frequently performed beyond their expectations. Combat reports tell of holes driven through a six-foot pillbox wall, of masonry walls blasted with holes big enough for a man to crawl through, of tank crews killed by fragments spalled off the inside of eight-inch armor plating, although the shaped charge did not penetrate the armor.

Experience in the Pacific showed that even when the bazooka did not destroy the heavy Japanese pillboxes, its concussion stunned the occupants and gave infantrymen an opportunity to rush in and dispatch the enemy at close range. The bazooka was highly effective against Japanese tanks, which were more lightly armored than the German.

In one fierce action on Luzon, soldiers of the 6th Infantry Division fought a close-range battle against the Japanese tanks which, firing at point-blank range, were mowing down American antitank gunners as fast as they manned their weapons. "We tore into them with rifle grenades and bazookas, the only weapons we could use under the circumstances," a sergeant reported. His battalion claimed fifty-seven Japanese tanks in the battle.

Combat experience was translated into modifications which made the bazooka a more convenient weapon. A two-piece launcher permitted easier carrying and better concealment from observation than was possible with the original one-piece launcher. A trigger-operated magneto replaced battery ignition. The sight also was improved.

Versatility of the bazooka was increased with the development of a bazooka smoke rocket loaded with white phosphorus. This was particularly effective against Jap bunkers and caves. Ingenious American soldiers who knew that the longest way around was sometimes the shortest way home also used rockets to project telephone wire across ground that was mined or exposed to enemy fire. And they used dummy rockets to carry detonating cables out over minefields where the cables were set off, exploding the mines.

The American answer to heavier German armor and to Germany's large rockets consisted of two improved rockets — the super-bazooka and the 3.5-inch rocket. The superiority of the super-bazooka motor over that of the original bazooka was achieved by the use of an improved igniter and a heavier charge of propellant, the latter consisting of many thin disk-shaped grains, stacked in a stepped-back column to allow freer flow of the gases toward the nozzle.

The explosive power and the 4000-yard range of the Army's folding-fin 4.5-inch aircraft rocket indicated that it could be used as a ground force weapon to supplement the artillery. As compared with artillery, the rocket lacked range, velocity, and point accuracy; but the absence of recoil made possible the launching of rockets from lightweight devices which were easily moved and quickly set up in places where artillery could not go. Furthermore, by massing a number of launching tubes or rails on a single mount, our forces could fire a great many rockets from one launcher in a very short time.

When such multiple launchers were used, the inherent dispersion of rockets became an advantage for certain types of fire; for without changing the position of the launcher, our forces could spread rockets over a beaten zone of predeterminable size. Rockets were able in this way to lay down a drenching fire upon an area target such as a patch of woods, a town, or a supply depot so quickly that enemy personnel had no time to take cover.

The 18th Field Artillery Battalion in the United States First Army, equipped with 75 launchers, went on an offensive mission in support of infantry in mid-November, 1944. It continued in action until the seventeenth of December, and on the last two days helped materially to resist the German surprise offensive which opened the Battle of the Bulge. The intensity of drenching rocket fire was demonstrated on one occasion when the battalion fired approximately 1800 rounds in 18 minutes. Even official reports, usually restrained in their language, described the effect on the morale of enemy troops as "terrific."

"Calliope," another launching device, was designed to permit a tank to lay down its own artillery barrage. After the rockets were fired, the Calliope could be quickly jettisoned from inside the tank, if so desired, without exposing any of the tank crew. Eleven Sherman tanks of the 710th Tank Battalion, equipped with Calliope launchers, had sufficient fire power to lay 660 rockets on a breakthrough area in a matter of minutes.

The rockets' ability to hurl heavy projectiles from light launchers provided a countermeasure to the Japanese tactic of holing up behind cocoanut log bunkers deep in the jungles of Pacific islands. The folding-fin 4.5-inch rocket had the power to blast these bunkers, and the Ordnance Department developed an expendable plastic tube launcher in which the rocket was shipped and from which it was fired.

The Marines in the Pacific theater used Navy 4.5-inch finned barrage rockets extensively in ground operations. Four Provisional Marine Rocket Detachments each had twelve one-ton trucks mounting three twelve-round automatic launchers, supplemented by lighter installations. These rocket detachments supplied concentrations of fire for special needs. When ground advance was held up by a local Jap strongpoint, the commanding officer called up as much rocket equipment as seemed necessary. With this equipment came a skeleton crew, which was supplemented for ammunition passing and launcher loading by whoever was available on the spot — riflemen, cooks, signalmen, or machine gunners. If these localized concentrations of rocket fire did not completely knock out enemy machine-gun positions and troop concentrations, they drove the Japanese under cover long enough for other Marines to get to them and overwhelm them.

Ground-fired barrage rockets were used effectively in this fashion on Guam, Saipan, Tinian, Iwo Jima, and Okinawa. One restrained report sums up the verdict on them: "The rockets are very popular with the various combat units because of the effective support they provide."

Before the end of the war, California Institute of Technology developed chemical warfare rockets which the Army and Navy standardized. The 7.2-inch chemical rocket had a range of 3300 yards and carried a pay load of 20 pounds of gas or other chemical agent. Had the enemy resorted to gas, rockets as a means of laying down gas would have fulfilled a requirement imposed on the Allied Forces by this sort of warfare. A modification of this 7.2-inch chemical warfare rocket was also designed for the laying down of smoke screens.

Whiz Bangs (launchers mounted on General Sherman tanks) and 7.2-inch demolition rockets were included in the invasion army which landed in Southern France in July 1944. The Navy also used the 7.2-inch demolition rocket, and for its firing from LCM's developed a 120-barrel launcher nicknamed the Woofus. The Navy tried many rounds of this rocket at Salerno, at Anzio beachhead, and during the invasion of Southern France.

The spinner and its launchers were late developments in the war, and the first Honeycomb launchers and the spinner rockets sent as a special mission to the European theater pursued the retreating Germans across Central Germany and into Czechoslovakia, before they found a suitable target in the remnants of a Panzer division dug in at the edge of a woods. From a range of 4670 yards three Honeycombs threw 71 rounds in 15 seconds against the enemy with good effect.

Towards the end of the war, five rocket battalions were being organized and trained by the Field Artillery at Fort Sill, Oklahoma. Each was equipped with 36 Honeycomb launchers for firing Army 4.5-inch spinners. One of these battalions was on Okinawa and another in the Philippines, in preparation for the assault on the Japanese home islands, when the war ended.

Radar gave the infantrymen early warning of the approach of enemy planes and a hitherto unheard-of accuracy in antiaircraft fire. It made possible, moreover, much more effective air support of ground troops. Under favorable conditions Microwave Early Warning sets could pick up a heavy bomber over 200 miles away and at altitudes over 30,000 feet.

Two microwave SCR-584's and one 545 reached the hard-pressed

Anzio beachhead on February 24, 1944, by LST from Naples. It was their job to help our AA guns keep the skies clear above the 100 square miles of beachhead, for the enemy had done a thorough job of jamming the longer-wave SCR-268's.[8] On the second night after they were installed, twelve enemy bombers came over in formation, believing the eyes of our flak gunners had been blinded. In a few minutes half the formation came plummeting down in flames. That was the end of formation bombing at Anzio. Thereafter, enemy planes scattered before getting into flak range, resorted to violent evasive action, and bombed less accurately than before. In one night the new radars had virtually transformed defense against air attack on the beachhead. By May 6, when the certified account of downed planes was 46, the AA batteries equipped with SCR-584's claimed 37.

Still another use to which this versatile radar set was put toward the close of the war was in locating enemy mortars. This was only moderately successful in Italy, on account of the difficulty of moving cumbersome equipment in mountainous terrain.

When a mortar projectile was detected, the equipment was thrown into automatic tracking. Three five-second readings were then taken on slant range, azimuth, and elevation dials. The parabolic path of the shell was then determined by plotting, and the mortar's location computed by backward extrapolation. This point was checked closely against maps and aerial photographs. Under favorable conditions accuracies as high as 10 to 15 yards were obtained, although under most operational conditions an accuracy of 75 yards was average.

Although the proximity fuze had been jealously guarded and used at first only at sea, the Allied High Command determined to use it for howitzer fire in the offensive planned for December. Before this could be launched the Germans beat us to the punch, starting the great struggle known as the Battle of the Bulge. Fortunately the VT-fuzes were on hand to help stop the drive towards Liège and Antwerp. They were used against the *Luftwaffe* on December 16, the first day of the German drive, and against ground troops for the first time two days later. As

---

[8]The 268's were long-wave radars and could not see through the enemy's Window at all. The 545's were long-wave except for microwave fire control. Their vision through enemy Window was half good and half poor. The SCR–584's were all microwave; and though the enemy used ever-increasing quantities of Window as the battle of Anzio progressed, and though tracking consequently became more difficult, the operators of the SCR–584 developed ever-increasing skill in tracking on cluttered scopes.

familiarity with the fuze and appreciation of its capabilities grew, its use was extended to include harassing and interdiction fire by night and in fog, as well as counter-battery operations on all parts of the front.

The coming of the VT-fuze to relieve our hard-pressed infantry in the Bulge was as timely as the arrival of the *Monitor* at Hampton Roads. The effect on the Germans was devastating. In one area the Germans, believing that the fog would prevent accurate time-fuzed fire — even with the help of radar — massed their formations within easy range of our guns and were massacred when the air bursts of our VT-fuzed shells rained down upon them. There were not many survivors and those whom we captured were confused and dazed. A captain with long experience in battle said he had never seen anything like it. Foxholes were useless. Some prisoners said they didn't know how we did it, but that it must be contrary to the Hague Conventions.

The tests earlier made by the Army Ground Forces had indicated that howitzer fire with the VT-fuze would inflict three to four times as many casualties as anything previously available for use against personnel in the open or entrenched, or in unarmored vehicles. Battle experience showed these forecasts to be conservative. An officer from General Patton's headquarters observed some enemy tanks entering a patch of woods east of Bastogne one evening. Our artillery gave the tank crews time to get settled for the night, then saturated the area. When our troops overran it they found seventeen German tanks surrounded by German dead. The same officer saw a company of German infantry caught by a barrage of VT-fuzed shells as they tried to cross a river. None survived to reach the other side.

In the battle of the Ardennes, in January 1945, a column of advancing Germans were seen goose-stepping along a highway near Veilsalm. When VT-fuzed shells burst over them, many of them were killed, and the survivors took to their heels. When they re-formed, two batteries fired simultaneously, wiping them out, and with them a horse-drawn enemy battery in the rear. "Never," said an observer, "have I seen so many dead Germans at one time." A forward observer of the 82nd Airborne Division saw heavy traffic of vehicles, horse-drawn artillery, and foot soldiers crossing a bridge, paralyzed by two salvos of 8-inch proximity-fuzed shells.

Between December 15, 1944, and the following March 6, our forces in the E.T.O. fired over 776,000 proximity-fuzed shells. These comprised 12 per cent of all the heavy and 8 per cent of all 105-mm. fire.

In the Mediterranean theater the artillery of the II Corps used the VT-fuze for the first time on January 3, 1945, with excellent effect. On Okinawa field artillery began to use it on April 20, but with less effect because of the terrain and the tendency of the Japanese to stay in caves. On Luzon by the end of May all 105-mm. and 155-mm. howitzer battalions were firing proximity fuzes.

At the same time great efforts were being made to get the VT-fuze for 81-mm. mortar shells into large-scale production. Tests against ground targets had indicated that, because of the high trajectory of mortar fire, the VT-fuze applied to these shells would yield an improvement in fire even greater than that for AA or for howitzer fire. Not only would the GI be able to reply to Japanese mortar fire in kind, as before, but he would be assured an immense superiority in fire. The war ended before this last development could be completed but not before the ingenuity and energy applied to this unbelievably difficult development had won the admiration of all those privileged to behold it.

Part Two: New Weapons and Devices

CHAPTER VIII

THE SCIENTIFIC FRONT EXPANDS

LOOKING back over the whole course of the Second World War it is easier to appreciate the importance of the creation of the National Defense Research Committee as early as June, 1940, nearly a year and a half before Pearl Harbor. The benefits of this early start were enormously enhanced by the prompt establishment of scientific interchange with Great Britain and Canada. This reciprocity in science probably had more important strategic consequences than the exchange of destroyers for naval bases.

The pioneer in this achievement was Professor Archibald Vivian Hill, Member of Parliament for Cambridge University, who had won the Nobel Prize for Physiology and Medicine in 1922 and served as Secretary of the Royal Society since 1935. Convinced that a frank interchange of scientific information and service experience would be indispensable to both countries, he arrived in Washington in May 1940, as a temporary scientific attaché to the British Embassy. His chief, Lord Lothian, had already proposed that such an offer be made, but the authorities in London were hesitant about giving information to a neutral power, inclined to think that they had more to give than to get in the proposed exchange, and doubtful of the ability of Americans who were not at war to keep secrets. As no authorization had been given for disclosures, Hill soon realized that his hands were tied, and he returned to London to press for action there.

The fall of France made the proposed scientific interchange urgent. Before July was out President Roosevelt had approved it, on the basis of an *aide-mémoire* of Lord Lothian's. A British scientific mission, headed by Sir Henry Tizard, Rector of the Imperial College of Science and

Technology and Scientific Adviser to the Ministry of Aircraft Production, reached Washington in late August and early September, 1940. Its members included representatives of the British Army, Navy, and Air Force, the Canadian defense services, and the National Research Council of Canada. They brought with them a black box filled with blueprints and memoranda of the highest importance, and they were authorized to disclose any secret information in the possession of the British Government in exchange for secret information possessed by the United States. They meant this to include radar, fire control, underwater detection, communication, turrets, superchargers, chemical warfare, rockets, and explosives.

This distinguished group arrived before our Army and Navy had authorized NDRC to disclose anything to them. The ban was lifted, however, when the Army granted the necessary permission on September 12, 1940, and the Navy, in more limited form, four days later. Both the British and the Americans discovered that the other party to the interchange was much further advanced in secret developments than they had anticipated. The British gave us the fruits of twelve months' war experience and priceless information about the resonant cavity magnetron which became the basis of our great development of microwave radar. In return they were given access to the arsenals, flying fields, and experimental laboratories of our Army and Navy and the research departments of the principal producers of electrical equipment. The conversations of the Tizard Mission with the armed services and NDRC touched nearly every scientific aspect of the war. The result was a great stimulus to research on new weapons on both sides of the Atlantic. There is no question, however, that in the early days of the scientific interchange the British gave more than they received.

Tizard and three other members of the British Mission met with the members of NDRC on September 27, and worked out with them the broad lines of an arrangement for continuing scientific interchange between Great Britain, Canada, and the United States by way of Ottawa.

This was designed to supplement, not to supplant, the exchange of information through military and naval attachés. The Secretary of War, the Secretary of the Navy, and NDRC approved on October 25 a detailed agreement prepared by Carroll Wilson, the liaison officer of

NDRC, Professor J. D. Cockroft, who had become the head of the British mission on October 5 when Tizard returned to England, and by his colleague Professor R. H. Fowler, the liaison officer for the British Director of Industrial and Scientific Research at the Canadian capital.

Through no fault of Fowler's the exchange by way of Ottawa proved inadequate. The establishment of a London office by NDRC had been discussed from an early date, and Cockroft recommended the establishment of a British scientific office in Washington. The United States authorities were quite ready for both these moves, but there was a renewal of hesitation in London, and it was not till January 20 that the hoped-for invitation was cabled.[1]

Conant was impatient to overcome this reluctance and asked that he be assigned to launch the London Mission. Though reluctant to spare one of his chief colleagues, Bush finally consented and President Roosevelt asked Conant on February 1 to undertake the mission, expressing to Bush his delight at Conant's selection and his confidence that he would do "a grand job."

The President of Harvard had been the first of American educators to advocate entry into the war against Germany. Shortly before sailing for Lisbon on February 15 he was asked to testify before the Senate Committee on Foreign Relations on the pending Lend-Lease bill, and with Willkie and La Guardia made a strong argument in its favor. The release from the White House which was featured in the press on the morning of his departure gave the public its first news of the scientific interchange. Conant and Carroll Wilson, it was announced, were to stay in England about a month and be followed by other scientists from time to time. Frederick L. Hovde, assistant to the President of the University of Rochester, would remain in London as head of the NDRC office. The White House emphasized that "firsthand observation of recent English scientific research and experience is important for the prosecution of America's program of research on problems of national defense." The German propaganda agency forthwith announced that Conant had been dispatched by President Roosevelt to help the British start gas warfare.

When Conant's plane touched down in England on March 1 he found himself in a beleaguered fortress. The Germans were hammering it by

[1]Bush had written to Sir Henry Tizard on December 13, 1940, expressing hope that a mission would be invited.

night from the air and were expected to follow up the blitz by attempting a landing. His companions, Wilson and Hovde, reached London three days later in the midst of an air raid, a nightly occurrence in the first three months of the mission. On March 11 President Roosevelt signed the Lend-Lease Act, and issued a resounding challenge to Germany. The British, in their dark hour, were deeply moved.

All hesitation about the interchange vanished. The Lend-Lease Act afforded a broad base for the exchange of information as well as supplies. When Conant and his companions left their office in the American Embassy to thread the maze of the British scientific effort, they found the doors of the ministries and research laboratories wide-open to them. Arrangements for the exchange of documents and visits of scientific personnel were made with the greatest cordiality, and important discussions took place as to possible division of the fields of research. It was natural to assume that the British would undertake the larger share of short-run development, for the front was there and with it an abundance of user experience, while much of the important work of longer range could be best handled in the United States. As Conant put it, we Americans "must be willing to take the long gamble, do the long-range research as insurance against a war lasting four years or longer."

The British repeatedly emphasized to their visitors the importance of having the research scientists carry through to the user stage and collaborate closely with the service groups who were actually using the new devices. Only through such an arrangement had they found it possible to produce complex devices in a form that worked satisfactorily in actual combat. Conant consequently recommended that teams of American scientists and engineers be dispatched at once to England to familiarize themselves with the operation of rockets, fuzes, radar, and other devices under actual battle conditions. Here he was ahead of his time, but the idea bore fruit two years later in the establishment of two NDRC laboratories in England devoted to radar and radar countermeasures.

Akin to this idea was his suggestion of sending a number of Americans with some knowledge of electronics to England to learn how to operate the various parts of a radar warning net under conditions of actual combat. If our status as a nonbelligerent permitted such a course, it would serve two ends — furnishing the British with additional operators, of whom they stood in need, and ensuring that if and when we entered the war we should have a sizable group of radar specialists with battle experience. On his return to Washington Conant obtained President Roosevelt's hearty approval for this project, and in a short time the Signal Corps was dispatching several hundred members of the Electronics Training Group, who did good work in England and proved of great value to their own country in the days after Pearl Harbor.[2]

With liaison so well established in England at high levels from the outset, the path of the London office was a smooth one. Twenty-six American scientists visited England in the first nine months of the London mission, bringing back information of great value, especially in the fields of radar, fire control, rockets, explosives, chemical warfare, and underwater detection. The two-way exchange was facilitated by the establishment in Washington in April 1941 of the British Central Scientific Office, with Dr. Charles Darwin, Director of the National Physical Laboratory, as its first director, and Dr. W. L. Webster as secretary. They built skillfully on the foundations laid by the Tizard Mission and the work of Professor Fowler.

The pooling of scientific reports, and still more the exchange of visits, speeded work on both sides of the water. It was not just a matter of eliminating needless duplication of effort — men of each nation helped to catalyze thinking in each other. The British with their head start and great strength in science contributed a large number of good ideas. The Americans on their side were rich not only in ideas but to an unrivaled degree in engineering skill and the techniques of large-scale production. For some time, however, we received more benefits than we gave.

Another result of great importance was the increase in the number of possible customers for new ideas. If an NDRC scientist found Navy ears deaf to his proposals, he tried the Army, and vice versa. The developing relationship made it possible to turn to one or more British agencies if both of the American services were at first cool to the proposal. If the British gave something a try and it succeeded, there would be no dearth of customers. Even an expression of interest, or a remark that the Ger-

[2]George Bailey, then President of the American Radio Relay League, later in charge of the Scientific Personnel Office of OSRD, did a first-rate job recruiting the Electronics Training Group. Between August and November 1941, 350 men were sent to England, and a total of 2000 by December 1943.

mans were active on the line in question, might do more to get a project under way than a brief case full of memoranda.

A sudden decision of President Roosevelt's in May 1941 extended the field of Bush's activities to include research on military medicine. The Executive Order creating the Office of Scientific Research and Development greatly enhanced the powers of the Director.[3] The National Defense Research Committee and the newly created Committee on Medical Research were made advisory bodies, reporting to Bush, who could reject proposals or proceed without their recommendation. The form and details of contracts became therefore the responsibility of the Director and his delegate, the Executive Secretary, Irvin Stewart. Conant took Bush's place as Chairman of NDRC and became his deputy as Director of OSRD. Roger Adams relieved Conant as Chairman of Division B and became a member of NDRC. It is remarkable that this was the only change in the civilian membership of that body in over five years.

In a secret report to the President covering the first year's operations of NDRC, Bush stressed the pains that had been taken to concentrate effort on matters of pressing importance. Such secrecy had been maintained in the work which was being carried on all over the country under 200 contracts that no leak of important information had yet been brought to light. The greatest efforts thus far had been made in the field of microwave radar, which had been advanced in nine months to a degree which would ordinarily have taken years. Thanks to "teamwork of the highest order" other successes had been registered in developing night glasses, oxygen masks, fire control, rockets, antisubmarine devices, explosives, and chemical warfare.

In the years that followed, the responsibilities of OSRD grew by leaps and bounds. Most of the money went to NDRC, but the Committee on Medical Research spent $21,815,016 in the first four years. By the spring of 1945 the Army and Navy between them had purchased more than $4,000,000,000 worth of NDRC-sponsored equipment.

By the autumn of 1942 the increasing load of work had become too heavy for the original organization of NDRC. In a thoroughgoing reorganization the chairmen of the old divisions resigned their functions as division chiefs, and the Committee became a more effective one. The

[3]The text of this order, dated June 28, 1941, is reproduced in Appendix B.

The Committee on Medical Research

Left to right: Dr. R. E. Dyer, Public Health Service; Rear Admiral Harold W. Smith, Navy; Dr. A. Baird Hastings; Dr. Chester S. Keefer, Medical Administrative Officer; Dr. A. N. Richards, Chairman; Dr. Lewis H. Weed, Vice-Chairman; Brigadier General James S. Simmons, Army; Dr. A. R. Dochez; Dr. Irvin Stewart, Executive Secretary

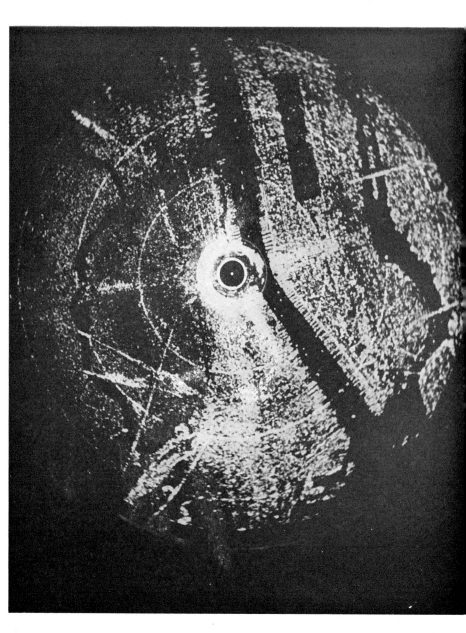

Radar scope photograph of New York City

*The outline of Manhattan Island clearly shows the Hudson River with its shipping
docks. The Metropolitan Museum can be seen jutting out into Central Park. On
the New Jersey side the Hackensack River is clearly visible. At the time the photograph was taken the plane was directly over the spot in the center of the circle.
Distance is indicated by the concentric circles used for navigation and bombing*

old divisions were recast into eighteen new divisions, some of which
had been sections hitherto. An Applied Mathematics Panel was set up,
to be followed in September 1943 by an Applied Psychology Panel:[4]

Fiscal Year Ending June 30	From the President's Fund	From Congress	Transferred from Army & Navy	Total
1940–41	$6,430,000			$6,430,000
1941–42	37,160,649*		$2,400,000	39,560,649
1942–43		$73,000,000	61,800,000	134,800,000
1943–44		135,982,500	9,500,000	145,482,500
1944–45		102,049,300	11,436,000	113,485,300
1945–46		13,898,208		13,898,208
Total	$43,590,649	$324,930,008	$85,136,000	$453,656,657

The race against time on the scientific front was not a short sprint
but a long-distance affair, consisting of several laps. "The entire program
of bringing a device into operation against the enemy," as Bush explained it to the Joint Chiefs of Staff, "consists of several stages. If any
one of these is omitted, the device will be ineffective. For a newly conceived device, these stages involve primary research, engineering development, initial production for extended field tests, and engineering for
quantity production. For devices that have gone through these stages,
as well as for older devices which are being adapted into new forms or
for new uses, there are also the stages of production, installation, maintenance, development of tactics, training and use."

To expedite production during the transition period Bush appointed
Frederic S. Gordon on December 23 as his special assistant to head what
was first known as the "few-quick" organization. This service unit,
acting as a broker between the research laboratory and the procuring
branches of the Army or Navy, endeavored to shorten the time from
the completion of a breadboard model in the laboratory to the standardization of the equipment. The "few-quick" unit, soon to become the
Engineering and Transition Office, had to be familiar with production facilities, supplies of strategic material, priorities, and a host of
other problems which the wartime demands on industry made increasingly acute.

[4]Division 19, "Miscellaneous Weapons," was created in April 1943, to meet certain needs
of the Office of Strategic Services.
*$28,160,049 from funds appropriated by Congress for the Office for Emergency
Management; $9,000,000 from the President's Emergency Fund.

As soon as a device gave promise of fulfilling a military need, it was necessary to find a manufacturer agreeable to the contractor and to the Army or Navy, who could produce quickly a few units for field test. Where radar was concerned a single set might suffice; with rockets or incendiary bombs, thousands might be required. For the "few-quick" production it was preferable to select a manufacturer able to undertake large-scale production if the device proved all that was hoped for. The demands on the broker were heavy and varied. He had to master the eventual service requirements and make sure that the equipment was sufficiently rugged to operate under most difficult conditions. Many a scientist writhed as he watched his delicate brain-child roughly handled in tests designed to ensure successful operation in the theater. Unless these needs were promptly understood, much precious time might be wasted.[5]

By January 1942, it seemed clear to Bush that it would be necessary to send scientists overseas to accompany new equipment into the field. Too frequently, if unaided, the man in the field imposed self-designed tests, misunderstood the device entrusted to him, and drew erroneous conclusions as to its potentialities and limitations. Explanation and initial training by an expert might make a world of difference. As the demands for this type of assistance and for scientific personnel for operational analysis multiplied, Bush, on October 15, 1943, established the Office of Field Service as a third major subdivision of OSRD, with Dr. Karl T. Compton as its chief.

The most difficult administrative problem which confronted OSRD and its contractors was to find and to keep sufficient scientific manpower. Both the contractors, who bore the heaviest burden of recruitment, and the agency itself were in competition for scientific talent with war industry — notably with the producers of explosives, synthetic rubber, high-octane gasoline, and electronics equipment — and with the technical branches of the armed services. At the same time 14,000,000 men were being inducted into the Army, Navy, and Marines.

The years between the two World Wars had witnessed a remarkable development of American science. It was estimated in 1941 that we

---

[5]As time went on large contractors developed transition offices of their own and spent an increasing portion of their effort on development as contrasted with primary research.

possessed 6800 physicists, 60,000 chemists, 3400 chemical engineers, 57,800 electrical engineers, 2570 radio engineers, 5500 mathematicians, and 3400 psychologists,[6] but these figures were based on each individual's estimate of his capacities and included thousands whose qualifications for research were nil. In the first week of NDRC's existence, Jewett and Conant undertook an elaborate survey of the personnel available in our leading educational institutions. Most of the technical societies had lists classifying their members by subjects, and on a far larger scale the National Roster of Scientific and Specialized Personnel spent $1,500,000 in registering 690,000 men and women.[7] Its punch cards were invaluable when one wished to know what American scientists spoke Italian, but as might be expected the Roster was used less to obtain key men than the rank and file. Those charged with recruiting chemists and physicists for OSRD and its contractors knew the outstanding men in each field already and through them got in touch with many young men of brilliant promise.

To obtain further assistance in the difficult task of recruitment, Bush turned in April 1941 to the National Research Council and arranged, by a contract with the National Academy of Sciences, for the establishment by the Council of an Office of Scientific Personnel, to assist the armed services and other government agencies as well as OSRD. Dr. Henry A. Barton, Director of the American Institute of Physics, took charge of the office, and one of the first important assignments of its Radio Section was the recruitment for the Signal Corps of the Electronics Training Group, destined for service in England as radar officers. This office performed many very useful functions, including the evaluation of records obtained from the National Roster.[8]

How was scientific personnel to be allocated between war industry, research, and the armed services? Bush, Conant, and many others in OSRD favored a National Service Act. Conant procured the insertion in the first draft of the Burke-Wadsworth bill in 1940 of a section pro-

[6]*Statistical Survey of the Learned World*, compiled by the National Roster of Scientific and Specialized Personnel, Washington, D. C., 1941.

[7]The Roster was organized in 1940 and was directed until late in 1944 by Dr. Leonard Carmichael, the President of Tufts College.

[8]It continued in operation throughout the war, though the NDRC contract with the National Academy was terminated on September 1, 1943. Dr. Joseph C. Morris served as Director from June 15, 1941, to September 15, 1942; Dean Homer L. Dodge, now President of Norwich University, from September 15, 1942, to July 1, 1944; and Dr. M. H. Trytten from July 1944 to the present.

viding for blanket deferment of physicists, chemists, doctors, and dentists, and students in training for those professions.[9] He pleaded eloquently for the principle that everyone should serve the nation in wartime in the capacity for which he was best fitted. The young scientist, in his view, should not be forced or indeed permitted to make the choice himself between the foxhole and the laboratory. It should be made for him by competent authority. Instead of a National Service Act, however, the Congress adopted in September 1940 a system of Selective Service which left the effective choice in local hands "with nothing but moral suasion flowing from Selective Service Headquarters to the State Directors and down to the Local Board."[10]

In four years of the First World War the British had learned something that we failed to grasp in a year and a half as co-belligerent. They had permitted some of their men of genius, still in their twenties, to leave their laboratories for combat duty.

In 1914 Britain sent into the front line trenches one of the greatest of modern physicists. He had revealed for the first time some of the secrets of the nucleus of the atom, and he was known throughout the world as one of the geniuses of his day. His name was Moseley. He was soon killed in action. . . .

This example was repeated, with men of lesser calibre, many times, the war effort of Britain in the first war was severely crippled by this act of folly, and the nation finally learned a lesson. In this present war Britain has utilized its young scientists well.[11]

Under our Selective Service system, on the other hand, blanket deferments were ruled out, save for ministers of the gospel and divinity students, and each case was left to be dealt with on its merits by one of the 6800 local boards. We assumed, correctly enough, that each qualified citizen should sacrifice equally, or at least be ready to do so. But we failed to devise a system under which every citizen put his efforts where they could best be utilized for the war effort. Looking back over four years of war, Bush put his finger on the heart of the problem: —

The fundamental reason for our course of action is that the numbers of men to be obtained by Selective Service have been determined in effect by military considerations and military needs alone. There has not been to my

[9]At the insistence of the military, this clause was dropped.
[10]Conant to Dean F. C. Whitmore, May 31, 1944.
[11]Bush to the Secretary of War, April 3, 1944.

knowledge at any time a body sitting on this subject which has considered the entire needs of the country, and which was in a position to balance further sacrifices of the prosperity of the country against the needs of the emergency. In particular we have not had in this country a War Cabinet. Accordingly, all of the machinery of Selective Service has operated within an arbitrary fixed frame of reference, namely to provide a certain number of men, and the resulting pressure has produced strange results.[12]

Scientific personnel represented a bottleneck even more serious than that of machine tools. "A scientifically trained man can hardly be produced in much less than ten years whereas great progress can be made in machine tools in a couple of years."[13] There was no difficulty in obtaining deferments prior to Pearl Harbor, for draft registrants who were employed in work "found to be necessary to the maintenance of the national health, safety or interest." Employees of OSRD or of its contractors fulfilled this condition. After Pearl Harbor the test of irreplaceability was more stringently applied. Bush and Conant, with the help of President R. G. Sproul of the University of California, who came east in January 1942 to assist them, devised a plan for a Scientific Corps which was sidetracked by higher authority in favor of the short-lived project for an Army Specialist Corps. At the same time Bush added a Selective Service Unit to the staff of his executive secretary to take care of the deferments of OSRD employees and to aid contractors to obtain deferments for their personnel. By the end of 1942 this unit had endorsed requests for 3602 scientific and technical personnel employed on OSRD projects. Since the list of critical occupations issued by Selective Service Headquarters covered most of these jobs, all but sixteen of these employees were deferred.

In March 1942 Bush had turned for assistance in the over-all problem to Dr. Frank Aydelotte, Director of the Institute for Advanced Study, whom he named chairman of an Advisory Committee on Scientific Personnel early in June.

After important conferences with Aydelotte and with the OSRD Advisory Council, Bush submitted on October 16 to Paul V. McNutt, whom the President had selected in April to head the newly created War Manpower Commission, an over-all plan for dealing with scientific

[12]To Major General S. G. Henry, August 27, 1945.
[13]F. C. Whitmore to Bush, December 14, 1940.

personnel. He pointed out that the country was facing an acute short-age of adequately trained scientific and technical personnel, urgently needed for research, for development and testing of new weapons, and for the solution of problems of military medicine.

Bush therefore suggested the creation by the War Manpower Com-mission of a Committee on Scientific Research Personnel. Its functions would be to prepare a list of reserved scientific and technical workers of professional grade engaged on research or development of new weapons or problems of military medicine; to determine the places in which their talents could be more effectively used, and to maintain a continuing study of the need for scientific personnel in the armed services and in civilian war agencies.

It was to be the duty of this Committee to furnish information regard-ing particular individuals to local Selective Service Boards and to the Army and Navy, so that these individuals might be reserved for the scientific work for which they were best fitted. The Committee, more-over, should recommend transfers of individuals on its reserved list from one project to another in accordance with the varying needs of research.

The group of specialists involved, Bush pointed out, was not large but was extremely important. Comparatively few additional young men could during the progress of the war be trained to the point where they became effective research workers. The men already available there-fore constituted a vital resource. They should not be forced to ask defer-ment for themselves, or to determine the particular place in which they could be of the greatest service. These decisions should be made for them by a board with a broad view of the whole war effort.

This statesmanlike proposal received no answer until February 26, 1943, when McNutt acknowledged it and set up within the War Man-power Commission a Committee on Scientific Research Personnel, com-posed of representatives of the armed services, the NACA, the OSRD, the OPRD, and the National Roster. He asked for Bush's suggestions as to nominees, accepted them all, and had the Committee at work by April 8. The mechanics of the reserved list were well cared for by the National Roster, whose director, Leonard Carmichael, became the chair-man of the Committee on Scientific Research Personnel.

In the long and difficult struggle for adequate scientific personnel the establishment of the reserved list was of fundamental importance. Until the crisis of 1944 it was respected by local Selective Service Boards and State Directors, and it went a long way, but not all the way, towards a solution of the problem.[14]

For scientists holding civil service appointments from OSRD itself a new hurdle was created by the President's executive order of March 6, 1943, setting up what came to be known first as the Barnett, then as the Puryear Committee to revise requests for deferment from executive agencies of the government and requiring each of them to set up an agency committee for screening purposes. As the Director of OSRD henceforth appointed no civil service personnel under thirty, relations with the Puryear Committee went relatively smoothly.

As D-Day in Normandy approached, and the Army found itself short of infantry divisions, a crisis was created by the President's order of February 26, 1944, to Selective Service Boards to review all deferments for men under twenty-six. The immediate reaction of the State Directors to the new directive threatened every scientist under twenty-six working on OSRD contracts, whether his name was on the reserved list or not.

For research the problem was much graver than for industry as a whole. Young scientists had taken to the new types of war work in electronics, underwater sound, and military medicine like ducks to water. An official of the General Electric Company testified that 30 per cent of the graduate electrical engineers in the important companies in his field were in the age group from twenty-two to twenty-five years. It seemed that young college graduates had the ability to absorb rapidly and in tremendous quantity facts and theories in these new fields which older engineers seemed to lack the capacity to absorb. Out of 1915 male employees at the Radiation Laboratory on March 8, 1944, 925 had staff ratings. Of these latter 50 were between eighteen and twenty-one years old and 240 between twenty-two and twenty-five. All of the 50 and all but five of the 240 had been nominated for the reserve list. If these men

[14]After Dr. Aydelotte resigned late in December, 1942, John V. L. Hogan, a well-known radio engineer and inventor, was appointed special assistant to the Director and entrusted with a study of all problems of scientific personnel. On his recommendation that they be centralized within the agency, Bush set up a Scientific Personnel Office for OSRD on June 1, 1943, with Hogan in charge and Bailey as his assistant, until March 1944, when the latter became head of the office. The earlier Advisory Committee on Scientific Personnel was dissolved; the Selective Service Unit was transferred from the executive secretary's office to the new office, and the contract with the National Academy for the services of the Office of Scientific Personnel, NRC, was terminated.

were taken, some of the most important "crash programs" for whose completion the services were clamoring might come to a stop. The percentage of young men was also high in the Field Service groups in overseas theaters.

Bush thought that his representations to the War and Navy Departments had put the problem on the way to solution, and left for the West Coast on OSRD business on March 10. In his absence McNutt set up a new group known as the Interdepartmental Agency Committee of the War Manpower Commission with himself as chairman. It included representatives of the War Production Board, the Petroleum Administrator for War, the Solid Fuels Administration, the Office of Defense Transportation, the Committee on Scientific Research Personnel of the War Manpower Commission, the Rubber Director, the War Food Administration, the War Shipping Administration, and the Army and Navy, but no representative of OSRD. This was important, for only the agencies thus represented were included as "claimants" with power to certify their own projects as essential to the war effort, and to designate representatives in each state to endorse special requests for deferment for key registrants under twenty-six.

On his return from the West on March 31, 1944, Bush found the morale of his organization "at an all-time low." By a strange paradox, just at the time that so many of their developments were powerfully affecting the course of the war, the OSRD scientists were made to feel "on the defensive, rather than as partners to a well-considered plan." At a time when the services were asking him to undertake new and large programs of research and development, he was deprived of the hope of expanding his scientific manpower and threatened with the loss of valuable personnel. With a National Service Act, young scientists and engineers would have been flowing from non-war work into OSRD; now they were moving into the ranks of the Army. He was being refused the means to perform the duties he had been asked to shoulder, and the gap between means and duties was widening rapidly.[15]

In this emergency Bush concentrated on three objectives: the inclusion of OSRD in the list of "claimant agencies" along with his principal competitors for scientific manpower; the preservation of the reserved list; and some assistance to scientists not included in the first two ob-

[15]Bush to the Undersecretary of War, May 3, 1944.

jectives. Obtaining the status of a "claimant" was the more important, because McNutt's Interdepartmental Agency Committee was proceeding on the basis of approving projects rather than individuals or classes of individuals. It soon appeared that the Army and Navy were ready to certify almost every OSRD project, which was not strange since they had requested their initiation. Bush was quite ready, indeed eager, to curtail his marginal projects, but an important principle was at stake in his right to certify projects. If the Army and Navy alone passed on the agency's projects all civilian initiative would be gone and there would be no hope for a project like the Dukw, in which the services at the outset evinced no interest.

In the first week of May Bush found a valuable ally in Judge Patterson, the Undersecretary of War. The two men met on May 6 and reached complete agreement. On May 11, thanks to the support of the War and Navy Departments, OSRD was made a claimant agency and Bush a member of the Interdepartmental Agency Committee.

The struggle to preserve the reserved list lasted until May 14. Although all requests for deferment made by the Massachusetts Institute of Technology had been endorsed by either the Army, the Navy, or the Committee on Scientific Research Personnel, the State Director in Massachusetts informed the Radiation Laboratory that he intended to refuse deferment to at least fifty of their radar experts then on the reserved list.[16] As President Compton promptly pointed out, the loss of these men would be "a major disaster." Demands of the Army and Navy for new types of microwave radar were pushing the Radiation Laboratory as never before.

Furthermore this ultra high frequency radar is a "young man's game." Practically no oldsters know it. Thirty-five per cent of this M.I.T. laboratory staff are under twenty-six years of age. In one of the component laboratories there is a group of nineteen research men working on a project which (1) was undertaken by the U. S. on behalf of both the U. S. and U. K. by arrangements between the Radio Board of the British War Cabinet and our Joint Chiefs of Staff; (2) was given next to top priority in radar research and development by our Joint Communications Board. Seventeen of these nineteen men are under twenty-six, and there are probably not another dozen men in the world who are now competent to do this job.[17]

---

[16]Similar difficulties were encountered in several other states.
[17]To the Undersecretary of War, May 11, 1944.

On May 12, 13, and 14 it still looked as if the reserved list were lost, but the tide had turned. A speech made under instructions by General Clay, Director of Material, Army Service Forces, at a meeting of the State Directors put this crucial problem back on the right track.

The third point in Bush's program covered a number of special cases. Some of the large pharmaceutical houses who were working for the Committee on Medical Research had undertaken at their own expense important researches on antimalarials and drugs to combat filariasis. Because the chemists so engaged, though working on war research, were not employed under government contracts, no agency was in a position to put in a claim for them. Bush pushed their case with the Army, and through a subcommittee of the Interdepartmental Agency Committee,[18] and with the help of Major General W. D. Styer, Chief of Staff of the Army Service Forces, a considerable number of these chemists were deferred.

By August the crisis of 1944 had been passed, though at a tremendous cost of time and energy on the part of top executives, which might have been expended to advantage on other sectors of the scientific front. It did make easier the solution of the problem raised by the Selective Service order of January 15, 1945, for the reviewing of all deferments in the age group twenty-six to twenty-nine years inclusive. This time there was no attack on the reserved list and OSRD was one of three agencies permitted to hold 100 per cent of their personnel. It was still a question whether industry, which was to lose 70 per cent of its scientists in this age bracket, could produce in time the equipment for which OSRD was charged with research and development. To Bush's way of thinking the proportion of scientific and engineering talent left in industry was dangerously low, but General Henry, the new Assistant Chief of Staff for Personnel, made a strong case for the Army's needs. Too often as our victorious armies swept through France, Belgium, and Germany, casualties could not be replaced and divisions had to be kept in line months at a time.

What stands out most clearly in the controversies over manpower is the lack of a War Cabinet to assess the needs of the Army and Navy, war industry, and war research. A National Service Act could have done far more than the system we had to shift manpower from unessential

18McNutt named him chairman of this subcommittee on June 10.

work to the place of maximum need. Though our decentralized Selective Service System, thanks to the loyal efforts of the thousands of draft boards, was a magnificent democratic instrument to ensure fair play through local judgment of individual cases, its difficulties and defects showed up stark and drear in the handling of special problems like that of scientific manpower.

To what extent was the effort of OSRD hindered by the shortcomings of our national manpower system? According to the records of the agency's Scientific Personnel Office only 64 men were lost to the draft by OSRD and its contractors out of 9766 for whom deferments were asked. This is not of course the whole story. When scientists are racing against time, the critical factor is not the amount of manpower but the amount of manpower of such high capabilities that solutions can be reached quicker than the enemy can reach them. A nation should not be satisfied with the organization of its scientific effort unless its best men are all at work in the jobs best suited for their talents. OSRD and its contractors did not ask for deferments of many able young men because, under the system in force, their chances seemed hopeless. It refrained from hiring many others in the younger age groups whose services would have speeded the war effort. And it saw hundreds if not thousands of scientists who were needed in its ranks choose instead to enter the armed services. Was it wise in total war to leave so much choice to the individual as to where he was most needed? Who can say? It is clear that the United States dealt clumsily with the problem of scientific manpower as compared with Great Britain, but we did far better than Germany.

The man in the street knew that wars could be lost because army divisions or warships were at the wrong place at the critical moment. Is it not just as clear that wars can be lost if the gifted and well-trained scientists are in the wrong place, in uniform or at the front or wholly outside the war effort? The German record is suggestive. In this as in so many other respects the experience of this war on the scientific front must be a guide to the future policies of the democratic nations.

CHAPTER IX

RADAR AND LORAN

Is RADAR in the same class with the atomic energy?" asked Senator Fulbright of Dr. Rabi. "Is it of a similar nature as far as its implications in warfare are concerned?"

"Yes and no," replied the great Columbia physicist. "Radar represents an extension of man's senses and power. He sees further. He sees more clearly. He measures distance more accurately. He can transmit information more readily. . . . Then you apply it to something. It extends your senses in dropping the atomic bomb, it extends your senses in guiding the missile. It gives you more information for navigation. . . ."

Radar is not a "death ray." It cannot reduce a city to ruins or hold out to a new age the promise of cheap power. But it does enable man to do an astonishing number of things he could not do before, and to do them with extraordinary precision. It has proved the most versatile instrument in modern warfare, revolutionizing one area after another.

The basic principles on which all radar systems work are reasonably simple. If you know the speed of sound and have a stop watch, you can stand opposite a cliff, shout, time the echo, and calculate easily enough the distance from the cliff. Your stop watch can time an echo in fifths of a second. The miracle underlying all radar is that men have learned, by means of a highly developed electronic tube called a cathode ray oscilloscope, to measure time in such infinitesimal amounts that radio echo ranges of objects miles away can be read with accuracy in yards. This new electronic "stop watch" reads in millionths of a second (microseconds), indeed in thirtieths of one microsecond. It is on that scale that the student of radar learns to think.

Like sound waves, radio waves can be projected in a beam to strike an object in space, whose distance can be determined by timing the reflected wave, or echo. The radio waves, like light, travel in a straight line at the constant velocity of 186,000 miles a second. In one microsecond a pulse of electromagnetic energy travels 0.186 mile, or 328 yards. The word "radar," coined by the United States Navy, means "radio detection and ranging." The fact that it can be read backward as well as forward may serve to remind us that it is an echo we are measuring, a pulse traveling out into space, a small portion of which is reflected back to the transmitter. If the round trip takes a microsecond, the distance of the target is 0.093 mile, or 164 yards. Since the time of the round trip can be measured in units as small as one thirtieth of a microsecond, the distance of an object twenty miles away can be determined with an accuracy of one thirtieth of 164 yards, or a little over five yards.

If you have tried to time the echo of your voice reflected from a cliff, you will recall that instead of shouting continuously, you shouted and then waited in silence while your watch ticked. In the early experiments with radar, men used continuous-wave transmission, but before long they found it much more satisfactory to use pulses lasting a microsecond or two, with relatively long resting periods in between, to give the pulse time to reach the target and return before being obscured by the next outgoing pulse. The longer the resting time, the greater the range. With a resting time of 2000 microseconds, objects can be detected out to 200 miles.[1]

So much for ranging, now for direction. Turn on your electric flashlight, step into a dark room, and try to locate an object, say the brass knob on a cupboard. To locate the knob accurately in space, as a gunner tries to locate a plane, you need to know the range and two angles, one of elevation, the other of azimuth or bearing. Swing your flashlight from left to right, or vice versa, and note the angle when the light strikes the knob. That gives you azimuth. Move the light up and down and note when it strikes the knob. That will give you the angle of elevation. It is easily seen that the narrower your beam of light, the more accurately you can measure the two angles. The same is true of radar. The radar beam, focused by a parabolic reflector like that of your portable electric heater or the reflectors in your automobile headlights, can be pointed steadily in one direction or made to sweep through (that is, to "scan") a full circle. A small portion of the transmitted energy will be picked up by the receiver.[2] You get the direction by noting the angular position

[1]Range depends not only on the power generated by the transmitter, but on the success with which the pulses can be concentrated in a narrow beam. The range of a radar system can be improved by raising the transmitter power, using a larger reflector, and increasing the sensitivity of the receiver.
[2]In the physicist's phrase, this power picked up at the receiver varies inversely as the fourth power of the distance to the target.

that gives the strongest signal or echo. As was true with your flashlight, the narrower the radar beam, the more accurately you can determine the angle in elevation or azimuth. Elevation is the harder of the two angles to determine, because the beam, unless very narrow or high above the ground, will strike the earth and be reflected, causing complications.

The theory was simple enough, but the application of it ran into many a difficulty. The receiver must be a delicate affair of great sensitivity. How were you to keep the huge outgoing pulse from burning out the crystal detector of the receiver? The answer is the "T.R." (transmitter-receiver) box which provides almost complete insulation of the two circuits.

The cathode ray oscilloscope which serves you as a stop watch has a glass face, painted inside with a fluorescent material. This tube face is familiar as the television screen. In the simplest type of radar indicator, known as the A-scope, a small spot of light, or "pip," appears on the screen and indicates the outgoing pulse. A smaller spot, or pip, somewhat to the right of the first, indicates the echo as it arrives at the receiver. The distance between the two pips gives the range, for the tube enables the operator to translate time instantaneously into range and to read the range off what is both a time scale and a range scale.

One of the great advances in the radar art was the development of the Plan Position Indicator (PPI), which followed the introduction of the rotating antenna. The time base, in this type of presentation, is a radial one, a line of light rotating like the large second hand or "sweep hand" on a wrist watch, in exact time with the rotation of the antenna, so that it represents the same direction as the radio beam. Distance is measured along this radial range and time scale, with zero at the center of the tube face. The returning pulse illuminates a section of a circle, and gives the operator both the distance and the direction of targets.

But this is only part of the story. After the sweep moves on, the persistence of the fluorescence leaves on the screen a maplike outline of the area scanned by the radar. In the PPI picture,

seas, lakes and waterways remain black . . . coastlines, with their cliffs, bays and inlets, show up clearly as outline map features because they scatter radiation back to its source; . . . the inland landscape is of a nondescript intermediate tone; and . . . "the works of man" — camps, hangars, and above all towns and cities — stand out brightly. . . .[3]

[3]Sir Robert Watson Watt, C.B., F.R.S., "Radar in War and in Peace," *Nature*, September 15, 1945, p. 323.

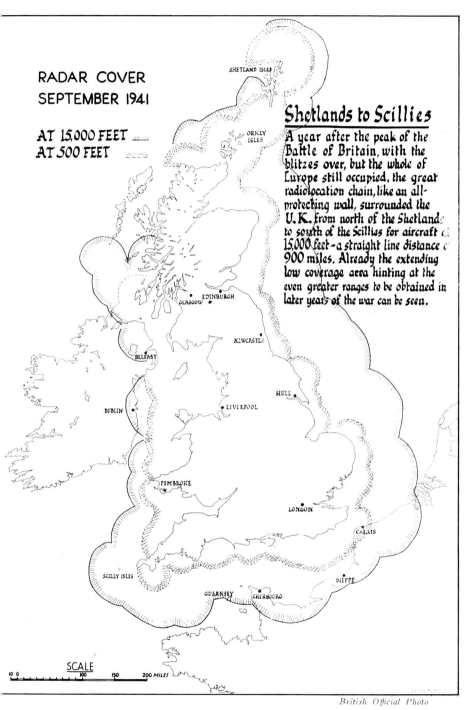

RADAR COVER
SEPTEMBER 1941

AT 15,000 FEET
AT 500 FEET

Shetlands to Scillies

A year after the peak of the Battle of Britain, with the blitzes over, but the whole of Europe still occupied, the great radiolocation chain, like an all-protecting wall, surrounded the U.K. from north of the Shetlands to south of the Scillies for aircraft at 15,000 feet—a straight line distance of 900 miles. Already the extending low coverage area hinting at the even greater ranges to be obtained in later years of the war can be seen.

SHETLAND ISLES

ORKEY ISLES

GLASGOW EDINBURGH

BELFAST

NEWCASTLE

DUBLIN LIVERPOOL HULL

PEMBROKE

LONDON

CALAIS

SCILLY ISLES DIEPPE

GUERNSEY CHERBOURG

SCALE
10 0   100   150   200 MILES

British Official Photo

Britain's radar coverage in September 1941

The Unknown Scientist solving the problems of microwave radar

By the time war broke out in September 1939, the United States, Great Britain, France, and Germany, working secretly and independently, had all made great progress with radar. Back of this lay the experiments of Heinrich Hertz, the discoverer of radio waves, who proved in 1886 that they were reflected from solid objects; and a number of suggestions that they could be used to detect obstacles in fog or darkness. In the autumn of 1922 Dr. A. Hoyt Taylor, now Chief Consultant and Chief Co-ordinator of Electronics at the Naval Research Laboratory, and his associate Leo C. Young noted a distortion or "phase shift" in signals reflected from a steamer on the Potomac, and suggested to the Navy Department that by means of this principle, "destroyers located on a line a number of miles apart could be immediately aware of the passage of an enemy vessel between any two destroyers of the line, irrespective of fog, darkness, or smoke screen."

Scientists at the Naval Research Laboratory, while experimenting with radio direction-finding equipment in the summer of 1930, observed that reflections of radio waves from an airplane could be similarly detected. A report from the Director of the Laboratory in November 1930 led to orders from the Bureau of Engineering to the Laboratory to "investigate the use of radio to detect the presence of enemy vessels and aircraft." The method adopted required at least two widely separated stations, one for transmitting and one for receiving, using continuous waves and detecting moving objects by the interference of the main ground wave with the wave reflected from the aircraft.

The Signal Corps had been working in the twenties on infrared detection and radio detection, using microwaves to produce echoes from near-by targets, but had been finding it impossible at such short wave lengths to generate sufficient power for a practical detection system.

Meanwhile great interest had been roused in the world of science by the use of radio pulses by Dr. Gregory Breit and Dr. Merle A. Tuve of the Carnegie Institution of Washington, in 1925, to measure the height of the ionosphere, the layer of ionized air at high altitudes which acts as a mirror, reflecting radio waves back to earth. This method of sending up a train of pulses and timing the echo soon became a standard practice among investigators of the ionosphere the world over.

The idea of using this pulse technique to detect aircraft and ships seems to have occurred almost simultaneously to scientists in America,

England, France, and Germany. Young, at the Naval Research Laboratory, proposed it in 1933. His colleague, Robert M. Page, made important advances in the pulse technique in the next few years, in transmitters, receivers, and methods of presentation. At the same time the Naval Research Laboratory was developing the highly important "duplexer," which permitted the use of the same radar antenna for transmitting and receiving.[4]

The Committee on Naval Appropriations of the House of Representatives, at the request of Rear Admiral Harold G. Bowen, allocated $100,000 to the Naval Research Laboratory in 1935 for the development of radar and continued its warm interest in the project. By April 1937 the Navy had radar working over salt water on the old four-stacker *Leary*. During the next two years, two much improved experimental models were built, one at NRL and the other by the Radio Corporation of America at Camden, New Jersey. These were installed on the battleships *New York* and *Texas* in 1938. After the successful tests of the prototype on the former ship in battle maneuvers early the next year, the Navy placed its first production order with RCA for six sets of NRL design, known as CXAM's, which were installed in 1940 on the battleship *California*, the aircraft carrier *Yorktown*, and the cruisers *Chester*, *Chicago*, *Northampton*, and *Pensacola*.

Meanwhile the Signal Corps Laboratories developed an antiaircraft detector for searchlight control and gun laying. Tested by the Coast Artillery Board in November 1938, it detected antiaircraft shells in flight and guided back to a safe landing an Army bomber which had been blown out to sea. An improved long-range set was adopted as a standard item of Army procurement in May 1940. It was one of these sets which detected Japanese aircraft approaching Pearl Harbor and was turned off too soon.

When the National Defense Research Committee was established, the first suggestions from the armed services of fields for NDRC investigation included basic research at ultra-high frequencies and studies of pulse transmission. The Air Corps was looking for solutions to the problem of fog and haze and was interested in the possibility of bombing through the overcast. Compton, Chief of Division D, promptly established a sec-

---

[4]Lieutenant (now Rear Admiral) W. S. Parsons, U.S.N., who armed the atomic bomb at Hiroshima, was a member of the NRL group.

tion to study the applications of microwaves (radio waves 10 centimeters or less in length) to detection devices. This Section D-1, which later became Division 14 of NDRC, was headed by Alfred L. Loomis, a New York lawyer and a pioneer in the field of microwaves. It included scientists and engineers drawn from the American universities and industrial concerns which had done the most to develop microwave techniques. The Microwave Committee, as it was commonly called, continued with remarkably few changes in personnel throughout the war.[5]

During the summer of 1940 members of the Committee investigated the radio-detection work being carried out by the United States Army and Navy. They concluded that great progress might be made if microwave techniques were adopted for the purpose. A small group from M.I.T., who worked during that summer at the Loomis Laboratories, in Tuxedo Park, New York, found their advances in this direction blocked by the lack of a vacuum tube which would generate microwave pulses sufficiently intense for practical pulse-detection equipment.

Meanwhile the possibility of a German attack by air had led British scientists to push the development of radio detection at an even faster tempo. At the end of 1934 the Air Ministry was so convinced of the inadequacy of visual and acoustic means to detect aircraft at high speeds that they formed a working partnership with British scientists. Development proceeded so rapidly that by December 1935 the Air Ministry decided to establish a chain of five radio-locating stations on the east coast of England, the first operational radar system installed anywhere in the world. Fifteen additional stations were authorized in August 1937 to complete the coverage of the east and southeast coasts. An uninterrupted 24-hour radar watch was kept on the North Sea approaches from Easter, 1939, to the end of the hostilities.

The British made a great advance by developing the Plan Position Indicator, first used for the control of night fighters, then more importantly in antisubmarine warfare and in blind bombing. But the greatest of their contributions to radar was the development of the resonant cavity magnetron, "a radically new and immensely powerful device

[5]The original committee included Dr. Ralph Bown of the Bell Telephone Laboratories, Hugh H. Willis of the Sperry Gyroscope Company, R. R. Beal of the Radio Corporation of America, George F. Metcalf of the General Electric Company, J. A. Hutcheson of the Westinghouse Electric and Manufacturing Company, Professor Ernest O. Lawrence of the University of California, and Professor E. L. Bowles of M.I.T., who acted as secretary.

which remains the heart of every modern radar equipment."[6] This revolutionary discovery, which we owe to a group of British physicists headed by Professor N. L. Oliphant of Birmingham, was the first tube capable of producing power enough to make radar feasible at wave lengths of less than 50 centimeters. When the members of the Tizard Mission brought one to America in 1940, they carried the most valuable cargo ever brought to our shores. It sparked the whole development of microwave radar and constituted the most important item in reverse Lease-Lend.[7]

In less than a decade American radar grew to a billion-dollar industry surrounded by a wall of secrecy which has only recently been removed. Let us suppose that the automobile industry had developed in the same way and that for the first time we had a glimpse of their output: "the sleek body, the compact engine, the dashboard bristling with controls."[8] Salesmen approached us with a lingo strange to us, talking about performance in terms of horsepower, gasoline consumption, and automatic gearshifts. It would be all very confusing, and perhaps the four best questions we could put to each of them would be: "What does this new thing do, how does it do it, what is your company's place in the industry, and how did it get there?"

Up to July 1945 there had been delivered to the services $3,000,000,000 worth of radar equipment and $71,000,000 worth of equipment for Loran, the closely related navigational aid. NDRC participated in the development of more than half this radar equipment and practically all the Loran; $25,000,000 worth of radar gear was supplied directly by the Radiation Laboratory established by M.I.T. under an NDRC contract, and by its glorified experimental or model shop, the Research Construction Company, under "crash" programs to meet the services' most pressing needs.

To grub-stake Division 14 in its exploration and pioneering on the frontiers of radar, OSRD allocated $141,000,000. Out of this expenditure came approximately 150 distinct radar systems. They varied in size from the lightweight compact sets designed for fighter planes and PT boats,

---

[6]Watson Watt, *op. cit.* p. 321.

[7]It was first shown to members of the Microwave Committee by Professor J. D. Cockroft and Dr. E. G. Bowen on the week end of September 28–29, 1940, while guests of Alfred Loomis at Tuxedo Park.

[8]I am indebted for this part of the analogy to the excellent article on radar in *Fortune*, October 1945, pp. 139 *ff.*

to the huge Microwave Early Warning system, which was housed in five trucks and manned by a company of soldiers. One thing they all had in common: they operated on microwaves.

In emphasizing the importance of the microwave field, the writer does not mean to disparage the sets of long or medium wave lengths built by or for the Army or Navy. There are applications for which each is best fitted. All the sets issued to the American forces prior to 1942 operated on these long or medium waves. As time went on, many of them gave place to microwave sets, which performed better. Furthermore, the microwave technique made possible a great number of new types of radio sets and new kinds of applications of this art which would have been completely impossible with the longer-wave radar. It is important for the reader to understand why.

Listen to a radar salesman, and you will find him talking about frequencies. The shorter the wave length the higher is the frequency in cycles — that is, the number of wave crests of energy that leave the transmitter within a given period of time and go rippling through space. A wave length of one meter corresponds to 300 megacycles (million cycles) per second. The first experimental pulse equipment tried out by the British was on a wave length of 50 meters, corresponding to six megacycles. Radar designers before 1940 usually operated in what is called the ultra-high frequency range, from a wave length of about 10 meters down to one of about 50 centimeters, corresponding to 30 and 600 megacycles.[9] Above this frequency are the super-high frequencies, the region of the microwaves, for which special techniques had to be evolved to produce and transmit the waves.

The boldest jump in the history of radar came when British physicists, after producing an effective radar set on a meter and a half, went directly to 10 centimeters, in the region of the microwaves. Nobody could do it without the magnetron, for no other tube could produce a strong enough pulse at so high a frequency. With the magnetron, the microwave region could be explored and exploited.

The higher the frequency (that is, the shorter the wave length), the narrower will be the scanning beam. The advantages of the narrow

[9]This ultra-high frequency band is sharply set apart from the longer radio waves because 30 mc. is the frequency at which waves are no longer reflected from the ionosphere but pass on through that "radio roof." The wave length in meters is obtained by dividing 300 by the frequency in megacycles.

beam are many: greater range of detection for a given amount of power; a higher degree of accuracy in determining the height or angular bearing of the target; and less interference from ground reflections, sea waves, and clouds. Narrow-beam radar is harder for the enemy to jam. And above all it allows higher resolution; that is, it permits two targets close together to be distinguished, instead of appearing as a single unseparated signal. The number and disposition of enemy ships and sometimes even of aircraft can thereby be determined.

The reader devoted to the camera knows all about high resolution, which gives fine detail to the picture.

Narrow-beam radar is easier to install in aircraft or on shipboard because, for a given size of beam, an antenna for short waves is smaller than one for long waves. The narrow beam is a great advantage on shipboard because it minimizes interference caused by reflection from the waves and enables vessels to be detected much farther away. This "low coverage" over land and water helps to prevent enemy aircraft from sneaking in under the radar beam.

The members of the Tizard Mission urged NDRC to specialize in the microwave field and to establish a large laboratory for the purpose staffed by scientists and engineers from both the universities and industry similar to the three created by the British — the Telecommunications Research Establishment of the Ministry of Aircraft Production, and the Air Defense Research and Development Establishment of the Ministry of Supply, both at Great Malvern, and the Admiralty Signal Establishment at Farnborough. They urged Section D-1 to give top priority to an airborne radar which could be installed in a night fighter for interception of enemy bombers. At its meeting on October 18, 1940, the Microwave Committee agreed to undertake this project and unanimously voted to recommend the establishment of a laboratory at the Massachusetts Institute of Technology.

The order of the Advisory Committee to the Council on National Defense which established NDRC had not empowered it, like NACA, to build and operate laboratories of its own. But it was free to contract with others to do so; and it early considered the possibility of arranging for the Carnegie Institution to set up a laboratory at its Department of Terrestrial Magnetism or at Bolling Field in Anacostia, or of contracting for some space in the Bell Telephone Laboratories. The conclusion was reached that it would be easier to build up a group of academic scientists at an educational institution and that M.I.T. had three important advantages for this purpose: proximity to the sea, a point stressed by the British Mission; the possibility of obtaining adequate facilities at the Boston Municipal Airport; and the presence on the staff of nearly a score of men who had been actively working in the microwave field.

Research began at what was soon called the Radiation Laboratory on November 10, 1940, under an NDRC contract with M.I.T., which was signed in the following February. Professor Ernest Lawrence rendered invaluable aid in recruiting physicists in the early days, including the Director of the Laboratory, Dr. Lee DuBridge, of the University of Rochester, a most happy choice. Dr. E. G. Bowen of the Tizard Mission joined the staff as British Liaison Officer, bringing with him wide knowledge of radio detection gained under Watson Watt. He exerted a profound influence on the development of the laboratory in its formative stage, and outlined the specifications for the proposed AI (airborne interception) equipment. At the same time, from its earliest days, the Radiation Laboratory established the basis for that intimate collaboration with the great industrial laboratories to which much of the American success in the field of radar was largely due.

If the writer attempted in this chapter to characterize all or even a large number of the 150 radar systems developed by Division 14, the reader would soon be overburdened. In a full-length history of the Radiation Laboratory it might be possible to portray the systems in detail, trace their lines of descent, their intermarriages, their individual characteristics, and their war records, and produce a portrait gallery as striking as the *Forsyte Saga*. Here one can high-light only a few of the major systems, indicate the line of descent, and show in other chapters the part that they played in changing the forms of warfare.

The genealogical tree consists of three main branches — ground radars, ship radars, and airborne radars. In each branch there were some specializing in early warning or fire control, and others, more versatile, which combined two or more functions. The superb SCR-584, the first Allied ground radar to surpass the German Würzburg, excelled not only in the control of antiaircraft fire but in directing the operations of a tactical air force. Several other systems starred in two roles, both as navigational aids and as devices for blind bombing, like Mickey and Eagle. The large family of radar beacons changed its name to racons. Some of the first patriarchs in the radar world founded lines of descent in which no black sheep can be discovered. Others experienced the common lot of man and produced some descendants who failed and others who were shining examples.

The Radiation Laboratory and the five large companies to whom the development of the first components had been assigned got under way with extraordinary rapidity. The first American microwave pulse radar system was put together in about two months of feverish activity in a laboratory on the roof of the main M.I.T. building. When first successfully operated on January 4, 1941, two days ahead of schedule, the screen showed echoes from the buildings on the Boston skyline across the Charles River. The first attempts to pick up aircraft signals were failures, but to the immense relief of the Microwave Committee, which was holding a gloomy session in Washington on February 7, a telephone call reported that the system had just tracked a small plane out to two and a half miles. In its first airborne test on March 10, in a B-18 A plane, it detected planes up to five miles, and it did better than that before the month was out. Another set, dispatched to England in June for comparison with the British airborne interception set, proved to be about equal in performance. The American system had the more powerful transmitter, the British the more sensitive receiver. The combination of the two produced good results.

In response to an Army request in February the Radiation Laboratory embarked on its first "crash program," the construction of fifteen AI sets for the early experimental models of the P-61 plane.[10] Two other airborne interception sets were built for installation in the Douglas A-20 attack bomber. One, after flight tests in September 1941, was flown to California soon after Pearl Harbor, where for a time it was the sole night fighter on the West Coast equipped to intercept hostile aircraft in the dark. The other set, with two Radiation Laboratory engineers, was lent in May at the Army's request to Bell Telephone Laboratories to help in engineering the first production AI set. The descendant of this production set, Western Electric's SCR-720, became our standard night-fighter radar in 1943, installed in the celebrated Black Widows.

---

[10]The British asked for ten more, for installation in Beaufighters.

The defeat of the *Luftwaffe* in the Battle of Britain somewhat lessened the interest in aircraft interception, just at a time when the U-boats, operating in larger numbers from longer coastlines, were increasing their ravages. The splendid performance of the first AI-10 set in the B-18 over water on March 27, in what was probably the first time an airborne microwave radar was tried out for surface search, was highly encouraging. At New London soon after in a plane flying at an altitude of 500 to 1000 feet, strong echoes were obtained from a surfaced submarine three miles away. The airborne interceptor systems were modified for this purpose and greatly improved by incorporating the first airborne Plan Position Indicator. This new equipment, installed in the U.S.S. *Semmes* in May 1941, was the first microwave radar with PPI presentation to be used on shipboard.[11] It proved so successful that before the summer was over the Navy placed a production order with the Raytheon Manufacturing Company for what became one of the most widely used and effective of all shipboard radars, the famous SG. A somewhat similar set saw day and night service on Deer Island in Boston Harbor for surface search after Pearl Harbor. The Radiation Laboratory's new model shop, the Research Construction Company, produced fifty of these sets, known as the SCR-582, for the Signal Corps in 1942. Five of them were used by the American forces in the invasion of North Africa, and were the first microwave ground equipment to see action. Two improved versions went to the Panama Canal to improve the low coverage of its longer-wave early-warning network.

In its first program adopted on October 18, 1940, the Microwave Committee had undertaken to develop a device for long-range navigation suggested by Alfred Loomis, and a microwave fire-control radar of high precision for use with antiaircraft guns. Although a parallel development, entrusted primarily to the National Research Council in Ottawa, proceeded along lines already being followed in Great Britain, the development at the Radiation Laboratory broke new ground. It was decided to adopt wholly automatic tracking, in both azimuth and elevation, and to incorporate Alfred Loomis's novel suggestion of conical scan. In the latter method, the antenna is rotated at high speed about the axis of a paraboloid, so that the beam produces a narrow pen-

[11]By November this system was giving four miles range on submarines, eight miles on aircraft, and twenty-six miles on land. The Naval Research Laboratory also made important contributions to the development of the SG.

cil along the axis. The strongest signal will then come from a target at which the beam is directly pointing. Despite the immense amount of work required to develop this equipment, involving novel circuits and complicated data transmission mechanisms, a mobile unit installed in a truck was ready for trials not long after Pearl Harbor. When tested by the Coast Artillery Board in February 1942, it located objects within less than six one-hundredths of a degree in azimuth and elevation and within twenty yards in range.[12] The production model, engineered by the General Electric Company and produced by them and Westinghouse, was standardized by the Army as the SCR-584. One of the greatest NDRC contributions to the war, it was still in 1945 one of the best and most versatile of all ground radars.

While one group at the Radiation Laboratory drove ahead with the development of complete systems, others pushed research in radar fundamentals or, with the help of industrial contractors, produced better components. One of the toughest problems in all radar history was the development of a satisfactory junction box which permitted transmitting and receiving on the same antenna.

If the reader examines a radar system, he will discover that the transmission lines do not resemble the wiring with which he is familiar but look like plumbing. Indeed that is just what the radar men have nicknamed them. If one tried to use ordinary wire at the super-high frequencies of the microwaves, the loss of radiation would be prohibitive. One has to use either coaxial lines or wave guides (hollow metal pipes) — some circular, some rectangular, in which there is no radiation loss because the outer conductor acts as a shield which forces the magnetic and electric fields to stay inside. The reader must not think, however, that the design of wave guides is as simple as that of house plumbing, for it is an abstruse chapter of the radar art. Electric and magnetic fields are more difficult to move through pipes and around corners than water, waste, and soapsuds. Their behavior differs at different frequencies, and raises novel and extremely difficult problems for the mathematical physicist.

Although not a single American microwave set was in use by the end of 1941, the basis for the new industry had been well laid.

In the history of Division 14, 1942 was the *annus mirabilis*. Under the

12In the parlance of the artillerist, .06° = 1 mil.

spur of actual war Radiation Laboratory personnel jumped from 450 to over 1700 during the year, requiring two new buildings. The 10-cm. systems, now coming from the production lines, proved brilliantly successful in combat and exerted great influence on tactics. The number of radar systems under development rose from twenty to nearly fifty, and included a huge outlay of funds and manpower to develop radar with a still sharper beam and higher resolution on a wave length of three centimeters.

The activities begun or planned in 1942 occupied most of the Laboratory's attention for the rest of its existence. Their success rested on a highly flexible and effective administration, extensive research in fundamentals, steady improvement of components, and close liaison with the Army and Navy, and the British.

The crying need of the day was no longer radar for night fighters to intercept enemy planes but airborne radar for patrol planes searching for surfaced submarines. We and the British had long-wave airborne radar, but microwave sets would be better. As the U-boats began to operate boldly in our coastal waters, their kill steadily mounted till it became doubtful whether we should have shipping enough to send adequate reinforcements overseas. Radio direction finders might locate submarines when they talked to each other or with their home ports by wireless, but radar for surface search was of the utmost importance.

While the Bell Telephone Laboratories were converting the first production radar set for night fighters into the first production set for patrol planes, the Radiation Laboratory pushed the development of another system for installation in Liberators which were being supplied to Great Britain under lend-lease. Dumbo I, the first of these specially modified B-24's, flew the Atlantic in March 1942, for tests in Northern Ireland. Dumbo II was demonstrated in April to Secretary Stimson and high-ranking Army officers. Seventeen of these sets were produced on a crash basis by the Research Construction Company, of which fourteen were delivered to the British between August and December, 1942, in time for a hot campaign in the Bay of Biscay.

Meanwhile ten similar sets were rushed to completion to outfit a squadron of B-18 planes under the command of the late Colonel William A. Dolan of the Army Air Forces. One of the planes, piloted by Dolan, with two members of the Radiation Laboratory staff in charge of the radar, located a Navy plane that had been forced down fifty miles at sea on April 2, and guided a destroyer to the rescue. Another B-18, the previous night, picked up a U-boat on its radar screen from eleven miles away, homed on it, and sank it.

Operating from Langley Field, Virginia, as the First Sea Attack Group, from July 1942, and for shorter periods from Key West and Trinidad, with hand-built radar from the Radiation Laboratory and the first of the SCR-517's and SCR-717's that were available, Colonel Dolan's Group played a notable part in the antisubmarine campaign.[13]

Officers at the Naval Air Station at Lakehurst, New Jersey, had become interested in October 1941 in putting radar on nonrigid airships. At a conference at the Radiation Laboratory on February 17, 1942, representatives of the Bureau of Aeronautics decided that a 10-cm. set should be designed around a new lightweight pulser, under production by the Stromberg-Carlson Company. The production contract was given to the Philco Corporation of Philadelphia, which had recently turned out for the Air Forces the first twenty-six American sets of IFF radar, an adaptation of the British identification system, in the sensational time of three weeks. The new search set, destined to become known in blimps and patrol planes the world over as the ASG or "George," was immensely superior to its predecessors because it gave a radar map of the territory ahead.

This set, weighing only 300 pounds, was the first production aircraft radar to present on its screen a complete map showing the shapes of coastlines, ships, and other targets scanned by the radar beam. With this type of presentation it is easy to tell the range of the target and its exact direction in degrees. The radar operator could spot convoys at 85 sea miles, coastlines at 100, and squadrons of enemy fighter planes at a distance which permitted the patrol bomber to take evasive action. Philco engineers developed long continuous assembly lines for rapid mass production of this ASG set, and several hundred test instruments to assure its satisfactory performance. A Government press release has well described the job as "a superhuman effort on the part of the development and production engineers."

If aircraft were to operate at long distance at sea, new navigational aids would prove of great significance for them and for surface vessels

13See Chapter III.

rendezvousing for convoys. In October 1940, Alfred Loomis had proposed a scheme in which pulsed radio waves from shore stations would
produce a grid of hyperbolic lines from which a ship or airplane carrying
a suitable receiver could obtain a fix. Let us suppose two stations sending
out simultaneous pulses. If we draw a line joining the two stations and
a second perpendicular to the first, a ship on any point in the second line
within range of the transmitting stations would receive the two pulses
simultaneously. Anywhere else within range they would arrive separately.
The interval between the times of receipt of the two signals will vary
with the position of the receiver. All positions having the same interval
will lie on a hyperbola, and there is a different hyperbola for every interval. Every Loran receiver is supplied with a set of charts having these
hyperbolae drawn in and marked with their time intervals. The time
difference gives a line of position. When a second line of position is obtained from a second pair of stations the point of intersection gives a
highly accurate fix.

In this simple and highly successful system which was soon to be named
Loran (Long Range Aid to Navigation), two stations are needed to provide one set of lines of position. In consequence, at least three stations,
one called "master" and two called "slave," are necessary. The signal
from the master goes directly to the navigator and also to the slave station, which, after synchronizing properly, retransmits the pulse. The
navigator notes the difference in time by means of a receiver-indicator,
which presents the signals on the screen of an oscilloscope, so that they
can be read to less than a millionth of a second. By means of Loran charts,
issued by the Hydrographic Office, the operator can plot his position
accurately in about two minutes.

The beauty of Loran for wartime use was that the ship or plane which
used it emitted no signal that might give away its position. Although
severe electrical storms might upset the system, it was otherwise unaffected by weather. Fixes could be obtained up to 700 miles from the
transmitting stations by day and 1400 miles at night, with an accuracy
comparable to that of good celestial navigation — that is, about one per
cent of the observer's distance from the station. The operator got either
a good fix or no fix at all.

This great contribution to navigation was developed at the Radiation
Laboratory during 1941 by a group headed by Melville Eastham, and

research was virtually completed by September. The tests, which proved highly successful, roused great interest in the services. Five stations were set up in 1942 on the coasts of Nova Scotia, Newfoundland, Labrador, and Greenland, and the four southernmost, linked to provide three pairs, operated regularly from October 1, 1942. As the war progressed, Loran coverage was extended over more than half the globe. Triplets in Assam and near Kunming guided aircraft over "the Hump," and others covered most of the Pacific. A modification, using the reflected sky wave at night to synchronize the master and slave stations, proved so accurate that the British used it for blind bombing as far east as Warsaw. The R.A.F. used this "sky synchronized" (SS) type of Loran for about 22,000 bombing sorties. Few developments of the war have greater peacetime possibilities.

The greatest triumph of the Radiation Laboratory in 1942 was the completion of the development of 3-cm. radar. Scientists were bold indeed who attempted the enormous task of developing components and systems on a shorter wave length when the new 10-cm. radar was only just going into production.

Wherever the 10-cm. sets had proved themselves superior to sets of longer wave length, the 3-cm. sets showed a further advance, especially in resolution. Production sets of 3-cm. radar for night fighters were manufactured by Sperry and by Westinghouse; and contracts for sets on the same wave length for patrol planes and torpedo bombers were given to Sperry and to Philco. These showed remarkable improvement in the clarity and detail of the pictures on the scope.

If the night fighters were to operate successfully from a carrier, it was necessary not only that they have radar to detect their enemy but that they be properly controlled by radar from the carrier itself. To meet this need, the Radiation Laboratory started work on a new system, incorporating conical scanning to give accurate bearings in elevation and azimuth, and the instantaneous presentation of height. This shipboard set, the SM, was manufactured by General Electric; but the prototype was built at the Radiation Laboratory and was installed in March 1943 on the new Essex-class carrier, the Lexington. It saw much service in the Pacific before it was replaced by a production set, the first of which came from the General Electric assembly line in August 1943.[14]

[14]A somewhat similar set, the SCR–615, was developed at the Radiation Laboratory for the Army and produced by Westinghouse.

The greatest of the high-power warning radars, the MEW (Microwave Early Warning), was conceived early in 1942 when there was still fear of Japanese attacks on the West Coast. It might be termed the "Big Bertha" of radar as it was the most powerful radar set ever built. The antenna system consisted of a linear array, backed by a cylindrical parabolic reflector. Since it was proposed to use a megawatt (1,000,000 watts) of power, special circuits and waveguides were required.

The coverage was so extensive, with ranges out to 200 miles, and the amount of information received was so large, that four scopes were provided to enable the operators to control tactical aircraft with greater flexibility. These amazing and historic equipments did not see service until 1944, when their performance exceeded all expectation. One of them, set up on Start Point on the Devon coast, enabled its operators on D-Day to control a patrol of Thunderbolts flying off the Brest peninsula, to dispatch fighter bombers over various targets, and even to have a hand in air-sea rescue operations in the Channel. The scopes were photographed and the film preserved as an historic record of the fighter sweeps over Normandy.

Meanwhile the work under way in England on radar beacons and blind landing had led late in 1941 to the creation of a group headed by Luis W. Alvarez at the Radiation Laboratory to study these problems. The first line of attack, using a pulsed glide path, required a receiver in the aircraft. While work on this was under way, Bush appointed an *ad hoc* Committee on Instrument Landing, with Alfred Loomis as chairman to recommend programs. A solution was reached by combining the linear array antenna recently developed for Microwave Early Warning with a new radar bombsight. The result proved highly successful in its first test at Quonset Point, Rhode Island, on December 26, 1942; and by the end of the war Ground Control of Approach systems had been installed by the Air Transport Command and by the Navy at numerous bases. They saved the ships and the lives of their crews in many cases where bad visibility had blanked out the possibility of landing without this aid. This method should prove of great importance to civil aviation.

As the war developed from its defensive into its offensive phases, more and more of the attention of British and American scientists came to be focused on radar bombing by night or through the overcast. The PPI picture lent itself extraordinarily well to this development. In it seas, lakes, and waterways remain black; coastlines, with their cliffs, bays, and inlets, show up clearly because they scatter radiation back to its source; and towns and cities stand out brightly. The British, committed to the policy of bombing by night, had a pulse navigational system called Gee, which guided their Pathfinder planes satisfactorily to targets as far east as the Ruhr, but they wished to go farther. Bomber Command consequently decided to try to navigate and to bomb by means of the data shown on the radar screen. This system, known as H_2S, was not very accurate, partly because 10-cm. radar lacks something in resolution.

On the wave length of three centimeters the fidelity of the scope picture was so great that better results might be hoped for. The Radiation Laboratory, which had long been working on radar bombsights, flung itself with enthusiasm into the development of H_2X, a 3-cm. version of the H_2S, which became famous as "Mickey."

The year 1943, as Dr. DuBridge characterized it in his summary report on the Radiation Laboratory, was primarily one of engineering and production. "By June 1943 nearly 6000 radar sets of Radiation Laboratory design had been delivered to the Army and Navy, 22,000 were on order, and production was climbing past the rate of 2000 sets per month of all types. The total dollar value of Service orders had by that time grown to three quarters of a billion dollars. Production mounted rapidly during the latter half of the year, and equipments with trained personnel were reaching the theaters in large quantities."

The total number of employees at the Radiation Laboratory rose during the year from 1700 to 2700, but the changed character of the work was far more significant. Instead of a small organization concentrating on fundamental research and leaving engineering strictly to others, the Microwave Committee had steadily expanded the operations of the Laboratory, with emphasis on development, assistance to manufacturers, and field service. Some in NDRC had argued that the Laboratory had become too large for efficient operation, and that it should be divided among several universities. These counsels were rejected; but during 1942 two major contracts for research on radar were let by OSRD: one to Harvard for a radar countermeasures laboratory and one to Columbia for a special microwave laboratory headed by I. I. Rabi. A score of lesser

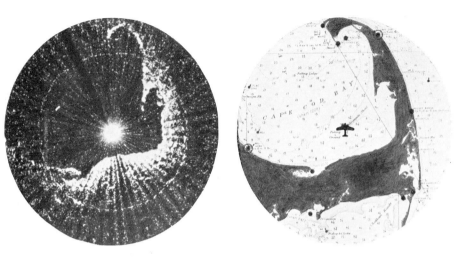

Cape Cod as it appears on a radar scope and on a chart

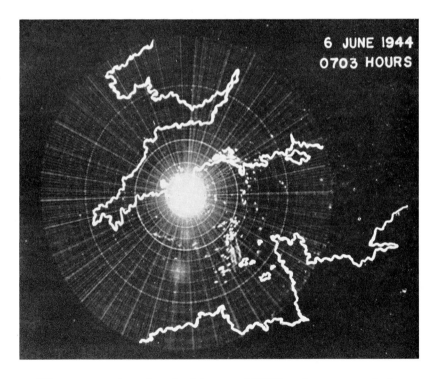

6 JUNE 1944
0703 HOURS

The greatest invasion in history: MEW radar scope of the
English Channel on D–Day

Intricate mazes of radar antennae watch over a carrier and guide a Navy
Hellcat on its mission

contracts were now concluded with other institutions, mainly concerning problems of microwave theory or basic electronic research.[15]

The original idea had been that the Radiation Laboratory

> would develop a piece of radar equipment, prepare a breadboard model for trials, and then, if accepted by the Army or Navy, turn this model over to a manufacturer, who would take full responsibility for carrying it from the breadboard stage to final use in the field . . . this technique was possible only in a very few cases. . . .[16]

Either the Radiation Laboratory detailed staff members to the manufacturer, or the latter sent his engineers and production men to Cambridge for indoctrination and collaboration in the production of prototypes. The latter practice was initiated by Philco in January 1943 and was more and more followed. Since the Radiation Laboratory dealt with over a hundred industrial contractors, this type of liaison came to constitute a large and increasing part of its activity.

The enthusiasm of the Laboratory staff was due not merely to the challenge of the services' needs and the fascination of the subject matter, but to the good sense with which all personnel and administrative problems were handled by the associate director, Dr. F. Wheeler Loomis, and his assistants. Above all, perhaps, it was due to the inspiring leadership of the director, Dr. Lee DuBridge, and the extraordinary group who constituted the steering committee: F. W. Loomis, I. I. Rabi, L. N. Ridenour, K. T. Bainbridge, L. C. Marshall, L. W. Alvarez, R. F. Bacher, L. A. Turner, J. R. Zacharias, and J. G. Trump. The latter subsequently rendered invaluable service as head of the British Branch of the Radiation Laboratory.

A visitor to one of the evening lectures for the staff will not soon forget the closely guarded auditorium, the youthful appearance of the lecturer, Dr. Ivan Getting, Chief of the Fire Control Group, and of the two thousand or more men listening to him with rapt attention. Getting was one of the world's greatest masters in the field, and the story he had to tell of the systems that made it possible for gunners to measure range to

---

[15]Among these contractors were Brown University, the California Institute of Technology, Cornell University, the Franklin Institute, the Bartol Research Foundation, Georgia Tech, Kansas State College, Brooklyn Polytechnic Institute, Purdue, Rensselaer Polytechnic, Stevens Institute of Technology, and the University of Pennsylvania. A staff member from the Radiation Laboratory was assigned to each of these contractors for liaison purposes.

[16]DuBridge, *Summary Report*, p. 28.

within a few yards well illustrated the revolutionary quality of radar. One got the impression not of a large audience listening to a lecturer, but of a conference of members of a large team, one of whose key players was analyzing some of the moves of past games so that all present, out of the analysis of past performance, would learn how to score fresh victories in the contests to come.

No division of NDRC had shown itself keener to follow its equipment into the field, learn its merits and shortcomings under combat conditions, help in the "debugging," and lend a hand to those at the front who were seeking to get the most out of the equipment. At the front or at Army and Navy bases the possible tactical uses of radar were explored, operating procedures were established, problems of installation and maintenance were met, and the training of operators and maintenance personnel went forward.

To make the collaboration closer yet the British Branch of the Radiation Laboratory was established at Great Malvern in 1943. Its first important job was collaboration with the near-by Telecommunications Research Establishment in developing Oboe, a microwave navigational and bombing aid widely used by the R.A.F. and the 9th Air Force. One of the most extraordinary members of the radar beacon, or racon family, descended from Gee and from the British IFF system designed to identify friend from foe, Oboe enabled two men sitting in trucks on British soil to know within a few yards each way the position of a British or American airplane over the Ruhr, and to know it much better than did the crew of the plane.

The job of the laboratory worker sent out to Great Malvern or to other bases closer to the front was not merely to demonstrate equipment, aid in its "debugging," revise or prepare training manuals, and develop modifications of sets to make them more useful under the shifting conditions of battle, but to aid the most alert of the air-force officers in devising tactical plans that would squeeze from the new gear the last drop of offensive power. Typical of this work was the development of methods for the control of aircraft in the assault of the Normandy beachheads, in the breakthrough which followed, and in the advance to and across the Rhine. As the ground forces pushed on, the British Branch of the Radiation Laboratory set up an Advanced Service Base in Paris and sent men to operate close behind the front, frequently under fire.

Before the war ended, Radiation Laboratory sets of the second and third generation had seen service in the European, Pacific, and China-Burma-India theaters. The Laboratory, which had worked out the techniques for the great shift from ten centimeters to three, had completed, with the help of its branch at Columbia University, the still more difficult transition to sets of a still shorter wave length. Despite the loss to the Manhattan District of some of its key men, such as K. T. Bainbridge, Alvarez, Bacher, and for a time Rabi, its numbers continued to increase, reaching a peak of nearly 4000.[17] Some long-term projects were begun in the belief that the war with Japan would outlast that in Europe by at least two years. Progress on some of these showed great promise, but they are still veiled in secrecy.

The 150 radar systems which the Radiation Laboratory had produced or helped to produce had speeded the day of victory. The high resolution of 10-cm. radar as compared to that of longer-wave sets had come to seem dull and unsatisfactory compared with the wonderful clarity of the 3-cm. radar and that of still shorter wave length. With these glowing outline maps before their eyes navigators had guided our bombers over Italy, Germany, and Japan. Thanks to the blind-bombing techniques they made possible, the pressure of strategic bombing had been kept so steadily on the Axis powers that they could not rebuild their towns, cities, and railroads, when they were bombed and blasted into ruins.

[17]At the end of the war nearly 5000 persons were engaged in radar development under Division 14 contracts.

CHAPTER X

RADAR COUNTERMEASURES

I N MARCH 1941 the Germans sent their only battleships, the *Scharnhorst* and *Gneisenau*, to sea as commerce raiders. On their sorties into the Atlantic they destroyed an entire convoy of almost 100,000 tons carrying war materials from the United States to Britain. When they holed up in Brest, British bombers swarmed over them like angry hornets, but had trouble hitting them through smoke screens and artistic camouflage. The two battleships and the heavy cruiser *Prince Eugen*, which had joined them in May, suffered some damage and decided to make a break for home before they suffered more. When these bottled-up ships left Brest on February 11, 1942, under cover of fog and snow and made their way through the English Channel, the world stood aghast at their success. The public was quite unaware of the fact that it was due to their jamming of British search radar.[1]

But the British authorities knew it full well and pushed their own program with redoubled vigor. They had used radio countermeasures successfully to parry the navigational and blind-bombing beams along which the *Luftwaffe* had sought to fly in the Battle of Britain. At the Telecommunications Research Establishment they had been studying radar countermeasures along with radar development. Now they got busy with counter-countermeasures.

News of this British activity led L. A. Alvarez's section at the Radiation Laboratory to give this problem some attention. The first need was a search receiver to furnish information as to what the enemy was doing with his radar, what frequencies he was using, what pulse width, what pulse repetition frequency. For this purpose OSRD contracted with the General Radio Company in July 1941 for an intercept receiver to cover the range of frequencies from 70 to 1030 megacycles, the equivalent of wave lengths of approximately 4.3 meters down to 29 centi-

[1]The Germans had jammed British radio communications to cover the escape of the *Goeben* and *Breslau* to Turkish waters in August 1914. The British had jammed the German gun-laying radar opposite Dover for months prior to February 1942 to cover the passage of convoys.

meters. At the Naval Research Laboratory, where radar had been under development for years, the possibilities of countermeasures had also been explored. Prior to our entry into the war NRL had developed a wideband crystal receiver to pick up enemy transmissions and determine their frequency, and had led a contract with the Panoramic Radio Company for a receiving set to cover the range from 50 to 700 megacycles.

As a result of conferences called by Admiral Furer on December 11 and 22, 1941, at the request of the Bureau of Aeronautics, NDRC was asked to undertake the development of radar countermeasures search receivers and jamming equipment in collaboration with the Naval Research Laboratory and the Signal Corps Laboratories. The project was assigned to the Radiation Laboratory, and entrusted to Dr. Frederick E. Terman, Chairman of the Department of Electrical Engineering of Stanford University. He had an encyclopedic knowledge of the field of radio and an unusual gift for helping a research associate over some difficult phase of the work.

Terman flew to England in April 1942 to get the latest information about German radar. Such information as was available came from secret agents and from the monitoring stations set up on the British coasts. Soon this was supplemented by captured enemy equipment, such as the set captured by British paratroopers on a moonlight night in February 1942 by their daring descent on Bruneval, near Le Havre.

It appeared that the Germans were using five major types of radar at frequencies from 100 to 600 megacycles for early warning, coast watching, aircraft interception, ground control of interceptors, and flak control. The task was to devise equipment capable of neutralizing all these systems plus any new ones at higher frequencies that might later appear. It was a big order to fill all these oscilloscopes with "hash."

Because the work of the RCM group grew out of enemy activity rather than our own, information from the front was desired at the earliest possible moment. The scientists chafed under the high security classification imposed on this material. Information available at the Radiation Laboratory flowed to the countermeasures group along a one-way pipe, with no return. Partly because of the security problem, partly because of the belief that different objectives required a separate locale and a separate *esprit de corps*, it was soon decided to set up the RCM project at a different institution. Harvard was a natural choice, close to the airport, with easy access to the Radiation Laboratory, and with sufficient space available for an expansion of the work. OSRD concluded a new Division 14 contract with Harvard on March 20, 1942, for what soon came to be called the Radio Research Laboratory, and in July 1942 Terman's group, now numbering 110 people, of whom 60 were technically trained personnel, moved from the Radiation Laboratory to a wing of the Harvard Biological Laboratory. By October of that year the group had become an integrated research and development laboratory with a total staff of 205, of whom 78 were technically trained.

At this time, coincident with the reorganization of NDRC into eighteen divisions, a new Division 15, entitled Radio Co-ordination, was set up. This new Division included the Radio Research Laboratory at Harvard, together with the communications countermeasures work also in progress in units of NDRC which subsequently became Division 13 (communications). This new Division 15, with a broad responsibility to all phases of electronics countermeasures work, was headed by Dr. C. G. Suits, now Vice-President in Charge of Research of the General Electric Company and director of its great laboratory at Schenectady.

Suits visited Great Britain in December of 1942 and was impressed by the opportunities of using radar countermeasures against the Germans. As a result, the Division embarked upon an expansion program aimed at trebling the effort at Radio Research Laboratory and bringing in additional university and some industrial contractors on all phases of countermeasures work. This task was accomplished during a period of great shortage of engineers and scientists.

Nine months later Radio Research Laboratory[2] had built up to a total of 475 people and in August of 1944 reached an all-time high of 810, of whom 212 were technical personnel. At this time physicists were in short supply, and the Army and Navy and the divisions of NDRC were clamoring for more. One group of highly valued recruits had been working on television for the Columbia Broadcasting System. Another came from the American Telephone and Telegraph Company and its subsidiaries. A training program was established to convert some chemists

---

[2]The original space available there was expanded by means of a temporary addition of two stories on the roof and a three-story temporary building located behind the main structure.

and biologists into radar technicians. One windfall came when RRL was permitted to tap a manpower pool established by the Signal Corps. Most of the men obtained from this source were engineers rather than physicists. Over half of the technical staff was composed of amateur radio operators. This group of "hams" and "ex-hams" turned their hobby into an important contribution to the war effort.

For the past three years [declared one of their number] the engineers of this laboratory have made Cambridge, Massachusetts, the noisiest city, electronically speaking, in the United States. This electrical plague has dwarfed all previous amateur efforts in the creation of QRM (interference), but for once, with a useful end in view.[3]

Out of this chaos on the Cambridge air came the larger part of the radar countermeasures equipment used by the American armed forces. Service orders totaled upwards of $300,000,000, more than two thirds of which represented equipment developed with the help of NDRC.

It took almost a year to place security on a workable basis, through the assistance of the Countermeasures Committee of the Joint Communications Board. This was one of the big jobs for the new Division 15, but with the fine co-operation of the Army and Navy RCM officers, satisfactory channels for the exchange of intelligence were worked out. Army-Navy-NDRC teamwork was never closer than in the RCM task and accounted to a large extent for the effective work of the Division.

The Army Air Forces established the Florosa Field Station at Eglin Field, Florida, in June 1943. This field was operated as a test area for countermeasures equipment in research, development, and early production stages. Division 15 set up a small laboratory unit at Florosa Field administered by Harvard University under the RRL contract. This laboratory served all the Division contractors for field testing of search receivers and jammers against the excellent array of captured enemy radar and communications equipment maintained at this field.

In January 1944 Division 15 took over the responsibility for the Airborne Instruments Laboratory at Mineola, Long Island, from Division 6. This laboratory, directed by Dr. D. G. C. Hare, under a contract with Columbia University, had successfully completed a previous task for the Navy Department, and now set out to develop countermeasures methods and equipment for a variety of new electronics problems posed by the

[3]Paul Robbiano, *QRM, The Electronic Life-Saver.*

enemy, including the newly launched guided missiles and flying bombs. At its peak period of operation the Airborne Instruments Laboratory engaged a total personnel of 301, of which 76 were of technical graduate grade; about three quarters of this staff went on the countermeasures job, the balance continued on final stages of the Navy's problem.

Early British and American jammers used electronic tubes which had been developed for other purposes because they were the only tubes available. The plea for more and ever more jamming power was apparent early in the countermeasures war, particularly when the problems of the Navy came to the fore. Because of this need, Division 15 undertook an extensive program of development of the special vacuum tubes required for high-power jammers. This work was largely centered in industrial laboratories under NDRC contract. The research laboratory of the Westinghouse Electric and Manufacturing Company had an old Division 14 contract for the development of a new type of tube called a "resnatron." This work, under Dr. David Sloan, was transferred to Division 15 and reoriented with super-power jamming of German radar as a new objective, and subsequently led to the development of the "Tuba" transmitter described below.

The Bell Telephone Laboratories developed some of the special tubes required for the RCM program, and the laboratories of the Federal Telegraph and Radio Corporation under Mr. Deloraine undertook to extend the design of the resnatron for other applications. A group in the General Electric Research Laboratory under Dr. A. W. Hull undertook an extensive program which eventually led to the production of a whole new series of high-power magnetrons which became the basis for the U.S. Navy's jamming equipment and which was subsequently adopted as standard by the British Admiralty as well.

Radar, as pointed out, sends out no intentional intelligence, and is basically easier than radio to jam. As it repeatedly sends out strong signals it can be heard at long range, much farther, indeed, than the greatest distance at which it can detect an object. If one hears the radar pulse, one can readily determine its exact location by means of a direction finder. Since the echo returned by most targets is weak in strength, relatively little power is required to drown out the echo by jamming. It is necessary, of course, to ascertain the particular frequency of the radar set, and tune the jammers to that same channel. If the jamming signal

The voice and ears of airmen adrift at sea: "corner" radar

The metal straw which blinded enemy radar: Window

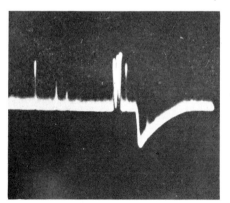

No jamming

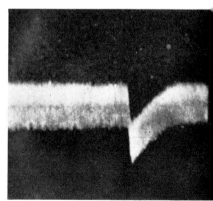

With jamming

Effect of Window: jamming a radar scope

is heard on a loud-speaker it sounds like a hiss. In a radar set, however, information is presented to the eye, not the ear, and the "noises" appear on the screen like grass covering up the blips caused by returning echoes.

The problem of radar countermeasures may be considered under three heads: search receivers, jammers, and counter-countermeasures. To monitor the enemy's radar effectively it is necessary to cover all the frequency ranges used in the radar art. To do this requires the development of numerous receivers and antenna systems and direction finders operating over a wide range of frequencies. When this equipment is installed in planes and ships one is prepared to analyze the enemy's radar transmissions.

The specialized planes in which this complicated gear is flown got the name of Ferrets. Often highly peculiar in appearance — one of them is said to have carried 36 different antennas — they were sent on long missions to collect information on which maps could be based showing enemy radar coverage. In the Pacific they had the help of our Fleet submarines, which were equipped with radar search receivers as soon as satisfactory sets were available.

Once the search receiver had supplied the necessary information the stage was set for jamming either by mechanical or by electronic means. This could be effected mechanically by dropping the metallic strips called Window or Chaff, cut to such a length that they are resonant at the frequency of the radio waves sent out by the radar. A packet of such strips can return an echo similar to that produced by a plane. The Germans investigated such reflectors early in the war, but realized that they had much more to lose than to gain if their use were adopted by the Allies. They consequently wrapped the system up in secrecy and it was not used by the *Luftwaffe* until six weeks after the R.A.F. introduced it in a raid on Hamburg in July 1943. Its first use caused consternation among the German radar operators, who cried, "The planes are doubling themselves."

The losses of the R.A.F. were cut to a small fraction of those sustained in earlier attacks, but the Germans soon showed that two could play at the game by executing, with the help of Window, a devastating raid on the Allied base at Bari. For use against long-wave radar, long ribbons of foil called Rope had some advantages. The Radio Research Laboratory made important improvements in the manufacture of Window, which heightened its effectiveness. The high-speed Chaff cutter opened the way to mass production. A total of over 10,000,000 pounds of aluminum foil were dropped over Europe by the 8th Air Force alone.

German radars could likewise be put out of action by electronic jammers. This achievement was not as easy as it might seem to the reader who has noted how a fifteen-dollar electric razor can prevent a costly home radio from receiving a high-powered broadcasting station. At the start there were no really good tubes for operation at frequencies higher than 600 megacycles. In pulsing, where the resting time is long in proportion to the transmitting time, you can overload the tube without difficulty. In jamming you cannot tolerate these long intervals of silence, for the tube must transmit continuously. To screen a plane by jamming, little power is required. For screening ships the new high-power magnetrons developed at the General Electric Research Laboratory under the supervision of Dr. A. W. Hull provided an ideal solution.

The first use by the Japanese of torpedo bombers using radar as an aid in launching a torpedo took place during the invasion of the Philippines in the Battle of Leyte Gulf. These "blind" torpedo attacks became a serious menace to the Fleet operations. Search receivers in the Fleet determined that the frequency of the radar sets in these torpedo bombers was below the lowest frequency of the magnetron jammers then installed in the Fleet. As soon as this fact was known, an emergency call was sent to the Navy Department for help. An urgent request was placed with the General Electric Company for some new tubes to cover a lower frequency range than was possible with the jamming transmitters then in the Fleet. Although the development of a new tube, even in wartime, frequently takes many months, experiments were performed immediately in the laboratories and within twenty-four hours a new low-frequency design was determined. By working night and day the scientists and tube engineers delivered over fifty of these new tubes to the Navy within one week of the original request.

As a result of remarkable teamwork all along the line, the new tubes were flown to the Pacific and were in successful operation shortly thereafter. Operational reports brought back the gratifying story of the success of this equipment against the Japanese torpedo bombers, which, when the jamming was turned on, were observed on the radar scope to waver from their course and finally turn back. Many grateful skippers authorized their countermeasures operators to paint a Japanese flag on their jamming transmitters after each successful action.

Although the rapid development of the electronic art made many new devices and techniques available, countermeasures raised new research problems, especially by the requirement of wide-range tunability and large continuous-wave power outputs. It was also necessary to devise methods of obtaining wideband modulation. Each transmitter ought to have the widest possible tuning range to reduce the number of transmitters required to cover all enemy radar frequencies. Each should have sufficient modulated power output, and be light and compact enough for airborne use. The British had found that random noise was the best jamming signal and had used a noisy diode for the purpose. RRL got much better results by using first a photoelectron multiplier tube and later a miniature gas triode.

During 1942 the Radio Research Laboratory developed an airborne electronic jammer known as Carpet, designed to cripple the small Würzburgs which were controlling German flak and inflicting substantial losses on Allied bombers. The more closely the subject was studied the more vulnerable the German radar defense appeared, for, except for the low-frequency Freyas, most of their radars were bunched in the frequency range between 550 and 570 megacycles, a narrow band which simplified the problem of electronic jamming.[4] One of the strange scientific facts of the war was revealed by studies of Window at Radio Research Laboratory. The weight of material required to make an echo equal to a four-motored bomber is a minimum in this German frequency range around 500 megacycles. Whatever the considerations were which led the Germans to standardize on this frequency range, it was a fateful choice. The British had been similarly vulnerable in 1940 before they introduced microwave radar, and by expending a few millions on suitable jammers at the time, the Germans might have altered the course of the Battle of Britain, and with it the fate of the world. Now the Germans were vulnerable: they had an immense investment in a narrow range, and it looked like a pushover.

Barrage jamming, spread over a broad band of frequencies, is like

[4]Originally all Freyas were contained within a band about 8 megacycles wide. Our jamming made them disperse over a band about 100 megacycles wide.

shooting with a shotgun, and much of the effect is wasted. "Spot" jamming, tuned to the frequency of the radar to be countered, is more like rifle fire.

Carpets are tuned to send down into ground radars signals having the same frequencies as those on which the radar sets operate. A Würzburg looking in the direction of a jamming Carpet has its entire scope filled with "grass," whereas Chaff affects only that part of the screen corresponding to the range at which the Chaff is located.

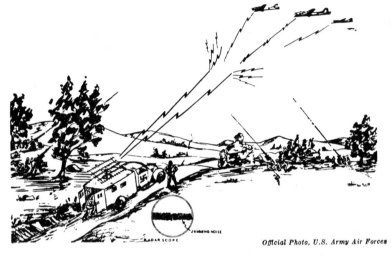

Official Photo, U.S. Army Air Forces

CARPET

Airborne transmitters, tuned to a slightly different frequency in each aircraft, radiate a torrent of "noise" which obscures the position of the formation in the enemy radar, causing inaccurate gunfire

Two hundred Carpets were produced by the Signal Corps, flown to England in the summer of 1943, and installed in planes of two groups of the 8th Bomber Command. First used on a raid over Bremen in October, the 68 planes equipped with Carpet suffered losses much less than those of planes not so equipped. It was soon discovered that Carpet and Window together were even more effective, and Carpet went into large-scale production.

The Germans, in consternation at the jamming of their best defensive weapon, had two courses before them. They could shift to microwave radar which is much harder to jam, or they could concentrate their efforts on applying anti-jamming techniques to their existing systems. Fortunately for the Allies they first chose the latter course, spending immense sums of money and man-hours on such modifications. Toward the end of 1944, half and sometimes more of the German experts on high-frequency radio were frantically trying to devise anti-jamming attachments for the Würzburg radars. To avoid Carpet they tried to shift the operating frequency. To avoid Window, they perfected methods of distinguishing between moving and stationary targets. To their dismay, the anti-Carpet devices made their radars vulnerable to Window and the anti-Window devices made them more vulnerable to Carpet. We and the British continued to use both at once. When the Germans turned to microwave radar they were too late to get it into effective use.

Late in 1942 the Germans began to take a heavy toll of British night bombers by sending night fighters equipped with radar to hover over British airfields. This led the British to develop a super high-power jammer. It was impractical to use jammers carried in their bombers, for the jammer itself provided a signal which might lead the fighter to its target. To jam effectively over a 200-mile path leading to Germany required an immense amount of power, a thousandfold more than any previously attained at that frequency.

The remarkable resnatron tube developed by Westinghouse presented a possibility of satisfying this requirement for tremendous jamming power. RRL studied this tube and its methods of operation and, as a result, produced a monster transmitter known as Tuba, one of the great curiosities of the electronic art. The greatest output reached (average continuous-wave power, not peak power) was 87 kilowatts delivered into a dummy water load, but in actual field operation the conservative output of 20 to 30 kilowatts was used.[5] The gain from the huge parabolic antenna was about 600 to 1, giving a field strength equivalent to 18,000 kilowatts radiation. By the time it was set up on the northeast coast of England the *Luftwaffe* was so depleted that the jamming of night fighter sets had lost much of its importance. This extraordinary research undertaking, however, should do much to advance the development of ultra-high frequency broadcasting.

[5] Its power was comparable with that of the most powerful United States broadcasting station, 50,000 watts, but the frequency of operation was 500 times as high.

Mechanical reflectors and electronic jammers could be used not only to blind but to deceive the enemy. Both sides in the war used small, lightweight conducting surfaces of the proper size and shape as decoys, to create radar echoes similar to those from airplanes, surface vessels, or submarines. This gave the impression that a force was about to attack which in reality was either nonexistent or of much smaller size. A small diversionary force which carried sufficient confusion reflectors might appear indistinguishable from the real attacking force which carried jammers for its own protection.

Fear that the Germans might put on a large jamming program led the British to speed up their study of anti-jamming techniques. Suits, on his return from England in November 1942, got an active program of counter-countermeasures under way.

Because of the secrecy which shrouded the countermeasures program, practically no information about jamming had reached radar designers and they had given little or no consideration to the vulnerability of their sets. An Anti-Jamming (AJ) Committee of Division 15 was organized, with representatives from all the governmental and industrial laboratories concerned with radar research and development. It was just in time, for the enemy was making rapid headway. The Joint Communications Board agreed to disclose to the extent required the information about German jamming and British counter-countermeasures. A technical group was set up under Lynn C. Smeby which prepared an AJ handbook, to help radar designers make their sets as jam-proof as possible. At the Radiation Laboratory Dr. James L. Lawson was assigned to review the Laboratory's microwave radar designs and to revise them if necessary to decrease their jammability.

Of all the scientific developments of the war, radar countermeasures were the most closely tied in with actual military operations, and, of course, with the equipment and tactics employed by the enemy. In the autumn of 1942, at British request, two representatives of Division 15 from RRL were attached to the British research laboratories. A better solution was proposed by Air Commodore Addison during Compton's visit in May 1943 — that a Division 15 Laboratory be established in England. Its main function was to be of technical assistance to the 8th Air Force in introducing new RCM equipment into combat, but it was also to secure information needed by the Division contractors.

An OSRD contract was concluded with Harvard University for the operation of the "American British Laboratory of Division 15" (ABL-15) under the supervision of RRL, to serve as a field laboratory in the European theater for the whole countermeasures program of the Division.

It was a novel enterprise for a university to run, in a foreign country, a laboratory so closely entwined with an operating air force, but the venture was a huge success. The first group of about thirty persons, under V. H. Fraenckel of the General Electric Company, was established at the chosen site, across the road from the Telecommunications Research Establishment. When Fraenckel went to General Spaatz's staff as an advisory specialist in RCM, John N. Dyer of CBS became director, with John P. Chase as his associate in charge of administration. The staff eventually reached sixty-eight and took a most active part in the work.

The contracts awarded by Division 15 totaled about $31,000,000. Approximately $23,500,000 of this was spent on radar countermeasures, of which $15,000,000 went to the Radio Research Laboratory; $1,000,000 to ABL-15; $7,500,000 to research and development in other laboratories. The remaining $7,500,000 went into other radio countermeasures.

While the Radio Research Laboratory and ABL-15 were straining every nerve to get the maximum results in countermeasures to jam German radar on D-Day, Dr. Suits was looking ahead to the period after victory in Europe. He toured the three operational theaters of the Pacific in May and June 1944 to explore the possibilities of expanding Division 15 activities there, and as a result the program of the Division was reoriented. All of the new projects were focused on Pacific objectives, and equipment originally developed for the European theater was re-examined for its application against the Japanese electronic weapons.

The operational use of countermeasures equipment involved some of the most extraordinary duels of wit in the history of war, and it helped mightily to speed the day of victory. It has been estimated that radar countermeasures saved the United States Strategic Air Force based on England alone 450 planes and 4500 casualties. But that is only part of the story. They played a major part in the masterly deception which covered our landings in Normandy and in Southern France. By blinding the eyes of our enemies while permitting our own radars to scan with little or no interruption they struck from the hands of the Germans and Japanese new and potent weapons, while leaving us free to do our utmost.

CHAPTER XI

CONTRIBUTIONS TO SUBSURFACE WARFARE

THE SENSE of urgency which spurred NDRC scientists to toil late into the night, seven days a week, was nowhere stronger than among the men working on antisubmarine devices. Unless the U-boats could be destroyed, the Germans had the war won already. Knowing that they had nearly won the First World War with their submarines, they had taken infinite pains to strike harder than before under the surface. Captured U-boats alongside a New England dock may look drab and scantily equipped compared with our latest models. Yet these ships came within a handsbreadth of mastery of the world. Thanks to them and to their like, Germany, till past the spring of 1943, seemed to hold victory in the hollow of her hand. Of what avail to build up an American Army of eight million men, if it could not be transported across the Atlantic to come to grips with our principal foe?

Better designs, better materials, and new methods of welding enabled the U-boats to dive to three, four, and finally to six hundred feet, as compared with the hundred-foot limit of 1917. To offset the progress of enemy listening devices they were much more silent than earlier types. When the British captured a German submarine in 1942 they found her crew wearing crepe rubber soles and supplied with rubber-covered hammers. The new U-boats were harder to detect and much harder to kill once contact had been established. The improvements which enabled their hulls to stand the great pressures at these depths made it possible for them to withstand heavy depth charges unless they exploded under water close to the skin. And these submarines were produced in large numbers by mass production methods.

In the First World War the chief means of detecting submarines were radio direction-finding and sonic listening devices. If the submarines surfaced and used their radio, the listening stations could establish an accurate fix with surprising rapidity. Detection of a submerged vessel was another matter. Knowledge of the transmission of sound through water was in its infancy.

Despite this handicap good work was done in 1917–1918 on listening devices at audible frequencies[1] for installation on submarine chasers and destroyers. The United States Navy assembled groups at Nahant and New London which included some of the great names of American science. Irving Langmuir and his associates developed hydrophones able to detect submarines effectively under quiet listening conditions from a stationary or slow-moving ship. They took the first step towards determining the direction of the target submarine by applying the principle of binaural listening which enables a blind man to sense the direction of a speaker. Max Mason made a further advance by devising an array of hydrophones that made it possible to establish the direction of the target even when the listening ship was in motion. Similar progress was made contemporaneously in England.

During the fifty-one months of World War I, 4837 Allied merchant vessels of 11,000,000 gross tons were sunk. These losses would have been much greater but for the adoption of the convoy system in 1917 and the equipment of about 3000 assorted escort craft with the new sound gear. Allied surface vessels and submarines sank 178 U-boats.

Toward the close of the war, too late to be of use during the hostilities, the French physicist, Langevin, made possible a great advance by demonstrating the possibility of echo-ranging or "pinging" at supersonic frequencies. He used the piezo-electric effect of quartz crystals to convert an electric voltage into a mechanical pressure, and vice versa. By this means he could transmit sound under water at higher than audible frequencies, and obtain the range by timing the echo. This method was further developed by Rutherford and his associates in Great Britain, where the initials of the Allied Submarine Devices Investigation Committee gave the world a new name, Asdic, for supersonic gear.

In the United States between the two wars the Naval Research Laboratory and the Submarine Signal Company made notable contributions to supersonic echo-ranging gear. Our equipment was fundamentally the same as the British save that we relied on the magnetostriction effect (that is, the ability of certain metals to change dimensions under the influence of magnetism) in preference to the piezo-electric effect obtainable with quartz sandwiched between steel plates. The British gear was simpler than our own, used a recording rather than an indicating

[1]Average ears respond to frequencies of 40 to 15,000 cycles per second.

means for the range, and had certain conveniences which made it easier to train operators. The Germans had been doing work in underwater sound comparable to our own; and the Japanese had bought good sound gear abroad.

Supersonic gear was used to detect the sound of a submarine's propeller or to receive the echo reflected from the hull of the submarine. Under favorable water conditions submarines could be located at ranges up to several thousand yards. Unfavorable factors were excessive refraction of the sound beam, reverberation, and false echoes. Rough seas might cause the ship to roll so heavily that pinging became difficult or unreliable. The apparatus, moreover, failed to indicate the depth of the submarine, an important factor in the geometry of attack. And echo contact with the submarine was lost throughout approximately the last 200 yards of the approach of the stalking ship.

On June 27, 1940, the day NDRC formally came into existence, Secretary Knox requested the National Academy of Sciences to appoint a committee[2] to advise him and his technical aide, Rear Admiral Harold C. Bowen, then Director of the Naval Research Laboratory, on the scientific aspects of defense against submarines and the adequacy of the Navy's preparations. This committee set up a subcommittee headed by Dr. E. H. Colpitts, who had recently retired as vice-president of the Bell Telephone Laboratories.[3]

After two months of visits to Navy shore establishments, antisubmarine craft, and the Submarine Signal Company, the Colpitts subcommittee found that the Navy, with the limited funds at its disposal, had done a fine job with supersonic echo-ranging, but had not had money enough to explore other approaches as fully. On January 28, 1941, they consequently recommended that a much broader and more vigorous attack be undertaken. Since the existing detection gear was far ahead of the training of those who were to operate it, they stressed the importance of better methods of selecting and training sound operators. Improvements in attack tactics and in instruments for guiding the attack seemed to them imperative. In view of the great advances in acous-

[2]Max Mason, chairman, R. A. Millikan, C. F. Kettering, F. B. Jewett, and John Johnson.
[3]The other members were W. D. Coolidge, H. G. Knox, V. O. Knudsen, and L. B. Slichter.

tics since the First World War they urged that audio-frequency as well as supersonic methods be studied intensively. And they insisted that greater attention be paid to the fundamentals of the problem, including the production of instruments for the measurement and recording of underwater sounds, the determination of the sound spectra of the noises from various types of ships under different conditions of operation, the study of underwater sound-absorbing and -insulating materials and techniques, further investigation of the propagation and attenuation of sound in typical oceanic waters and of the background noise in the listening ship when under way, and the study of magnetic devices and microwaves as supplements to acoustical detection.

When this report came to the attention of the General Board of the Navy late in March 1941, they called Jewett and Bush into conference and asked them to make recommendations concerning the best type of organization for a comprehensive study of the submarine problem. As a result, Admiral S. N. Robinson, Chief of the Bureau of Ships, on April 10 requested NDRC to enter the field.

The scale of the problem demanded the enlistment of great numbers of American civilian scientists. It was not merely a question of more warships and airplanes using existing weapons. The desperate race called for better weapons, for weapons more readily used, especially from airplanes; for the technical training of thousands of Navy men, many of them new recruits, and for solutions of all the complex problems of installation and maintenance at far-flung points.

Division 6, as the NDRC group came to be called, wove itself into the warp and woof of the Navy, conceiving its mission to be a joint effort with the Navy and with other divisions of NDRC. Scientific personnel were encouraged to feel themselves a part of the armed services. The efforts of NDRC in no degree led the Navy to relax the effort of its own development laboratories or to limit development work under Navy contracts with industrial companies. Rather, NDRC participation stimulated such Navy activities.

Prior to Admiral Robinson's invitation, NDRC's activities in this field had been confined to a contract with the Gulf Research and Development Company for the detection of magnetic masses from aircraft, the development of airborne microwave search radar to detect surfaced submarines, and a contract with the Woods Hole Oceanographic Institute.[4] The contributions of both radar and oceanography proved to be of the first order of magnitude.

Bush's first step was to set up a new section, C-4, in Jewett's division, charged with the development of new and improved methods of detecting submerged submarines. Later, this section and its successor, Division 6, found their responsibility greatly increased, but both the radar and the rocket divisions made contributions of great importance.

At the outset Jewett set up two laboratories, one at New London, operated by Columbia University, and one at San Diego, run by the University of California. The latter laboratory was supposed to stress fundamental research and special problems in the Pacific, the former was to stress the finishing stages of the development of new devices. Both were founded on naval reservations so that the Navy might more easily furnish buildings, ships, naval personnel, and policing.

In actual practice the San Diego Laboratory[5] devoted about one third of its efforts to fundamental studies, one third to training and to the development of training devices, and one third to sonar (underwater sound) devices and methods of submarine evasion. It scored notable triumphs in all three fields, extended the knowledge of reverberation and wakes, and produced charts of average sound-ranging conditions for Pacific areas comparable to those produced at Woods Hole for the Atlantic. San Diego scientists developed the equipment which later in the war helped our submarines to penetrate Japanese minefields and operate in the Sea of Japan.

The New London Laboratory[6] continued throughout the war to be concerned mainly with the perfecting of new devices, first for antisubmarine use, later for submarines themselves, and for the training of their personnel. The weapons which it devised or improved were numerous and varied. We can never know how many German submarines or Japanese surface ships its efforts helped to sink, but we know that a high percentage of the problems it tackled were brought to successful completion.

[4]From the early days of NDRC Bush and Jewett had been eager to get to work on the antisubmarine problem which seemed "absolutely the kind of thing on which NDRC ought to take off its coat and get busy." (Bush to Jewett, September 16, 1940)

[5]It was established on the premises of the Navy Radio and Sound Laboratory at Point Loma and was directed first by Dr. V. O. Knudsen and later by Dr. G. P. Harnwell.

[6]It was first directed by T. E. Shea, Vice-President of Electrical Research Products, Inc., and later by T. K. Glennan, formerly Chief Engineer of Paramount Studios, under Shea's general direction.

To assist the Navy on installation and maintenance of new devices, Rear Admiral E. L. Cochrane, Chief of the Bureau of Ships, induced the New London Laboratory to set up the Bureau of Ships Field Engineering Group,[7] which rendered valuable technical assistance throughout the Atlantic and Pacific areas and at innumerable shore bases.

One single incident will epitomize all this work. Two field engineers worked thirty-six hours on end supervising the readying of antisubmarine equipment on the destroyer escort U.S.S. *Bangust* at Pearl Harbor. When the DE's captain thanked them they laughingly said, "You'll pay us back if you will sink a Jap sub on this trip." Within a week the *Bangust* did so. The Navy sank the enemy vessel, but the *Bangust's* equipment was at top efficiency because of the field engineers' feverish efforts.

One of the cornerstones of the Division's program was the development of accurate methods for measurement of sound in water. The improvement of underwater sound gear depended on improved measuring equipment. The Bell Telephone Laboratories, anticipating coming events, had done some exploratory work. In July 1941, NDRC contracted with the Western Electric Company for the Laboratories to develop hydrophones which would serve as standards for underwater sound calibrations, projectors to furnish sound fields for this work, and testing and calibrating procedures applicable to a wide variety of devices. Test stations were set up at Mountain Lakes, New Jersey, and Lake Gem Mary, at Orlando, Florida, where tides, waves, ship motion, and background noise would not interfere with the most delicate tests.

For nearly a year the Bell Laboratories carried this work through the pioneering stages and established reference testing stations. Though the Laboratories had vast experience in measuring sound in air and were a natural choice to develop similar test equipment and procedures for underwater sound, it became advisable for the Laboratories to suggest a change in sponsorship. For the Navy had, in the meantime, asked the Western Electric Company, the Laboratories' associate, to become one of its suppliers of underwater sound gear; and a standards laboratory, to be effective, must of course be regarded as independent of any product

---

[7]Under Shea's general oversight this group was directed first by J. W. Kennard and later by Woodman Perine.

whatsoever that it may have to test. On May 1, 1942, therefore, this work was organized under Columbia University, which established the Underwater Sound Reference Laboratories.[8]

When this work started in 1941, Bell Telephone Laboratories had already developed some equipment for the measurement of underwater sound. By the end of the war it was possible to measure sound as accurately in the water as in air.[9] NDRC gradually built up a stock of standard instruments, constructed and repaired by the Bell Telephone Laboratories, calibrated by the Underwater Sound Reference Laboratories, and issued to authorized agencies including Allied nations.

The introduction of pulse techniques comparable to those of radar revolutionized sound testing and promised important contributions to air as well as to underwater acoustics. Thanks to all these new techniques, sonar gear could be given accurate production tests at the factory and calibration could be performed in test areas under conditions much nearer than formerly to those of service use.

The third of the major laboratories of Division 6, the Harvard Underwater Sound Laboratory,[10] made valuable improvements in existing sound gear, and developed a radically new type, to which it proposed to apply the name "sonar," for sound navigation and ranging. The name seemed to the Navy to be too good to be applied to a single device and it came to be applied to underwater sound devices used for listening, depth indication, echo-ranging, and location of obstacles. At least half of the highly important work done in this Harvard laboratory is still veiled in secrecy. As is true of other distinguished contributors in this field, such as the Westinghouse Electric Corporation, the Leeds and Northrup Company, the American Can Company, and the Armour Research Foundation, no adequate record of its work can be given at this time for reasons of security.

By the time of the Japanese attack on Pearl Harbor work was well under way in all the laboratories in Section C-4 and mutual understand-

[8]Professor R. S. Shankland (on leave from the Case School of Applied Science) was the director.

[9]The equipment installed at Mountain Lakes covered the range of 2 cycles to $2\frac{1}{2}$ megacycles per second and permitted measurements at powers up to 1500 watts, hydrostatic pressure up to 300 pounds per square inch, and throughout the temperature range from zero to 100° Centigrade. Here were established the basic reference levels with which all underwater acoustical measurements were ultimately compared.

[10]Dr. F. V. Hunt of Harvard was director, and later Dr. Paul Boner of the University of Texas, associate director.

ing with the Navy was growing. One incident at this time made a deep impression on the NDRC scientists. A general conference had been called at New London for December 10, 1941. The question arose, Would the naval officers come in their usual numbers, now that war had laid such heavy burdens on them? The Navy came in almost triple its former numbers, as if to emphasize that here was not an academic discussion of research, but a survey of some of the hopes and expectations for more efficient warfare, soon to be so direly needed.

During the following three and one-half years the division not only operated its three great laboratories, which produced so much in knowledge and devices, but prosecuted similar work through the research staffs of Bell Telephone Laboratories, General Electric Company, Gulf Research and Development Company, Woods Hole Oceanographic Institute, and many other organizations. The muscles and nerves of the division spread all over the globe, wherever our Navy fought.

Its scientists flew on long blimp patrols as technical aides; they flew out of Iceland in long-range antisubmarine search planes; they helped detect mines off North Africa and Italy; they traveled on escort carriers in the Atlantic and participated in many carrier plane missions, perfecting equipment and analyzing attacks; they helped on shakedown cruises of destroyers and destroyer escorts; they helped to install and try out rocket ordnance on small ASW vessels; they applied mathematics to search operations off Brazil and in the Caribbean; they repaired and put back into use discarded equipment at isolated places like Trinidad; they aided in building or improving training courses and in installing special training devices, at Key West, San Diego, Norfolk, Boston, Midway, Pearl Harbor, and many other centers; they gave assistance on the installation and maintenance of weapons in every Naval District without exception; they gave on-the-spot instruction to destroyer personnel off Leyte, Manus, and in the Marianas, and helped overcome there the technical limitations of difficult supply conditions.

They made acoustical surveys of harbor or coastal waters in Long Island Sound, in Chesapeake Bay, at Key West, Coca Sola, Midway, Oahu, and Guam; they made countless dives in submarines on experimental tests and frequently underwent depth charging in tests of new devices; they produced and tried out quantities of pre-production equipment; they worked with production manufacturers on specifications and

design problems, and with the Navy on trials of manufacturers' equipment; they measured the noise of many submarines, aiding in the perfection of routinized tests; they devised, under naval officer guidance,
improved tactical methods and practice exercises; they assessed combat
results; they visited England and Canada in liaison exchange of information; they maintained research liaison with large numbers of naval
activities; they acted as technical advisers at our distant bases in Brisbane
and Perth, Australia; they were a part of an airplane antisubmarine
squadron in the Solomons; and they channeled the results of all this
effort through the authorities and commands of the Naval Bureaus and
fleet forces.

All this and much more, too. Many of them were nomads of science.
One of them, Shea, traveled over 300,000 miles, going from activity to
activity. Wherever they went they found those who had to combat the
enemy heartened by evidences of scientific help pouring out of the laboratories back home.[11]

Early studies made by Dr. S. S. Wilks and Dr. L. B. Slichter showed
the need for more accurate detection equipment, greater maneuverability on the part of the escort craft, and streamlined, fast-sinking depth
charges which would give the submarine less time to maneuver. These
studies indicated that with the best underwater detection system only
one attack out of twenty would be likely to succeed with the methods
then available. The precision of attack required to get depth charges
close to the strong U-boat hulls of 1940 was far greater than it would
have been with the submarines of 1917.

Later destroyers, destroyer escorts, and smaller patrol craft were designed to be much more maneuverable. Streamlined depth charges were
developed and methods to project them forward in pattern. For destroyers and destroyer escorts it sufficed to copy the British "Hedgehog"
or spigot mortar, which fired a ringlike pattern of small, fast-sinking
depth charges with contact fuzes. As smaller craft could not stand the
recoil of this weapon, Divisions 3 and 6 developed the "Mousetrap"
rocket device, which fired a straight-line pattern of similar projectiles.

Would these new weapons require new systems of fire control, or could

[11]On the invaluable work of the Antisubmarine Warfare Operations Research Group,
see chapter XXVI.

Official Photo U. S. Navy

Death for the U–boats: loading a Hedgehog

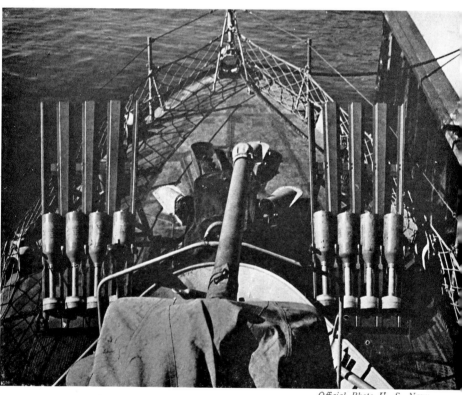

Mousetrap ready for the kill

the "seaman's eye" be relied on in making attacks on submerged submarines? British experience indicated that plotting and predicting devices, mechanical, chemical, or electrical, offered great advantages. Attack directors and plotters were developed by Division 6 to help the conning officers of antisubmarine vessels in determining the correct attack course and firing time. The Anti-Submarine Attack Plotter (ASAP), developed by the General Electric Company under NDRC contract, went into large-scale production. It furnishes a Plan Position Indication of the attack situation depicted on the screen of a cathode ray tube.

Radar had given long-range eyes to both ships and planes. But as soon as either type of craft approached the U-boat submerged. In the early stages of the war the aircraft lacked means of detecting submerged U-boats, or of damaging them while they were beneath the surface. The surface vessel could search only a much smaller area than the plane, but it was far superior for close-range work because of its sound gear and the ordnance it carried. Two major tasks were the development of better co-ordination between planes and surface craft and better detection devices and better weapons for the plane.

It became steadily clearer that however effective supersonic equipment was under ideal conditions, the vagaries of sound transmission through water varied its performance enormously. It depended upon the bouncing of a short ping or burst of sound off the target and upon the reception of the weak echo from this reflection. Under ideal conditions, it had much the accuracy of radar in air and, indeed, anticipated many of the technical features of the latter. Under bad conditions, wave motion, refraction of sound due to varying water temperatures, false echoes, the effect of rolling and pitching of the searching ship, and the noise of the latter when moving at considerable speed, severely limited detection.

Second, except upon the unlikely discovery of some moderate-range underwater system of detection based upon something other than sound energy, detection by supersonic sound would remain a vital tool and must be improved.

Improvements in ship detection gear took place, so far as NDRC was concerned, in the Harvard, New London, San Diego, and Bell Telephone laboratories. Electronic devices were made simpler and more accurate. Devices were developed to keep the projector pointed at the target in spite of one's own ship's motion, and to reduce the effect of reverbera-

tion from near-by water. Indicating equipment was made more convenient for operators' use, especially under conditions of fatigue. Based
in turn upon the measurements standards program started in 1941,
better projectors and hydrophones came to the fore, more efficient
and more accurately directional. Means were devised to reduce the
interference of one's own ship's noise in the operation of the equipment.

The use of the bathythermograph, developed at Woods Hole, to measure water temperatures' change with depth, spread recognition of the
importance of diffraction. Sound-ranging charts, developed at San
Diego and Woods Hole, showed average detection ranges to be expected
when diffraction existed in various areas and in various seasons. Numerous acoustical studies developed understanding of the peculiarities of
shallow-water transmission. Development, especially through ORG in
co-operation with the Navy, of improved tactical methods, enabled detection information to be used "while still hot," and made plain the
geometry and timing of the attack problem. Optimum shipboard performance of detection equipment was aided by the development of
portable testing equipment. None of these steps, or of others taken,
changed radically the nature of the detection equipment. Taken as a
whole, they assisted the Navy to make the best possible use of available
techniques, especially during the period of tremendous expansion in personnel and ships.

In the training field, the San Diego Laboratory did the largest part
of the Division's work. It operated in close co-operation with the staffs
of the two fleet sound schools. One of its sections developed highly ingenious apparatus for training purposes. The primary and advanced
Bearing Teachers are intended to give preliminary instruction to the
sound operators on Attack Teachers. Primary and advanced Listening
Teachers were likewise developed at San Diego. Recordings of various
underwater sounds prepared at New London proved of great assistance;
indeed, the demand for instructional records made New London one of
the important sound-recording centers of the country. A more advanced
teaching device for officers is the Conning Teacher, which presents the
conning officer with essentially the information he would receive from
a perfect sound operator and requires that he maneuver a simulated ship
so as to conduct a successful attack. Practice attack meters and practice
targets were developed for training at sea, together with a Shipboard

Attack Teacher, which is a portable device for simulated training at sea. These and other similar efforts furnished the Navy with thousands of well-trained operators.

Toward the end of the war radically different detection equipments, based upon sound transmission but capable of giving continuous target indications, had been developed. These equipments, though used for certain other special applications, arrived too late for the U-boat problem.

NDRC gave the airplane two important aids for underwater detection, the Magnetic Airborne Detector and the expendable sonobuoy.

When Section C-4 was organized, Dr. L. B. Slichter was put in charge of a group to examine the possibility of developing a magnetic means for detecting submerged U-boats. To this group was referred the work which had been done by the Gulf Research and Development Company under NDRC contract. In October 1941, trials in a PBY-1 plane of an automatically stabilized magnetometer were so successful that it was decided to expand the effort. First at Quonset Point Naval Air Station and later at Mineola, Long Island, where a complete laboratory was established, the work on the Magnetic Airborne Detector (MAD) was continued and brought to the production stage.[12] With this device submerged submarines were detected from altitudes of more than 300 feet, approaching 500 feet on occasion. On December 2, 1941, the Magnetic Airborne Detector Mark I, designed by the Gulf Research and Development Company, detected the submerged submarine *S-20* four times in nine tries in deep water 100 miles south of New London. Installed in blimp *K-3* it was used repeatedly from January 1, 1942, and was effectively used in the coastal campaign against enemy submarines. Fourteen units built by the Gulf Company of the improved Mark II for use in blimps were delivered to the Navy in March and April, 1942.

The demonstrated importance of magnetic-detection equipment now led to an intensive development campaign to increase its sensitivity and overcome certain limitations. This campaign centered around equipment stabilized by the magnetic field of the earth itself rather than by gyroscopic action.

[12]The staff of the Mineola Laboratory under the direction of Dr. D. G. C. Hare built hundreds of pre-production equipments, installed many of these in planes and blimps, helped establish training schools and tactical procedures, and flew almost 10,000 hours on observational and training flights.

Laboratory staff members were present during numerous bombing attacks on submerged targets, witnessed several torpedoings and rescues, and acted as technicians on the blimps and planes in which MAD apparatus was installed. The device produces a continuous trace on a moving tape which indicates when it has passed near a magnetic body such as a submarine. With the aid of flares and markers dropped from the aircraft, it is possible to chart the course of a submerged submarine as a guide for aerial bombing tactics or for attack by surface ships.

When Tate and L. B. Slichter visited Great Britain in April 1941 to inspect British antisubmarine devices they brought back the idea of an expendable sonic buoy which might be dropped by a ship in convoy. As the convoy continued on its course, the drifting buoy would pick up the sounds of any vessel approaching from the rear and send a warning signal by radio. A practical form of convoy buoy was developed for Division 6 by the Radio Corporation of America. The concept of dropping such devices from convoys soon lost its appeal, but the possibilities of adaptation of such a device for aircraft searching for submarines were most promising. This was developed at New London, in a form remarkably well adapted to U-boat hunts. Launched from an airplane, it floated in the water "free of all effects of ships' motion," and transmitted by radio to the plane whatever underwater sounds it heard. Light enough to be carried by planes in considerable numbers, the buoys were used in patterns to scour large areas of water within which a submarine was known or suspected to be. Then either an attack or an exhaustive waiting game, dependent on the submarine's ultimate surfacing, might be decided upon, depending on the circumstances. With each buoy having a different code signal, the moves of the submarine could be followed. If surface ships were called in to aid, the radio information could be transmitted to them, likewise. Developed with infinite skill and thoroughness, and sent into operation through most intimate co-operation between the New London Laboratory and the Air Force, Atlantic Fleet, the expendable sono-radio buoy became one of the outstanding developments of the war.

The important work of Division 6 in the field of mines and torpedoes was under the direct supervision of Dr. W. V. Houston and is still a Navy-OSRD secret. It occupied a large part of the attention of the Harvard Underwater Sound Laboratory, and of a group at the Bell Tele-

A depth charge blasts a U-boat to the surface

Radio sonobuoys used to track down U-boats

phone Laboratories under W. H. Martin. Groups at the California Institute of Technology threw fresh light on the behavior of projectiles under water, using a high-speed water tunnel and a 300-foot torpedo tube which was erected at Morris Dam. To take but a single example, the work done on airborne torpedoes at Cal Tech so improved the reliability of their performance when launched under battle conditions, and the probability of a successful hit, that the pilots were no longer reluctant to undergo the inherent great risks in making such attacks. No longer were our torpedo planes to be easy targets for the Japanese gunners, like the gallant Torpedo Squadron Eight in the Battle of Midway.

Operations analysis indicated that aircraft were to become more important if anything than surface craft in antisubmarine work. This led to heightened interest in the Magnetic Airborne Detector, in the expendable radio sonobuoy, and other airborne devices. When a submarine had been detected by aircraft, it was desirable to mark the spot in some way so that the plane might return to the same region and thus track the submarine. For this purpose special float lights were developed. To insure that they fell vertically, and landed as close as possible to the point of MAD contact, rocket projectors were developed at Cal Tech and compressed-air projectors at New London, to project the flare backward at a velocity substantially equal to that of the aircraft. Underwater flares, to be used from blimps and patrol aircraft, were designed to show up submerged submarines at night, either by direct underwater illumination or by silhouette against a bright background. Tests, however, showed the range of illumination to be so limited that further development was not undertaken.

In tests of these underwater flares, two Navy blimps operating off the New Jersey coast on the night of June 8, 1942, collided in mid-air and crashed into the sea. All hands aboard the two aircraft were lost, with the exception of one Navy officer who escaped through a gondola window and was saved. Five NDRC scientists lost their lives — Franklin C. Gilbert, Charles R. Hoover, Lawrence S. Moyer, Israel H. Tilles, and Arthur B. Wyse.

From 1942 on, the United States Navy was bringing terrible pressure to bear on Japan by means of our own submarine forces. The security aspects of subsurface developments were awkward, for if the Germans learned of our new devices for the war against the U-boat, they might pass the information along to the Japanese for use against our submarines. And what the Japanese learned of our new devices for submarines might find its way into German hands. This was one reason for delaying the entry of NDRC into prosubmarine activities.

Despite this reason for caution, certain devices developed for antisubmarine use were soon adapted for use on our underwater craft.

Thus the bathythermograph, originally perfected by Woods Hole Oceanographic Institute for antisubmarine work, found wide application in the submarine field and became a standard instrument for determining the acoustical character of the water through which a submarine traveled and the nature of the maneuvers which would provide greatest safety against a searching enemy. Likewise, a simple directional sonic listening gear originally produced for small ASW craft was adapted into a highly effective gear for submarine use. The value of this equipment lay partly in the ability which it afforded a submarine to detect its own noises, thus offering a precaution against Japanese sonic listening from small stationary or slowly moving craft; partly also in the frequent superiority of sonic listening for long-range observations of enemy targets; and partly in the simplicity of use of the device. Designated by the service, in improved form, as the JP-1 Sound Receiving Equipment, it has become standard on all American submarines as an addition to supersonic gear and many a Japanese target was brought within the submarines' ken by it. A modification of this equipment, for measurement of the submarine's own noises, was later developed and is known as the Noise Level Monitor. Details of the JP-1 and of its modified forms are still secret.

These examples illustrate how often in research work profit results from looking at "the other side of the coin." Intensive study of the strength and weaknesses of submarines as enemies led to an appreciation of the possibilities of applying recent knowledge to helping our own submarines.

As the summer of 1943 approached, Division 6 had gone so far with the development of antisubmarine devices and weapons that it became possible to transfer substantial effort to the prosubmarine field. Discussions within the Division had resulted in many suggestions for fruitful work. Moreover, the intimate relationships which had been formed with the Navy, especially in the offices and bureaus in Washington and with Commander Submarines, Atlantic Fleet, had made a great deal of preliminary assessment possible as to the urgency and probable value of improvements.

But time was pressing; the pace of the Pacific war was stepping up and careful choice of effort was necessary if improvements were to be made quickly of use. Accordingly, Shea and Glennan, acting as ambassadors of Division 6 and with the cordial support of the Navy, visited the Pacific Fleet Submarine Force and exhaustively reviewed the proposed program with about thirty squadron and division commanders and staff officers. Out of this visit, which proved a landmark in the Division's history, and out of further discussions in Washington, grew a practical, intensive, and speedy program on many valuable devices. The accompanying chart indicates the shift of effort within the New London Laboratory only, but it is significant of the trend in Division 6 as a whole.

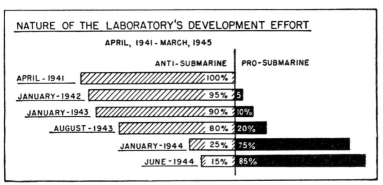

Anti-submarine: aids to detect and kill enemy submarines
Pro-submarine: aids to sink enemy shipping by our submarines

With the changing character of the war in the Pacific the number of NDRC scientists serving the Navy there increased. A Pearl Harbor Division of the New London Laboratory was established in August 1944 and its members were attached to the staff of Vice-Admiral C. A. Lockwood, Jr., Commander Submarine Force, Pacific Fleet, who welcomed and fostered the assistance of the civilian scientists.

Division 6 was the only one in NDRC to be given objectives as broad as a whole field of warfare. Its activities, as has been seen, covered the whole field of subsurface war, including methods of selection, training, installation, maintenance, and operational analysis, as well as the development of new weapons and devices. Throughout the whole field the NDRC scientists acquitted themselves superbly. Nowhere was collaboration with the armed services closer or more fruitful. The triumphs were a joint product of NDRC and the Navy, jointly conceived, produced, and applied. They went to the heart of two of the greatest problems of the war: the defeat of the U-boat, without which victory could not have been achieved at all; and the strangulation of Japan by sea power exerted beneath the surface, without which it could only have been won much later and at much greater cost of life.

CHAPTER XII

NEW DEVICES FOR AIR WARFARE

THE IMMENSE expansion of air warfare left to OSRD great fields of activity quite outside the area of aerodynamics and aeronautical design which had been properly reserved for the National Advisory Committee on Aeronautics. Division 1 of NDRC developed the gun liners which added so much to the life of airborne machine guns. Out of the studies of blast effect made by Division 2 developed theories adopted by the Air Forces as to the selection of targets, the proper missiles for use against a given target, and the best height for air bursts. This Division also developed the frangible bullet, for the training of aircraft gunners. The rockets developed by Division 3 became, in the opinion of many, the Navy's best airborne weapon. Division 4 developed proximity fuzes for bombs and rockets; Division 5 developed guided missiles. One of the chief sections of Division 7 made important contributions to fire control of airborne weapons. The chemists developed new explosives that increased the effects of bombs and depth charges, new hydraulic fluids, better methods by which airplanes could lay smoke screens, and new incendiaries which burned the hearts out of Japanese cities.

Division 12 devised improvements in aircraft brakes and Division 13 perfected speech secrecy systems which permitted air crews to talk from plane to plane without risk to security. Although it was first put to defensive uses in detecting aircraft and submarines, radar in its offensive aspects found its greatest usefulness in the air. Radar countermeasures permitted planes to ride above the flak as if they were on a magic carpet. As they blinded the eyes of enemy radar, so the camouflage paint developed by Division 16 rendered planes less visible from the ground. The studies made by Division 17 in acoustics greatly improved airborne communications. Division 18 made contributions in metallurgy which vitally affected the construction, equipment, and armament of planes, and helped, like the work of NDRC on fuels, towards a solution of some of the problems of jet propulsion.

Some of the most important contributions to air warfare came from the Committee on Medical Research. The close co-operation of its Division of Aviation Medicine with the air officers of both the Army and the Navy led to better methods of selection and training, important advances in the field of night vision, and new ways to protect the aviator from the lack of oxygen at high altitudes, the perils of quick decompression, and the effects of centrifugal force.

Though the design of planes fell in the research field allotted to NACA, the Office of Scientific Research affected it in two ways. The Division of Aviation Medicine of the Committee on Medical Research studied with great care the causes of aircraft accidents and the nature of the resulting injuries, revealed faulty structural characteristics, and made recommendations for the redesign of seats, control panels, safety harness, and escape hatches. At the same time NDRC made great advances in the art of sound control in planes.

Prior to our entry into the war the intercommunication system of an airplane failed to function at an altitude of 20,000 feet or more. Even if a speaker shouted into a microphone, chose his words carefully, and enunciated clearly he could not be heard above the roar of the motors, let alone understood by the crew member he was talking to. American scientists led the world in the transmission of sound, but they had given little thought to the problem of designing earphones and microphones for use at such high altitudes. The road to a satisfactory solution was a long one.

In the summer of 1940 the Matériel Command of the Army Air Forces asked NDRC to undertake studies of the effects of noise on man and the best methods to reduce sound in combat vehicles. The project was referred to Professor Philip Morse of M.I.T. He sought the assistance of a young Harvard physicist, Leo Beranek, who had just completed a doctor's thesis on noise reduction. At a meeting of scientists, Army officers, and representatives of several companies working on acoustics, held in November 1940, Morse outlined a program for developing lightweight acoustical materials. When the question came up as to the amount of quieting that might be needed, Dr. Hallowell Davis, an expert on hearing from the Harvard Medical School, convinced the group that this was something best answered by psychologists. Colonel Frederick Dent of the Army Air Forces, who had been instrumental in getting the project started, multiplied Beranek's original estimate of $3000 for his research needs by ten, and added a substantial sum for a team of psychologists.

This dual approach to the problem proved of great value. The Committee on Sound Control in Combat Vehicles was first set up under the Division of Physical Sciences of the National Research Council, with Morse as chairman and Beranek as secretary. Under a subcontract with Harvard University, Dr. S. S. Stevens headed a group studying the effect of noise and vibration on psychomotor efficiency in the newly created Psycho-Acoustic Laboratory. Throughout the following four years they worked in close collaboration with Beranek's Cruft Laboratory group. The two groups spent over $1,750,000, made important discoveries in the field of electro-acoustics, and applied them to improve many types of airborne communications.

Their studies of the acoustical properties of materials used for sound-proofing aircraft showed that these must satisfy two demands. They must prevent to the greatest degree possible the transmission of sound through the side walls of the cabin, and they must absorb sound that has already arrived in the cabin. For a limited weight these two requirements of low transmission and high absorption are somewhat contradictory, so that at best the design is a compromise. The material most suited for the acoustic treatment of airplanes turned out to be not mica, or a similar substance, but a single layer of porous material spaced as far as practical from the fuselage skin.

The two Harvard laboratories produced many important papers on the control of sound in aircraft and tanks, culminating in 1944 in a magnum opus, *Principles of Sound Control in Airplanes*. As the Joint Aeronautical Board relied largely on these reports in writing its specifications, by the end of the war all combat planes were soundproofed in accord with these principles.

Soundproofing the plane was only one step towards better communications. It was Commander Malcolm P. Hanson, U.S.N.R., a farsighted authority on radio frequency, who initiated, in October 1941, the important project on airborne communication which more than any other contributed to the growth of these two Harvard laboratories.

At the Psycho-Acoustic Laboratory Stevens and his group created noise duplicating the sound spectrum of a plane and measured what it did to humans. Fifteen or twenty different tests were made of the effect of noise on hearing, vision, motor co-ordination, blood pressure, and metabolism, using high school students, undergraduates, Ph.D.'s, and conscientious objectors as subjects. Surprisingly enough it was found that noise alone did not make one half of one per cent difference in the scores. The tests furthered the development of improved communications, proved that speakers using airplane microphones should be selected by means of carefully prepared tests, and led to the compilation of a list of words from which standard commands might be chosen because they were more intelligible than others over a communication system.

Farsighted people in both the Army and the Navy recognized the shortcomings of existing communications and pressed for the standardization of airborne equipment. Thanks to the aggressive leadership of the Joint Aircraft Committee and the Joint Radio Board, objectives were set up for headphones, headsets, and helmets and an improved microphone was promptly put into production.

Out of a project for an acoustical device for determining the relative position of a glider in relation to the tow plane came the construction at Harvard, at a cost of $100,000, of a large echoless chamber known as "Beranek's box" or "the world's quietest room." This proved useful in other projects where it was desired to eliminate any trace of an echo.

The Harvard groups developed new methods of testing headphones and microphones and studied the transmission of sound through oxygen masks and gas masks. A laboratory for field testing was set up at Eglin Field where Army Air Force enlisted personnel were selected as members of articulation test teams.

The trouble with communication at high altitudes is due to the voice rather than to the ear end of the circuit. At 35,000 feet the voice level drops off 18 decibels, which is equivalent to a loss of 49/50 in energy. A second factor to contend with at higher altitudes is pressure. Since the air between the diaphragm in the earphone and the eardrum is more easily compressed, the headphone's task of transmitting sound is increased. Finally the voice changes in timbre.

Various interphone components, oxygen masks, helmets, and noise shields were studied under conditions of actual flight at different altitudes. It became clear that a good airborne microphone must be a faithful transducer of speech, so constructed or shielded from ambient noise that

it could be used in the presence of loud noise, and so mounted or suspended that a speaker could use it conveniently and comfortably without
the use of either hand. An earphone, by the same token, must be so fitted
to the ear canal that it excludes all extraneous noise. The Harvard scientists designed a number of ear sockets for various purposes and mounted
them in "kapok doughnuts" which comfortably and almost completely
excluded extraneous noise. They also redesigned aviation helmets to get
a snug fit.

Articulation tests under flight conditions confirmed laboratory findings. Up to approximately 20,000 feet, there was a gradual dropping off
in articulation scores with a sharper drop at progressively higher altitudes. At 33,000 feet, great effort was required by the speaker to make
himself understood even with the best interphone components tested.
After a few words he "ran out of breath." To overcome such difficulties,
an adjustable automatic-switching aneroid amplifier with greater output
and voltage gain was suggested to provide satisfactory performance at all
altitudes. The greatest single cause of poor speech intelligibility was attributed to the throat microphone, but recommendations for its withdrawal met opposition. However, a new microphone, to be used at high
altitudes in the oxygen mask and at low altitudes in a noise shield, suspended over the mouth, met with acceptance as did improved ear sockets,
earphones, headbands, and headsets.

In conjunction with these studies, ear wardens, small rubber or viny-
lite plugs inserted in the ear canal, were developed. The controversy
over the introduction of this small, inexpensive yet scientifically designed protector for the eardrum was not successfully resolved until the
last year of the war, when several million were ordered.

To enable aircrewmen to talk from plane to ground and plane to plane
without interception by the enemy, NDRC scientists devised speech
secrecy systems with a high degree of security. These broke up speech
into elements and transmitted them in various combinations, drastically
altered from the original order. The receiving set then reassembled them
correctly.

To camouflage our planes OSRD scientists developed a glossy black
enamel for night fighters which made it much more difficult for the
enemy to make them out in his searchlight beams. After model trials

at the Tiffany Foundation, Long Island, New York, and service tests in
late 1943 at Eglin Field, Florida, General Arnold ordered that all United
States night fighters be so camouflaged. This paint proved so successful
that it was adopted for the understructure of the B-29's as well.

Radar guided our planes to the target but what they needed when
they got there was the right weapons and the right choice of bombs.
The principal contribution of OSRD to aircraft armament was the
rocket. This was ideally suited to airborne use because the speed added
by the plane increased the accuracy of the projectile and because the
absence of recoil permitted the use of heavy pay loads without damage
to the aircraft from which they were fired.

Another great contribution to aircraft armament was the liner for
machine guns. Gunners who fired prolonged bursts ruined the barrels,
wearing away the rifling and destroying the accuracy of the weapon before its ammunition was exhausted. Frequently after a single mission the
machine-gun barrels of a fighter or bomber plane had to be replaced.
What was needed was a liner of erosion-resistant material.

In solving this difficult problem Division 1 had the help of the Crane
Company of Chicago, the Westinghouse Manufacturing Company, the
Geophysical Laboratory of the Carnegie Institution of Washington, and
other contractors who produced a highly successful liner. Beginning in
September 1944, the Crane Company supplied 2000 lined barrels a
month, meeting a demand which was so urgent that the barrels were
flown to the Marianas as soon as delivered, for installation in B-29's.
The Army Air and Service Forces hailed with delight these new weapons
which enabled machine gunners to fire long continuous bursts without
impairing the accuracy of their guns. This increase in their firing capacity
reduced the number of barrels which had to be transported. Today the
gun barrels with liners will outlast the guns themselves.

Besides the right weapon the aerial gunner needed a good system of
fire control,[1] and thorough training. To this latter, Division 2 of NDRC
made an important contribution in the frangible bullet, which enabled
the airborne trainee to shoot at a maneuvering plane rather than a towed
sleeve or a radio-controlled drone.

In view of the difficulties in the way it is not surprising that the
Ordnance Department and the Army Air Forces were skeptical. Assum-

[1]See below, pp. 217–220.

ing that a machine-gun bullet could be made of glass or plastic which would break on impact and do no damage to a lightly armored target plane, plenty of other obstacles loomed in the path. The standard .30-caliber machine gun had to be modified so that it would recoil properly with the lighter powder charge and mass of the breakable bullet. This bullet must have satisfactory ballistics. A hit indicator must be devised. And plans had to be worked out for scaling of bomber's and fighter's velocities, the bullet's muzzle velocity, and the ring sight's size.

Only enthusiasts convinced that a new approach to the training of flexible gunners was indispensable could have mustered enough courage and staying power to see this project through. Major Cameron Fairchild, AAF, Professor Paul Gross and his colleagues at Duke University, and members of the staff of the Bakelite Corporation and of Division 2 of NDRC showed persistence and ingenuity matched by their ability to shed the cold water thrown on them for two years. When glass failed to do the trick, they turned to lead-filled bakelite. By 1944 their dream had come true. Aircrewmen were firing .30-caliber machine guns from bombers at lightly armored, friendly fighter planes which dove and rolled in simulated attacks. When a frangible bullet struck the armor it caused a vibration which was amplified electrically. The gunner knew when he saw a bright light appear in the nose of the target plane that he had scored a hit which would be counted automatically. The first successful air-to-air firing trials took place on May 29, 1944. By V-J Day about 300 P-63 target airplanes were in use in seven American gunnery schools and student gunners had fired close to 13,000,000 rounds of frangible bullets without injuring a single pilot of a target plane.

Those who knew how big the pin was in "pin point" bombing, and how broad the "pickle barrel" was, were naturally led to wonder whether means could not be found to control a bomb in flight and steer it to its target. The idea was an old one. Most of the enthusiasts who overwhelmed the Patent Office, the services, and the National Inventors' Council with their suggestions overlooked the fact that all the fundamental principles were matters of public record dating back twenty-five to forty years to basic patents issued to Charles F. Kettering, Elmer Sperry, John Hays Hammond, Jr., and others. What was needed was not the idea that a bomb could be steered by an observer at a distance or could be made to steer itself toward a source of energy. The need, which NDRC supplied, was for the technological development of known principles, plus research to solve the thorny problems encountered as soon as one tried to merge the dynamic characteristics of a control system with the behavior of a bomb in flight.

The long, complicated, and still largely secret history of the development of guided missiles in the United States in World War II is divided into two periods which differ as night and day. On August 25, 1943, in the Bay of Biscay, German planes, maneuvering out of range of antiaircraft fire, released glide bombs and then zoomed upwards. In a few seconds a flare was ignited in the rear of each glider, and the ships under attack could see that the bombs were being steered by some sort of control. Within a few weeks, by means of two radio-controlled missiles, one a bomb fastened to a glider wing, the other a high-angle bomb, the Germans sank many Allied merchant ships in the Bay of Biscay and the Mediterranean, and inflicted heavy damage on H.M.S. *Warspite* and U.S.S. *Savannah*. Immediately there was complaint that American ingenuity had failed to keep up with that of the enemy, and a demand for prompt action to counter the new German weapons and develop some of our own.

For years American officers had been thinking of using drones or pilotless planes, which came to be widely employed for gunnery practice, on offensive missions. With the development of radar and the improvements in the field of television, the idea spread of controlling planes, gliders, bombs, and even tanks and boats to the target. Too frequently those familiar with the control mechanisms — the "brains" or "intelligence" of the missiles — knew little about aeronautics; and those who knew the aerodynamics of planes, gliders, and bombs were often ill-informed about recent developments in the electronics field.

Shortly after its inception in June 1940, OSRD undertook several projects in the field of guided missiles but these received little encouragement from top service circles. Even those enthusiastic officers at Wright Field or at the Naval Aircraft Factory at the Philadelphia Navy Yard who advocated guided bombs or planes enlisted little interest from their superiors. When the Germans, in August 1943, made the first recorded combat use of radio-controlled missiles, the climate of official opinion changed overnight. From that time on more projects were sponsored by the services than could be co-ordinated effectively or pushed rapidly to completion.

In the early days of NDRC two basic projects had been started, involving the co-operation of the sections of Tolman's Division A and K. T. Compton's Division D which were later combined into Division 5. One project started out as a radio-controlled aerial torpedo, with a television camera in its nose which transmitted what it saw back to the controller in the dropping plane. The other began as a high-angle bomb, fitted into standard bomb bays with just enough controllability to allow either a human or an automatic steerer to modify its trajectory sufficiently to convert near-misses into hits.

The first of these two projects, which was known as Dragon, followed a somewhat tortuous path. In January 1941, the Radio Corporation of America, realizing that they knew a lot about television but nothing about aerodynamics, brought their torpedo to the attention of Division A of NDRC. The National Bureau of Standards was asked to form a research group to design and build a suitable air frame to carry the torpedo.

Then came the submarine campaign, growing more and more menacing. The Navy asked the National Bureau of Standards group and the Radiation Laboratory to co-operate in designing an antisubmarine weapon. Using a scaled-down Dragon air frame, which by then had undergone encouraging tests, a standard depth bomb was to be carried directly to the submarine, steered by a radar-bombing device. As originally planned, the radar transmitter was to be carried by the dropping plane, while the bomb carried the receiver and flew along the reflected beam.

Before this weapon, known as the Pelican, was perfected, however, the submarine threat faded. The idea of a glide bomb which would follow a radar beam directly to the target was, nevertheless, too good to abandon. All that was necessary was to increase the size of the bird until it became capable of carrying a full-size standard bomb. This was done, and eventually there emerged a bird capable of homing on a steamer regardless of visibility conditions, and giving a good record of hits.

Pelican, despite a long and honorable history and an excellent record in tests, was fated to suffer an ignominious end, for the Navy's verdict was "no operational use." Nonetheless, the experience gained was put to good use in the development of Bat. Pelican had required that the dropping plane illuminate the target with a radar beam. This was not necessary with Bat, which used the same type of air frame and a combination send-receive radar set which was self-sufficient. It made its debut in Borneo in May 1945 and paid off with the destruction of a sizable tonnage of Japanese shipping.

Bat, the first and so far the only completely automatic target-seeking missile to be used in warfare, was a glider bomb which located its target by radar, then, like a bird dog, tracked down its prey, steering itself toward the chosen target by following the reflected radar beam. It was a splendid example of the results obtained by co-operation between the Navy and civilian organizations.[2]

Television as a source of information for the bombardier proved most beguiling. It seemed so sensible to put a television camera in the nose of a bomb. Then all that was necessary was to steer the bomb so as to keep the target centered on the television screen. Early in 1941, therefore, rival television studies were in operation, both for the high-angle bomb and for the glide bomb. Although several systems gave satisfactory performance as far as reproduction of the target image was concerned, nothing resembling a usable weapon came from all of this work.

For one thing, the steering turned out to be much more difficult than its sponsors had imagined. All of the birds oscillated in their downward flight, and it was a rash operator who would swear that he could be certain exactly where his bomb was heading. Then, too, there arose the mathematical paradox of the pursuit curve. In the presence of either cross wind or target motion, it is mathematically impossible to hit a point target with a very fast missile which is kept continuously aimed toward the target. In practice, these difficulties caused sidetracking of the original vehicles.

It remained for a late starter to overcome most of the hazards and reach serious consideration. In the autumn of 1941 the Radiation Laboratory had developed a radar receiver which would reliably track reflected

[2]Bat was conceived by the Navy Bureau of Ordnance, using principles developed at the NDRC Radiation Laboratory at the Massachusetts Institute of Technology. Its radar was designed and built by the Western Electric Company under Navy contract and fitted to an air frame developed at the National Bureau of Standards. The complete missile was tuned up and put into service under the eyes of technicians and research men from M.I.T. Field Experiment Station under a Division 5 contract.

pulses and could presumably steer a homing bomb. Division 5 asked the Douglas Aircraft Company to design the ideal vehicle to carry such a mechanism.

From the standpoint of aerodynamics the work done by Douglas proved of extraordinary interest and its influence will be long felt. Roc, the unorthodox bird which emerged from the Douglas Laboratory, avoided the aerodynamic troubles that plagued many another designer. But in the intervening years there had been many delays and changes in plans, some of them due to the difficulty of producing a "brain" for the bird, some due to the fact that there were no Navy carrier planes which could use Roc.

So it became necessary to rework the design and produce the "cookie-cutter" model finally accepted which could be slung beneath the wings of existing bombers.

Then it was learned that the radar signals, by which the target could be distinguished from its background, were not reliable at the moderately steep glide angle at which Roc was designed to fly. It became necessary to abandon radar intelligence and search for a suitable system of control.

Fortunately RCA had just about perfected MIMO (Miniature Image Orthicon), a compact television outfit which appeared to be ideal as a servant for Roc. Just at the war's end, it seemed that all the troubles had been eliminated, that Roc flew well and could be steered to a target anywhere within a relatively long radius of the original aiming point, that MIMO gave a good usable image, and that a computing television sight built by Douglas could eliminate the "pursuit curve" difficulty by steering the bird along a target-interception course.

Out of the studies of infrared radiation begun by Section D-4 of NDRC in 1940 came the idea that a ship could be detected at night by means of its own inherent heat radiation. By logical steps this program led to an airborne ship detector, thence to a heat-homing bomb, which was christened Felix.

It required months of work to develop a thermal element sensitive, rapid, and reliable enough to serve in the "eye." It took more months of laboratory analysis and field tests to eliminate the engineering difficulties. By midsummer of 1945, however, the production model had given good results in Army tests, and Felix was ready for use against Japan — just too late to see service.

The most important guided missiles project of NDRC was a standard 1000-pound general-purpose bomb fitted with an extended tail which carried a flare, a radio receiver, a gyro-stabilizer to prevent rolling, and rudders for steering to right or left at the will of the bombardier. Because the remote control was exerted in AZimuth ONly, the bomb was named Azon. It was designed in the summer of 1942 with alternative controls by radar-homing, heat-homing, and television or direct-sighted steering; but it was another year before it was ready for production design. In the meantime there occurred many a heartbreaking failure of this or that phase of the design. Most persistent was the tendency of the bomb to spin. Obviously, for the bombardier to steer the bomb satisfactorily to right or left, complete elimination of rolling was necessary. In the wind tunnel and on paper this seemed easy, but after many labor-filled hours had been spent preparing full-size bombs for the ultimate test, dropping from an airplane, the result too often was that the stabilizing forces were inadequate and the bomb would spin.

There was also official lethargy to be overcome. One colonel with considerable experience in Europe flatly denied that any guided missile could be of any use at all. Others wanted to wait until Razon came along, on the ground that Azon was too limited in its utility. (Razon was to be radio-controlled but steerable in both Range and Azimuth rather than in azimuth alone.) Furthermore, and this was the point that the Army stressed, steering the bomb had not yet been *proved* to improve accuracy of bombing, but *could* be proved to increase the risk to the plane crew due to continuation of the bombing run until impact.

It took several months of hard work by Gulf Research and Development Laboratory engineers, gathering reliable data and eliminating faulty components, to overcome these discouraging sentiments. It was May 1943 when the results of one crucial series of tests were presented to the Division and to the Army; of sixteen bombs dropped, eight were Azons and eight were uncontrolled. The average error of the uncontrolled bombs was twenty-nine times as great as that for the Azons dropped simultaneously.

These spectacular results led swiftly to production design and procurement. When most of the "bugs" had been eliminated, the Army Air Forces put the weapon to good use in the Mediterranean theater where it scored hits on the locks in the Danube at the Iron Gate and

Radio-controlled Azon bombs smack a Burma bridge

Azon tail assembly mounted on 1000-lb. M–44 bomb

B-29's rain incendiaries on Japan

on the Avisio viaduct just south of the Brenner Pass. At the end of May, 1944, as part of the bombing prior to the landings in Normandy, Azons were dropped on bridges over the Seine. Then interest lapsed until early in 1945 news came of amazing successes in Burma.

Because of Allied attacks on Japanese shipping, a large part of the supplies for the Imperial forces in Burma had to be routed east of the Malay Peninsula to Bangkok and thence by rail from Bangkok to Moulmein and Rangoon and thence north to Lashio, behind the north Burma front, or Prome, behind the Arakan front. The bridges on these vital rail lines had been frequently attacked by fighter bombers and by medium and heavy bombers with little effect, for bridges defended by flak are very difficult targets. When Azons were installed in the 493rd Squadron of the 7th Bomb Group for use against these bridges, there had been a good deal of skepticism, but it vanished after the first mission on December 27. The target was a three-span steel railway bridge, 380 feet long, at Pyinmana, on the line between Rangoon and Mandalay, which had survived numerous bombing raids during the previous two years. Three planes carried four Azons and four standard bombs each and dropped one of each on three passes, all at 9300 feet. The standard bombs all missed, but the center span of the bridge was destroyed and another span damaged with the expenditure of only nine Azons. During the period December 27, 1944, through March 3, 1945, the 7th Bomb Group expended 459 Azon bombs and destroyed 27 bridges. Ten to 15 per cent of these controlled bombs scored direct hits. It is small wonder, after these brilliant successes, that plans were under way for larger use of Azon in China when the war ended.

Except for the disruption of Japanese communications in Burma, the American guided missiles had no influence on World War II. Their future is quite another matter. General Arnold, in his Final Report, has stressed the dangers of attack by long-range missiles guided accurately to sources of heat, light, and magnetism: —

Drawn by their own fuzes such new rockets will streak unerringly to the heart of big factories, attracted by the heat of the furnaces. They are so sensitive that in the space of a large room they aim themselves toward a man who enters, in reaction to the heat of his body.

With our present knowledge a guided missile, in the form of an airplane, could be made to fly across the Atlantic, but it would be highly inaccurate and relatively easy to intercept. Whether a high-angle rocket similar to the German V-2 can eventually be developed to fly from one hemisphere to another, and, if so, how accurate it might be, we do not know. But the success of the Germans in developing the fastest missile yet known has placed this question high on the applied scientists' list of unsolved problems.

Off to battle with 5-inch HVAR's; a P-47N

THE FLYING RADAR SET

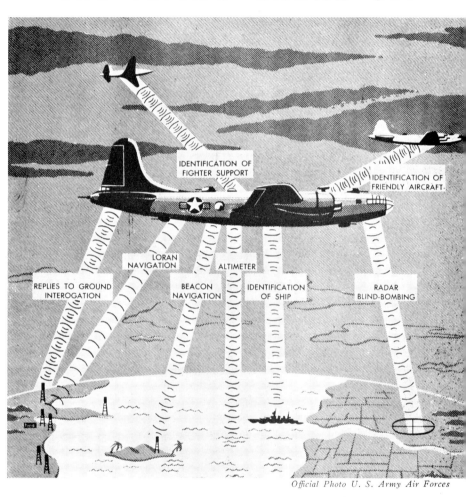

IDENTIFICATION OF
FIGHTER SUPPORT

IDENTIFICATION OF
FRIENDLY AIRCRAFT

LORAN
NAVIGATION

ALTIMETER

REPLIES TO GROUND
INTEROGATION

BEACON
NAVIGATION

IDENTIFICATION
OF SHIP

RADAR
BLIND-BOMBING

Official Photo U. S. Army Air Forces

THE B-29 IS SOMETIMES REFERRED TO AS A
FLYING RADAR SET. THE FUNCTIONS OF FIVE
TYPES OF RADAR EQUIPMENT ARE SHOWN HERE

CHAPTER XIII

ROCKETS

THE ROCKET, which assumed such extraordinary importance in World War II, was a weapon of ancient lineage, used by the Chinese against the Mongols as early as 1232. Within a century it was widely known in Europe, but its inaccuracy consigned it to the discard when rifled ordnance of great range and accuracy appeared, about 1850.

Backward though they were often said to be in matters of technology, it was the Russians who in 1941 first employed rockets on a major scale. They achieved a notable success, and made more use of the rocket as a ground-to-ground weapon than any other combatant. The Germans scored the greatest triumph in the rocket field with the celebrated V-2, the fastest missile yet made by man, with its pay load of a ton of high explosive.[1] The British had fortunately made a fine start on their rocket program before the war and were able to help us when, the last of the great powers, we belatedly entered the field.

What started all this activity was the desire for a weapon of great power which, because of its lack of recoil, could be fired from an airplane or from a light surface vessel. The rocket filled the bill. In a war in which air power and amphibious operations bulked so large, the demand for it was enormous.

What is the secret of this lack of recoil? The rocket consists of a tube, closed at one end and open at the other, filled with a propellent powder. When it is fired, the gas pressure inside the tube rises quickly, and is exerted with the same force on each square inch of the inside of the tube. The gas rushes out through the open end without exerting any force on the area of the opening, but it exerts its full force on the opposite closed end of the tube. There is thus produced a thrust on the tube, acting in the direction opposite to the nozzle.[2]

---

[1] The true rocket can operate in a vacuum since the fuel it carries has already in it all the oxygen necessary for combustion. The V-1 was not a rocket, but a pulse-jet flying bomb, which required air for its operation. See above, pp. 35–36.

[2] The magnitude of this thrust equals approximately the area of the orifice in square inches multiplied by the internal pressure in pounds per square inch.

The first suggestion that NDRC embark on a rocket program came from Dr. C. N. Hickman of the Bell Telephone Laboratories, a rocket enthusiast of long standing who had worked in 1918 and 1919 with Professor R. H. Goddard, then the foremost advocate of such missiles. Hickman proposed that NDRC start work on recoilless guns, jet-propelled armor-piercing bombs, rockets to be mounted on tanks and vehicles, infantry rockets, rockets for submarines and small boats, rockets for the projection of chemicals, and rockets for aircraft.[3]

The services were skeptical as to the value of an inaccurate weapon of low velocity, but the Navy nonetheless asked NDRC to develop a jet-accelerated armor-piercing bomb for low-altitude tests against heavy armor. Since such a rocket development would be both hazardous and secret, the Navy provided a small laboratory building tucked away in a corner of the Naval Powder Factory at Indian Head, Maryland, with range facilities on the Potomac River.

The work which got rapidly under way there, under the supervision of representatives of the Army, Navy, and Section H (for Hickman) of Division A of NDRC, soon indicated that rockets would prove of great value. The full interchange of scientific information with Great Britain, which resulted from the Tizard and Conant Missions, enabled the American scientists to catch up quickly and to save long months of trial and experiment. By the spring of 1941, Section H had several new weapons under development, including antiaircraft rockets of both low- and high-altitude types, the 4.5-inch aircraft and artillery rocket, and the jet-accelerated armor-piercing bomb.

The curse of the rocket was its inaccuracy. The crux of the problem was not so much the design of the rocket and its stabilizing fins, but the discovery of a suitable propellant, sufficiently strong mechanically, with just the right burning time, and capable of imparting a steady thrust.

At the time Section H turned to American powder manufacturers for assistance, it appeared that none of them had experience with such production or facilities adequate for the purpose. Ballistite, a double-base powder similar to British cordite, seemed to be the best thing available, but it was produced here only in the form of small grains for small-arms ammunition or in sheets for trench mortars. Neither form was suitable for rocket propellants.

[3]Hickman to Jewett, June 20, 1940.

A vigorous controversy raged around the best type of grain for rocket powder. The reader must not think of these grains in terms of a grain of sand, but rather of a three-foot length of rubber hose or cast-iron pipe. To produce them of just the right shape, diameter, and internal perforation so that the thrust would remain as constant as possible throughout their burning time was the neatest trick of any rocket program. Much depended on the "web thickness," or smallest cross-sectional thickness, of the grain, for this determines the time of burning. By the "wet-extrusion" or "solvent-extrusion" process, the only one practiced by American manufacturers, the Hercules Powder Company, with the help of Dr. R. E. Gibson of Section H, developed a new technique and produced a stick of powder 7/8-inch in diameter.

This looked good, but the British had something better. They were centering their efforts on a high-altitude antiaircraft rocket to supplement their flak guns which were still in short supply. As a ground-to-plane weapon these rockets left much to be desired but their influence on later British and American rocket design was profound. On a visit to England in the summer of 1941 Dr. Charles C. Lauritsen of NDRC found that the British were producing grains of much greater web thickness, indeed of almost unlimited size. They did this by what is called "dry extrusion" — that is, by squeezing the dry propellant in very heavy mechanical presses. Hickman did the same thing at Indian Head with a small press in June 1941, and in October with a good-sized one; but the process had two hurdles in its path on this side of the water. Our manufacturers were unfamiliar with it, and the massive equipment needed was not readily available.

On his return to the United States Lauritsen ran into much skepticism as to the dry-extrusion process; but he convinced the NDRC of the need of expanding the rocket program. The development at Indian Head was supplemented by contracts with the Bell Telephone Laboratories and George Washington University, and a new group known as Section L (for Lauritsen, its director of research) was set up at the California Institute of Technology. Here, on a tract of land leased in Eaton Canyon, just outside the city limits of Pasadena, a dry-extrusion press was soon built, which by December 11, 1941, had extruded 180 pounds of sheet powder in sticks nearly an inch in diameter. This "Little Giant" was followed early in 1942 by a 5-inch press capable of extruding grains 2.5 inches in diameter; and by the end of the winter an 8-inch press was extruding grains up to three inches. These were to make possible the manufacture of rockets of much greater accuracy and hitting power.

Meanwhile the experts of the Ordnance Department were racking their brains to find a good way by which an infantryman could fight back against an armored tank. They had long been familiar with the fact, known as the "Munroe effect," that a shaped or hollow charge of explosive which presents a concave rather than a flat surface to a sheet of armor will do much more damage than a flat charge.[4] They developed a 2.36-inch shaped charge, which, thanks to the Munroe effect, did not need a high velocity to penetrate armor. When they tried to project it as a rifle grenade, the recoil was too strong for an infantryman to fire it from his shoulder. They then suggested to NDRC, in July 1941, that a rocket motor might do the trick.

Captain (later Colonel) L. A. Skinner and Dr. Hickman designed a small rocket for this purpose. When the method of launching it from a bayonet proved unsuccessful, owing to inaccuracy and to the danger to personnel from the blast, they persuaded the Ordnance Department to accept a tube launcher. This and the rocket weapon were both standardized by the early summer of 1942, and were dubbed the "bazooka." The NDRC Laboratory turned over the finished machine drawings for the complete weapon, and the Army and industry cooperated to produce in quantity the ammunition and launchers in time for the campaigns immediately following the invasion of North Africa. For the first time the infantryman was equipped to fight back against a tank.

Though the bazooka proved a very successful weapon it was not a perfect one, for the blast caused by unburned particles of powder, particularly in cold weather, was a serious drawback. At the request of the Ordnance Department, members of the rocket and explosives divisions of NDRC teamed up to produce the "blastless bazooka propellant," known as BBP, which brought the infantrymen's weapon to a point nearer perfection.

In 1943 the Army asked Section H to develop a "super-bazooka,"

[4]See below, pp. 259–260.

much more accurate than the original weapon. Although its velocity was nearly doubled, its motor was safer than previous models. It would neither blow up at high temperatures nor blast the soldier's face at low ones.

As soon as the Eaton Canyon plant began to produce 2.5-inch grains early in 1942, the rocket program at Cal Tech expanded rapidly. The problem of developing a target rocket for antiaircraft gunners to shoot at proved quite easy. Work on a high-altitude antiaircraft rocket similar to the British one was never completed, since the danger from the *Luftwaffe* had passed and more urgent problems called for solution.

In the spring of 1942 the U-boat offered the most serious threat to the United Nations. New ordnance was even more in demand than new methods of detection. What was needed was an ahead-thrown barrage of small depth charges with contact fuzes. The British had solved the problem with a spigot mortar known as the "Hedgehog," which we duplicated, but the recoil was too severe to permit its installation on antisubmarine craft smaller than destroyer escorts. The development of a rocket weapon for this purpose was pushed with great vigor at C.I.T., and by midsummer the "Mousetrap" rocket, together with a simple multiple-rail launcher and a new fuze, had been developed, demonstrated, and accepted for installation on patrol craft. The urgency of the need led the Bureau of Ordnance to request NDRC to undertake the immediate manufacture of ammunition, launchers, and fuzes.

Physically the Mousetrap rockets were approximate copies of the British Hedgehog projectiles as to form, tail, and position of the center of gravity, but they were almost half again as heavy. The launcher, whose appearance when raised gave the device its nickname, was a simple arrangement of six standard 5-inch steel channel sections, which each held one round of the ammunition. These rails were fanned out slightly from parallel, with the result that, when the launcher was elevated at an angle of 45°, the six bombs fell spaced approximately 17 feet apart along a line 220 yards ahead of the ship at right angles to its course. To aim the Mousetrap installations it was necessary to aim the ship, since the launcher base was in a fixed position.

Deliveries of this material to the Navy were well under way by July 1942. Meanwhile Cal Tech had developed a subcaliber practice and training rocket known as "Minnie Mouse," and a new fuze of great merit. As the reader doubtless knows, the purpose of a fuze is to explode the projectile at the place where the greatest damage will be effected. To prevent the missile from exploding prematurely, as when stored or handled, it is equipped with an "arming" mechanism. In the new fuze developed at Cal Tech, this arming mechanism was actuated by hydrostatic pressure.

As the Mousetrap development was just getting under way some members of Section L conceived the idea of launching a projectile backwards from an airplane, by means of rockets, at a velocity just equal to the forward velocity of the plane, so that the missile would fall more accurately on the target submarine. The idea seemed even more promising a little later when Section C-4 produced the Magnetic Airborne Detector.[5]

Three rocket motors were rapidly produced to give the 7.2-inch antisubmarine bomb the right velocity for backward firing from the various types of aircraft then being flown on antisubmarine patrols. By using a ripple-firing technique a pilot could drop a line pattern of bombs across the target with a high probability of a hit.[6]

The naval officers planning the forthcoming amphibious operations agreed that with the weapons then available the most critical time in a landing operation would be the period from the lifting of the naval and air bombardment until the mortars and field artillery could be put ashore and in action. Machine-gun fire from the support boats would be inadequate. Heavier weapons were needed, but mortars and artillery were barred by their recoil and their weight. To fill this need, Section L proposed a recoilless rocket projectile which could be fired from simple lightweight launchers.

Vice-Admiral Wilson Brown, then Commander, Amphibious Forces, Pacific Fleet, enthusiastically supported this proposal and laid down the military requirements for the now famous "beach barrage rocket." He

---

[5]See above, pp. 181–182.
[6]The flight tests held on July 3, 1942, marked the first air firing of an American rocket.

called for a heavy weapon with a range of 1000 yards, capable of being launched from small landing craft, and having a high rate of fire to drench the landing beaches with high explosive.

Development proceeded rapidly, by making use of a 2.25-inch rocket motor similar to that developed for the Mousetrap. The first rounds fired at the C.I.T. test ranges in late June, 1942, proved satisfactory. To improve the model a special impact-firing fuze was developed which was "armed," or made ready to fire, by a wind-driven propeller. The launcher developed for these beach barrage rockets was a 12-rail crate projector, arranged in four tiers of three rails each and designed to be mounted on either side of the armored cowl of a support boat.

With the help of the Amphibious Forces Training Center at San Diego, operational trials were made at San Clemente Island off the California coast in late July. These tests were so successful that the Navy Department induced C.I.T. to embark on the manufacture of rockets as an emergency job to aid the projected landings in North Africa. The training of crews for new rocket boats equipped by C.I.T. began at Solomon Islands, Maryland. After a formal demonstration of this equipment on August 25, the Navy Department requested the NDRC to supply 6000 rounds of ammunition and 100 launchers. C.I.T. met the deadline, and the rockets produced during that strenuous month blazed paths for our troops in the landings in North Africa on November 8.

These highly successful beach barrage rockets played a part in practically all the subsequent landing operations in the Pacific, Mediterranean, and European theaters, at Sicily and Salerno, and in the invasion of Normandy and Southern France.

After their hectic experience of trying to combine pilot production with experimental work to meet the first delivery deadline, Section L assigned a portion of its staff under Trevor Gardiner exclusively to production. Eventually they set up a complete assembly and inspection plant in the C.I.T. buildings, operating with parts supplied by two hundred subcontractors, and producing nearly a million rockets.

Great improvements were made in the launchers developed for use on various types of boats and vehicles. The most versatile of these, the gravity-feed automatic launcher, adjustable to any quadrant angle between 30° and 45°, could fire twelve rounds in less than one minute.

The chief efforts of the rocket laboratories[7] in 1943 centered on the development of forward-firing aircraft rockets. The British had used their antiaircraft rocket known as the UP-3 for this purpose with much success, and had found that this long, slender, finned rocket had an unusually long and shallow underwater trajectory. Its use as an aircraft weapon for underwater attacks on surfaced submarines and ships appeared most promising. Aircraft of the Coastal Command with rocket rails mounted under their wings fired the UP-3 with a solid head with amazing success in the Mediterranean in the summer of 1943, scoring a very high percentage of confirmed kills.

In the meanwhile, the Navy Department asked Division 3, in March 1943, for a 10,000-yard rocket for ship-to-shore bombardments. Previous experiments with high-performance 3.25-inch motors for the high-altitude antiaircraft rockets now proved valuable, and the technical difficulties largely disappeared in April, when the tubular propellent grain was abandoned in favor of a cruciform grain.

The success of the British antisubmarine rocket shifted the emphasis. A parallel American development was required, since Great Britain could not possibly supply enough rockets to equip both its own and the United States aircraft. In order to expedite the entire program, Admiral King directed the Bureau of Ordnance and the Bureau of Aeronautics to collaborate with C.I.T. on the development of rockets and launchers for aircraft, with the active participation of the Commander, Fleet Air West Coast. This close joining of a research laboratory, two matériel bureaus of the Navy Department, and the operating forces provided the necessary teamwork, and development went forward with amazing rapidity.

Each Navy rocket had two lug bands on the motor tube, with a button or loop on top of each band. These slid into slots or onto tongues on the launcher mechanism. The launchers suspended the rockets in place under the aircraft's wing until they were fired. The early ones were rails with T-slots on which the lug buttons rode. Later, when it was found that a

---

[7]When NDRC was reorganized late in 1942 the work at Indian Head and at Cal Tech was placed under Division 3. Dr. John T. Tate of the University of Minnesota headed both this division and the one devoted to subsurface warfare until June 1943, when the activities of the latter claimed his entire attention. Dr. Lauritsen served as chief of the Rocket Division from June until September, 1943, when he was relieved by Frederick L. Hovde, who directed Division 3 through the rest of its life. Hovde, formerly the head of the OSRD mission in London, is now President of Purdue University.

A rocket barrage; new LSM(R) with automatic firing, remote-controlled rocket launchers

Official Photo U. S. Navy

Hit-and-run rocket fire on Iwo Jima

rocket launched from a fast-flying airplane tended to stabilize immediately in the airstream, "zero-length" launchers were introduced to reduce drag. These launchers are streamlined posts with short slots or
tongues at the bottom to hold the lug buttons or loops.[8] A rocket-firing
plane usually mounts three or four launchers on each wing, but some
carry eight per wing, or sixteen per plane.

On June 18, 1943, the first of the new rockets were fired from wing
sections of the Grumman torpedo bomber. After various improvements
had been incorporated in the rocket designs, the resulting 3A12's were
first fired in flight late in August at C.I.T.'s range at Goldstone Dry
Lake in the Mojave Desert, south of Death Valley. All day long, a
Martin torpedo bomber and a PV-1 made runs on the target. It was clear
to all beholders that the speed of the aircraft, added to the initial velocity
of the rocket, greatly increased the accuracy of fire. And the way in
which the solid war heads plowed up the ground boded ill for the
U-boats.

The Navy Department promptly requested NDRC to supply 10,000
rounds per month for five months in order to provide ammunition for
extensive service testing and training activities, and launcher rail installations for 200 Grumman torpedo bombers. Regular deliveries began
in September. The first squadron of these rocket-firing Grummans,
VC-7, was trained in November, soon followed by others at Quonset
Point and Pearl Harbor. In January the new rocket went to sea on small
escort carriers assigned to convoy duty in the Atlantic. The first attack
on a U-boat gave a confirmed kill.

During the manufacture of the first 10,000 rounds, further improvements in design were incorporated. In October pilot plant production
was changed over to this new design. The Navy asked C.I.T. to double
its production and to provide 100,000 rounds during those critical
months. In March 1944, the job was completed, overlapping by a few
weeks the start of full-scale production by the Bureau of Ordnance.

In the meantime Section H at Indian Head had completed its development of a rocket device to accelerate a 12-inch armor-piercing bomb;
had improved the 4.5-inch aircraft and artillery rocket, and had greatly

---

[8]The British had tried a zero-length launcher, but on too slow a plane, and had
rejected it in favor of rails, despite the fact that they cut down the speed of the plane.

improved both the rail and the zero-length launchers. To augment its facilities NDRC extended the George Washington University contract to cover the operation of a new undertaking, the Allegany Ballistics Laboratory in Cumberland, Maryland. Beginning here in February 1944, Section H developed a 4.2-inch recoilless chemical mortar and a rocket motor to project the mine-clearing "snake."[9] It also made important progress on jet-assisted take-off for airplanes.

The great success of the Cal Tech airborne rockets led the Navy to assign top priority to the development of aircraft rockets of higher velocity and still greater hitting power. By June 1944, C.I.T. had completed the development of a 5-inch high-velocity aircraft rocket known as the HVAR, or, because of the force of its blast, the Holy Moses. It was six feet long, weighed 140 pounds, and had a velocity, at 70° F., of 1375 feet per second. Division 3 proposed to Colonel H. L. Donicht, then in charge of rocket development for the Army Air Forces, that the Holy Moses be sent to the European theater for use against the V-1 launching sites on the French coast. When the AAF accepted the proposal, the Navy gave full co-operation. By Wednesday, June 28, Dr. C. C. Lauritsen and Dr. Carl Anderson of C.I.T., Colonel Donicht, and Group Captain Dixie Dean, R.A.F., were in England to start a training program to instruct pilots in the fundamentals of firing these rockets. One hundred rounds a day were manufactured by C.I.T. and ferried daily from California to England by Air Transport Command until 2000 of them had been delivered.

When the AAF rocket squadron was ready for action, it was thrown into the support of General Patton's tank columns in their famous breakthrough at Coutances at the end of July. On August 9, the squadron again was hotly engaged when the Germans launched a heavy counterattack from Vire and Mortain in an attempt to break through at Avranches to the sea. Rocket-firing P-47's and British Typhoons played no small part in halting this German drive.

An even more ambitious C.I.T. project for blasting Japanese pillboxes, bunkers, and larger vessels was the 11.75-inch aircraft rocket known as the Tiny Tim. Although work on it was rushed during the summer of 1944, it was held up by technical difficulties, mainly with launching

[9]See above, p. 102.

Official Photo U. S. Navy

Headed for action with Tiny Tims; an F6F

Official Photo U. S. Army Air Forces

A ripple of ten 5-inch HVAR's

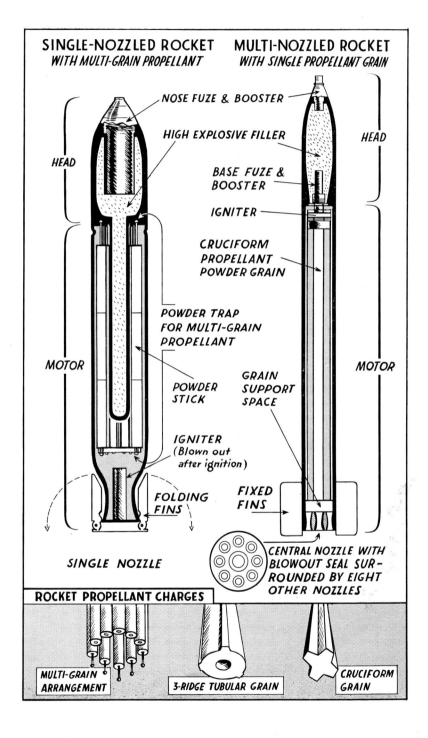

SINGLE-NOZZLED ROCKET
WITH MULTI-GRAIN PROPELLANT

MULTI-NOZZLED ROCKET
WITH SINGLE PROPELLANT GRAIN

NOSE FUZE & BOOSTER

HIGH EXPLOSIVE FILLER

HEAD

HEAD

BASE FUZE & BOOSTER

IGNITER

CRUCIFORM PROPELLANT POWDER GRAIN

POWDER TRAP FOR MULTI-GRAIN PROPELLANT

POWDER STICK

MOTOR

MOTOR

GRAIN SUPPORT SPACE

IGNITER
(Blown out after ignition)

FIXED FINS

FOLDING FINS

SINGLE NOZZLE

CENTRAL NOZZLE WITH BLOWOUT SEAL SUR- ROUNDED BY EIGHT OTHER NOZZLES

ROCKET PROPELLANT CHARGES

MULTI-GRAIN ARRANGEMENT

3-RIDGE TUBULAR GRAIN

CRUCIFORM GRAIN

mechanisms and blast damage to aircraft. Experiments with retractable launchers and wing zero-length launchers were abandoned in late 1944 when trials of a technique of drop launching from standard bomb racks showed promise. This latter launching method was standardized by the Navy, and early in 1945 several carrier squadrons were sent into the Pacific theater to give Tiny Tim its first trials against the enemy.

The C.I.T. development of spin-stabilized rockets which was initiated in the fall of 1943 established that this type is preferable to the fin-stabilized one for ground and surface forces because of the greater accuracy and ease of handling. New and difficult technical problems arose from this development. The first weapon of this type, the 3.5-inch SSR, and its launchers were standardized although no quantity procurement was made. However, several types of 5-inch SSR developed by C.I.T. were procured by the Navy. To utilize these rounds for the purpose of producing heavy fire power in landing operations, the Navy developed special rocket ships to fire 300 rounds a minute. The most advanced type mounted several rapid-fire launchers, each with powered elevation, traverse, and ammunition feed.

A number of simple launchers for the 5-inch SSR were developed by C.I.T. for use on ground and surface equipment. An 8-tube multiple-launcher unit was mounted on PT boats for the purpose of firing high-velocity rounds in attacks on lightly armored ships and barges.

Before the end of hostilities the Army and Navy were procuring rockets at the rate of over $1,000,000,000 a year. The time in which a new device could be designed and brought into actual full-scale use had been cut from the five to twenty years of peacetime to two years or even less. Among the advantages we enjoyed in this development, great weight must be given to our full interchange with the British, who had begun their own rocket work in 1936 and had pushed it with great imagination and vigor. But the chief reason for success was the extraordinary degree of co-operation evinced by the services, the civilian scientists, and industry.

CHAPTER XIV

FIRE CONTROL

W HEN THE German dive bombers flattened Rotterdam and teamed with the Nazi tanks to spearhead the sweep across France, thousands of Americans began thinking of ways to knock planes down from the skies. If they were duck hunters or quail shooters they knew the difficulty of tracking a small, fast-moving target, and the need to lead the bird by an amount that varied with its speed and course. If they were puzzled at all by the failure of the French and British to shoot down more German airmen, they realized, when they stopped to think, that both the speed and the effective altitude of the airplane had doubled or trebled since the First World War. The problem of fire control for field artillery against ground troops, or for coast artillery against surface vessels seemed relatively simple. Hitting the planes of 1940 was a different story.

Any sportsman who got to thinking about antiaircraft fire saw quickly enough where it resembled and where it differed from his own shooting. The projectile is not a charge of birdshot moving on a collision course with the bird but an explosive shell carrying a time fuze set to produce a burst within lethal range of the target. For success you need a good gun, a good projectile, and a fire-control system that enables the gunner to know the target's position at all times, estimate its future position, apply corrections to the gun controls, and set the fuze properly, so that it will detonate the projectile at the right instant.

If the sportsman turned to an ordnance officer for further light on the problem, he soon realized how complicated it really is. A device controlling antiaircraft fire may be regarded as a combination of a measuring instrument and a computing machine. Success in hitting planes in flight depends in the first instance on a reliable and accurate tracking mechanism. Because the target moves in three-dimensional space, three separate measurements are required to determine its position. The measuring instrument must then furnish the predictor, or computing machine, with these three co-ordinates, so that from these data the proper extrapolation can be made to determine the target's future position. As the amount by which the gunner has to lead the plane changes continuously, a system of continuous automatic calculation is needed.

When provided with the necessary indication as to the future position of the target, the automatic computer can tell how to aim it and how long it will take to get a shell to the right spot. This computer makes due allowance for a number of variables such as the velocity and density of the air, and passes its information along to the gun in the form of the two angles necessary for proper aiming and the time of flight for which the fuze should be set. For accurate antiaircraft fire the time of flight should be as short as possible.

The United States Army and Navy had both gone a long way in developing fire control. Much work on it had been done by the Army at the Frankford Arsenal in Philadelphia. Our Navy's systems of fire control were the best in the world. The industrial concerns which developed fire-control devices for our services had able research staffs and laboratories of their own, and they had accumulated much experience in this field. It was to be expected that the role of Section 2 of Division D of NDRC, which had been assigned the problem of fire control, would be to perform auxiliary tasks of analysis and scientific experimentation, rather than to launch broad new developments.

Dr. Warren Weaver and his associates in Section D-2 realized that they were dealing with a long-established art. But although most of them were little versed in the technical aspects of military affairs they could all see that improvement of the control of antiaircraft fire was one of the war's major problems. Colonel W. S. Bowen, President of the Coast Artillery Board, cordially welcomed their assistance and placed a wealth of technical information at their disposal.

Perhaps the greatest need was for a new idea in the directors for antiaircraft guns. Mechanical directors were complicated, expensive, and hard to produce in adequate quantity, and the accuracy of some types left much to be desired. They required a large amount of high-precision workmanship. Since motions of the plane in the sky must be scaled down enormously to be represented inside the computing device, tiny errors in the construction of the mechanism or even particles of dust could cause serious errors. An electrical director was something new, and it held hopes of equal or greater accuracy and lower cost of production, and offered the advantage of great flexibility in arranging the various parts of the system. The members of the Tizard Mission urged that the project be given high priority.

Within six weeks of the British visit the specifications for such a director for the 90-mm. gun had been worked out by representatives of Section D-2, the Army, and the Bell Telephone Laboratories.[1] The Bell Telephone Laboratories men had immense experience in the electronics field and were skilled in designing smoothing circuits which were as essential in a computer as in a communications system. To track a plane smoothly is a difficult business. No fire-control prediction will be accurate if there are marked irregularities in the data fed to the computer, any more than an automobile will steer well if the driver keeps jerking the wheel.

The great contribution of Section D-2 to the electrical director lay in its insistence upon careful analysis of the problem of tracking and of the mathematical problems involved in each stage of the system. Weaver and E. J. Poitras visited England in 1941 and brought back information of value. The combination of the Bell Telephone engineers and Section D-2 proved a great team, and the first of the new directors, known in the experimental period as the T-10, was delivered on November 29, 1941, to the Coast Artillery Board for test. The Board recommended the device, with modifications, and in February 1942 the Army standardized the director and designated it as the M-9.

The Army undertook large-scale production forthwith, placing contracts amounting to over $22,000,000. The M-9 director has operated with great success the world over under all sorts of battlefield conditions, and has proved itself one of the great scientific triumphs of the war. Its most brilliant success came in 1944 when, coupled with the SCR-584 radar set and the proximity fuze, all three OSRD developments, it enabled British and American gunners to shoot down German flying bombs with the astonishing figures of less than a hundred rounds per bird.

Soon after its first tests Army Ordnance placed contracts with the Western Electric Company for electrical directors for other guns, including the six- and eight-inch coast artillery pieces, and for the control

[1]They were completed on November 18, 1940, at a meeting held in Dr. Weaver's office in Rockefeller Center. NDRC authorized the contract November 29.

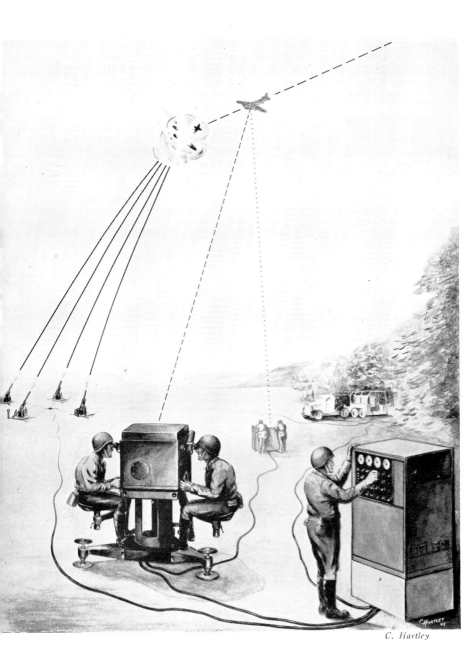

C. Hartley

Radar-controlled antiaircraft fire

SCR-584 WITH GUN BATTERY

SCR-584 OPERATING WITH GUN BATTERY

A. POWER GENERATOR M7

B. RADIO SET SCR-584

C. DIRECTOR M9

D. TRACKER FOR DIRECTOR M9

E. BATTERY 90mm

of fire against swift and evasive motor torpedo boats. The computing methods originated for the M-9 director have been applied to solve a wide variety of fire-control problems.

The fact that this first successful electrical predictor was a close counterpart of the standard mechanical AA director used by the Army permitted direct comparison between the mechanical and electrical ways of going at the problem. The M-9 director includes optical means for ascertaining the angular position measured by azimuth and elevation angles but must be supplemented by some form of range finder, either an optical height finder or one of four types of radar systems. All manual operations except those of tracking the targets are eliminated. Electrical networks perform all the calculations, which involve addition, subtraction, multiplication, division, differentiation, and electrical representation of tabulated functions.

The computer calculates the three quantities necessary to control the gun and transmits these values to the gun-control system by means of remote-control devices. Since these computations are made continuously, the gun is at all times correctly pointed, and the fuze correctly timed for firing at any instant. Means are provided for applying all the necessary corrections for wind, air density, and other variables.

The problem of fire control for heavy AA guns, so well solved by the M-9 director, is easier than that for guns of 20 to 40 millimeters, and much easier than that of plane-to-plane fire. If one is to hit a low-flying strafing plane, great speed is required in the fire-control system. Simple devices tend to be inaccurate; more complicated ones, too slow and heavy. In the summer of 1940, when NDRC came into being, the problem of a satisfactory director for 20-, 37-, and 40-mm. AA guns was still a thorn in the flesh of Army Ordnance. Professor Charles S. Draper of the Massachusetts Institute of Technology, working under a Navy contract with the Sperry Corporation, was developing the celebrated Mark 14 sight, a gyroscopic lead-computing device which worked wonders. It was this Sperry-Draper sight which enabled the battleship *South Dakota* to down so many Japanese planes on October 24, 1942, when defending the carrier *Enterprise* from heavy air attacks in the Battle of Santa Cruz.

The Army knew that the British had developed a new predictor for the Bofors 40-mm. gun but knew none of its details until the autumn of

1940 when they were furnished by Professor Cockroft of the Tizard Mission to Colonel Bowen. That same day a request for one of these directors, the invention of Colonel K. E. Kerrison, went from the War Department to the British Embassy. In less than a month British gun crews with a Bofors gun, a Kerrison predictor, a 3.7-inch heavy AA gun, and a supply of ammunition had landed in Canada en route to Fort Monroe. Their visit played an important part in the Army's decision to standardize the Bofors gun instead of the inferior 37-mm. gun we had under development, and it led to a request to Section D-2 to modify the Kerrison predictor for American use. The Eastman Kodak Company, under an NDRC contract, developed a stereoscopic range finder which was incorporated in this system, and the Singer Manufacturing Company received the production contract for the director, which the Army standardized and designated as the M-5 A2.

The important role that NDRC mathematicians played in the development of the M-9 and M-5 A2 directors was repeated in every phase of the agency's activity in the field of fire control. Whether the problem called for accurate analysis of tracking, the translation of a given set of measurements into rates of change, or of rates of change into orders to the gun, the mathematicians had tools of their trade that enabled them to devise more precise solutions. In the reorganization of NDRC in December 1942, Section D-2 became Division 7, with Professor Harold L. Hazen of the Massachusetts Institute of Technology as its chief. Weaver, the former chief of D-2, remained a member of the new Division, and became head of the Applied Mathematics Panel, whose creation was one of the most important features of the reorganization. Although its purpose was to make the most appropriate and advanced mathematical techniques more available to all NDRC divisions, its relations to Division 7 were particularly close and significant. As will be indicated later, the mathematicians broke new ground over the whole field of fire control. Before it was possible to devise a testing program on which advances could be soundly based, it was necessary for them to take the problems apart and discover what it was for which tests must be constructed.

In the happy phrase of Professor S. H. Caldwell, the theme song of Section D-2 and its successor, Division 7, had been "quality, by way of quantitative analysis." When NDRC came into existence both our Army and our Navy had means of testing fire-control systems statically, but neither could test them dynamically under controlled conditions. There was a world of difference. It is of fundamental importance to be able to test each part of a fire-control system by itself, and under closely simulated operating conditions. The conversion of both the Army and the Navy to this philosophy and the development of devices to make such testing possible constitute the most important of all the achievements of Division 7.

At the outset of their investigations the members of Section D-2 found it hard to get the real dimensions of the phenomena they wished to deal with. None of the existing devices for static testing gave significant answers. The automobile industry would not have made such efficient cars if it had not gone beyond static tests and developed dynamic tests of machines in motion. What was needed was a testing technique which combined the dynamic conditions imposed by fast-moving targets with the reproducible conditions and precise measurements possible in the laboratory. The necessary information could thus be obtained without the delays, the nonreproducible conditions, and the great cost inherent in field tests using actual targets.

Successful dynamic testers were developed under NDRC contracts by the Barber-Colman Company of Rockford, Illinois, and the Bell Telephone Laboratories. These devices revolutionized service thinking about testing and were used to test and improve a whole series of directors.

Much more difficult was the development of testers for airborne fire-control systems. It is hard to get any measurements from plane to plane in the air and harder yet to get measurements that have meaning. Yet measure you must, if you are to compare competing fire-control systems, analyze their shortcomings, and determine the bottlenecks of accuracy. To meet part of this need in the plane-to-plane field the celebrated University of Texas tester was developed under an NDRC contract at a cost of over a million dollars, and was completed in October 1944 in time to make possible important improvements in operation of the central fire-control system of the B-29 airplane.

The first stage of assessment of airborne fire-control devices can be carried out on the ground in the Texas tester. A second stage had to be undertaken in the air. It was necessary not only to take pictures of a fighter from a bomber and vice versa, but to take them at the same instant. Elaborate methods of assessment by means of synchronized cameras were developed by a group at Northwestern University working in close collaboration with another at the Naval Air Station, Patuxent River. Devices for controlling cameras in a fighter plane by radio from a bomber proved successful at a range of one mile, and photographic ranging was improved to give accuracy of 99 per cent to 700 yards.

The development of the dynamic testers afforded a sound basis for progress over the whole field of fire control. Detailed investigations of optical and photographic devices and techniques were launched by Division 7 and Division 16 of NDRC under contracts with Eastman Kodak, Bausch and Lomb, Keuffel and Esser, the Polaroid Corporation, the Foxboro Corporation, and Harvard University. These led to improvements in both sights and range finders.

From an early stage Section D-2 concerned itself not merely with testing and development of better instruments but also with the problems of physiology and psychology related to their design and use. The first of these important studies of man in relation to the machine was entrusted to Princeton University under an NDRC contract authorized in January 1941. This study of range and height finders was conducted both at Princeton and at the Psychophysiological Laboratory built for the purpose at Fort Monroe, adjacent to the Height Finder School. One of its first fruits was the discovery of the serious errors in existing range finders caused by the stratification of the gas in the tube due to temperature change. The Princeton group demonstrated that this could be eliminated almost entirely by charging the tube with helium, and their proposals, developed by the American Gas Association Testing Laboratory, were promptly adopted by the Army.

Equally important with the development of more accurate measuring instruments were the selection and training of the men to operate them. Here it was necessary to start from scratch, for the first thing to be determined was the qualities that made a man a good operator. The long series of Princeton studies and reports were supplemented by related investigations at Harvard, Brown, and Ohio State Universities, Dartmouth College, Tufts College, and the Eastman Kodak Company. They formed the basis of new selection techniques, training manuals, and training devices which contributed notably to improve the standards of fire-control performance in both services.

The work of Section 7.2, of which Samuel H. Caldwell was chief, on airborne fire control was extensive and varied. In the struggle for air supremacy weapons were packed within airplanes, hung on airplanes, and even mounted on catapults within airplanes. Whether propelled by gunpowder or gravity, these weapons had to be aimed, and sometimes they had to be steered after they were sent on their way. Section 7.2 undertook many assignments to develop the devices required by the men who used these weapons.

Most of the wartime work on airborne torpedo directors was done by Section 7.2 and several were accepted by the Navy. Although these developments were continued persistently and with great technical success, they never reached the stage of tactical use. The Fleet, which had seized the opportunities offered by hundreds of technical developments, fought the entire war with the anomalous doctrine that an aerial torpedo should be aimed by "seaman's eye," and used torpedo directors merely as training devices. By the end of the war a method had been found for using radar range in torpedo directors and design studies had been completed on a director for use against maneuvering targets.

For plane-to-plane fire both the British and the Americans developed devices in which the line of sight was itself shifted, by means of a small gyroscope mounted directly on the gun axis, in such a manner as to give approximately the correct lead. The precision was good enough for the control of aircraft turrets against targets at ranges up to 800 yards.

Other devices were developed which took advantage of the known nature of enemy attacks to provide simple but effective protection for bombers. These mechanisms were supplemented by the development of specialized rules which the gunner could use when he had no instrumental aids to help him. If the air gunner happened to be a good duck hunter, the rules for shooting down an attacking fighter plane required him to forget ducks if he wanted to live, for instead of aiming ahead of his target he had to aim astern of it in order to compensate for the forward speed of his own airplane.

But these developments attacked merely the outer ramparts of the problem. "The Navy is of the opinion," wrote Hunsaker to Bush, in August 1941, "that the first aircraft able to make consistent hits (in plane-to-plane fire) at 600–1000 yards will revolutionize air warfare." Before the month was out NDRC had arranged for a joint conference

with the Army and Navy on this thorny problem. From that time
forth it remained the major preoccupation of the airborne fire-control
group. Bush's comment at the time was that it was not enough to do
odd pieces of research for the services in this field. "We ought coura-
geously to look forward and plan the ideal gun control. I believe that
we ought not only to plan it, but that we ought to build it. It ought
to be so far in advance that it will at the present time be somewhat
unrelated to what is feasible, but it ought to have those features which
we believe will prove essential as air warfare continues."[2] The work of
Section 7.2 in developing basic methods for measuring gunnery performance was the foundation required to support this far-reaching program.

The work of Section 7.2 in the aiming of airborne rockets began
through its activity in the development of antisubmarine devices. Among
the latter was the Bombsight Mk 24, designed to make use of the swirl
left by a submerging submarine as a sighting point from which the
submarine's underwater motion could be allowed for in releasing depth
charges. When the rocket was introduced as an antisubmarine weapon,
the laboratories at the Franklin Institute were put to work on the development of a rocket sight for use on patrol planes. But the pace of
tactical evolution outstripped the specifications for this sight, and it
became necessary to begin all over again and build a sight for use in the
fighter type of plane.

By the end of the war the fighter plane had become a universally
effective weapon, carrying bombs, guns, rockets, and torpedoes. For the
pilot to use these varied weapons with maximum effect he needed a
single workable system of fire control. The development of such a Pilot's
Universal Sighting System (PUSS), had become a major responsibility
of Caldwell's group when the war drew to its close.

The scientists who had entered the outskirts of the fire-control field
with some hesitation in 1940 had long since made themselves every-
where welcome. They had made contributions of value whose importance was greatly enhanced by the simultaneous development of the
proximity fuze.

[2]Bush to Weaver, September 20, 1941.

CHAPTER XV

PROXIMITY FUZES

IN ANTIAIRCRAFT fire, the purpose of the fuze is to explode the projectile at a point where the maximum number of lethal fragments will pass through the target. Any duck hunter who studied this problem soon reached the conclusion that the best fire-control devices, no matter how accurate their tracking and how superhuman their computers, left much to be desired. In 1940 it was generally estimated that good antiaircraft brought down one plane for every 2500 rounds. This degree of inaccuracy resulted from poor range finding rather than poor aim, for the existing fire-control systems gave good results in calculating the angles of fire. Both optical and radar range finders, on the other hand, contained a lag which could be diminished but could not be eliminated. The most optimistic of gunners dared not hope for a direct hit with a shell fuzed to burst on contact.

Reliance had to be placed on time-fuzed shells. If these functioned perfectly the shell would burst at an instant when the plane would be within the cone of hurtling fragments. This *if,* however, remained very big. Even if the range had been estimated correctly there remained several possibilities of error: first, in the manufacture of the fuze, second in its manual or automatic setting, and third in the estimated allowance for "dead time," which is the interval between the instant the fuze is set and the instant of firing. In practice the explosion might occur anywhere along a thousand feet of shell path, so that, even if all other factors were favorable, the chances of a hit were few.

The stakes of the game were high indeed. The brilliant success of the German campaign in Norway had shown what land-based air power could do to checkmate sea power. Advocates of the plane against the capital ship crowed, "I told you so." The dive bombers roared down from the skies of Holland, Belgium, and France, opening the roads to Dunkirk and Paris. Unless some improved methods could be found to knock them out of the skies, the mobility of fleets and the security of ground forces were seriously threatened.

Fire-control methods could, as things turned out, be greatly improved, but not to the point desired. The obvious answer to the problem was a fuze operated not by time but by proximity to the target. It was easy enough to see what needed to be done, but incredibly difficult to find the ways and means. The only successful development of proximity fuzes for shells was American, sponsored by OSRD. Except for the development of the atomic bomb this constitutes perhaps the most remarkable scientific achievement of the war.

Patents on proximity devices of many different types had been issued in various countries, but all of them failed to indicate how the invention could be manufactured. The Germans spread their effort over thirty or more different proximity fuzes, and were working on more than a dozen different types as late as 1944. These included several different models of acoustic fuzes, which may be classified into passive or active according as they are triggered by the noise originating from the target or noise which the target reflects. They also devoted extensive efforts to radio and other types. When the war ended no model had seen service; only one, an overcomplicated radio fuze for rockets, was actually in production; and only one or two others were ready for mass production. Efforts had been largely confined to fuzes for bombs and rockets.

When the NDRC was established in 1940, the problem of proximity fuzes had already been under consideration for some time in the United States Navy, whose Council for Research was then headed by Rear Admiral Harold G. Bowen, the first naval officer to serve as a member of NDRC. It was clear that the airplane constituted a growing threat both to the surface ship and to ground forces and installations. Late in July, Lauritsen learned that the Western Electric Company and the Radio Corporation of America were manufacturing 20,000 miniature tubes for the British Army. He drew the correct inference that they were desired for experiments with proximity fuzes.

On August 12 Lauritsen and Tolman conferred with Commander Gilbert C. Hoover of the Bureau of Ordnance as to work which Division A might undertake for the Navy. Radio and other proximity fuzes were discussed. Captain (later Vice-Admiral) W. H. P. Blandy, Chief of the Bureau of Ordnance, was from the first interested in this problem. After further conferences with officials of the Bureau of Ordnance, the first research contract drawn up by the new agency was concluded on an actual-cost basis between NDRC and the Carnegie Institution of Washington for "preliminary experimental studies on new ordnance devices" to be undertaken at the Institution's Department of Terrestrial Magnetism. DTM became the base of operations of Section T of NDRC, whose chief, Dr. Merle A. Tuve, had performed with Dr. Gregory Breit in 1925 the celebrated measurements of the height of the ionosphere which led to such important consequences in the development of radar.

Discussions with Fowler and Cockroft of the Tizard Mission in September 1940 revealed that the British, in anticipation of air attacks, had been working on proximity fuzes for bombs to be dropped on hostile aircraft by interceptor planes. Here the problem was comparatively simple as the space limitations were less and the setback and centrifugal force, which seemed to make the shell problem insolvable, were not present. The British were also working on proximity fuzes for ground-to-plane rockets, and had considered their use as a plane-to-plane weapon. They were experimenting with various types of fuzes, but regarded radio proximity fuzes as the best of all both for rockets and for bombs as well. They had thus far, however, had little success, and they deemed the shell problem extremely difficult.

In the United States, as in Great Britain, the early emphasis was on the development of proximity fuzes for bombs and rockets, rather than for shells. A wide range of approaches was considered. The Bureau of Ordnance stressed the fact that unless the triggering pattern were properly related to the fragmentation pattern, so that the target was included within the cone of fragments, the fuze would have no value for combat and would simply, in Captain G. L. Schuyler's phrase, be "the world's most complicated form of self-destroying ammunition." Before the conversations with the British took place, work had begun on photoelectric, acoustic, and radio fuzes and a project for rugged tubes had been launched. After consultation with Fowler and Cockroft, work was started on a radio pulse fuze to be triggered from the ground by radio control.

Much of the research work during the first year was spent on the elimination of ideas and projects which were shown by laboratory and field tests to be impracticable for quick military application. This was true of the extensive studies of both acoustic and electrostatic fuzes.

Meanwhile the work of Section T shifted more and more to the radio

fuze for shells under increasing pressure from the Navy. It would be hard
to overstate the difficulties of the problem. Open the ordinary radio set
on your table and try to imagine how you would fit it, equipped with a
power plant and a transmitter as well as a receiver, into the nose of a
Navy 5-inch, 38-caliber shell in a space about the size of an ice-cream
cone. Remember the "setback" or translational force exerted on you
when you are standing in a bus which starts suddenly. A bomb dropped
from an airplane starts gently enough on its descent. When a rocket is
launched its various components are subject to an initial acceleration of
some hundred times the force of gravity (100g). The translational force
applied in firing to an antiaircraft shell, on the other hand, is approximately 20,000 times the force of gravity. An electronic tube weighing
less than an ounce must be subjected to a force of over 1000 pounds during the acceleration of the shell in the gun. Most conventional tubes
available in 1940 gave a high percentage of failures when accelerated to
ten to fifty times gravity.

To make the story complete, picture to yourself the immense centrifugal force applied to the radio set when the shell spins at speeds as high
as 475 rotations per second. It is not simply a matter of producing tiny
tubes whose glass or metal envelopes will not break when subjected to
these tremendous forces; their delicate cathodes, plates, and grids cannot be thrown out of alignment without impairing or destroying the
performance of the tube. To meet the Navy requirements, the fuze
would have to be sensitive and rapid in operation, but not subject to
being triggered by the passage of other shells or by the reflection of radio
waves from ground, water, and clouds. It must also be safe to handle and
not subject to serious deterioration in storage. Somehow, by some
miracle of design supplemented by another miracle of production technique, a radio set compact enough to fit within a shell must be made
rugged enough to stand these tremendous accelerations, and it must be
manufactured in large quantities.

The first requisite, as Tuve put it to his fellow workers, was to conquer
their fear of the gun. The first tests of the ruggedness of some existing
vacuum tubes proved surprisingly encouraging. A 22-caliber bullet fired
into a lead block on which was mounted a standard small tube produced
approximately 5000g without damaging the tube. Several types of
miniature radio and hearing-aid tubes, mounted in wax, were dropped

from the roof of the three-story Cyclotron Building at the Department of Terrestrial Magnetism to the concrete driveway below, with less damage than had been expected. Others were tested in centrifuges, and dropped in steel containers against lead and steel blocks. The experimenters then constructed a homemade smooth-bore gun out of steel tubing and fired electronic components from it.

By the end of November, 1940, contracts for the development of rugged tubes had been concluded by NDRC with the Western Electric Company for the Bell Telephone Laboratories; with the Raytheon Company, whose flat hearing-aid tube seemed most promising; and with the Hytron Corporation. Further assistance was derived from the Rogers-Majestic Company of Toronto, which had developed a larger rugged four-element tube for British use. By February 1941, three types of miniature vacuum tubes had been developed which were rugged enough to withstand firing inside a 5-inch star shell.

For testing these improved handmade electronic components, Section T acquired from the Navy some 37- and 57-mm. guns and the use of a field at Stump Neck, Maryland, until it could obtain a testing field of its own at Newtown Neck. At first the projectiles were equipped with parachutes which opened after firing. When this proved unsatisfactory, the shells were fired vertically so that they would land base down, and could be recovered by digging.

The first experiments were confined to testing an oscillator alone (radiosonde), to see if it could withstand the acceleration of a 37-mm. naval gun. When fired vertically at Vienna, Virginia, on April 20, 1941, it could be followed in flight by means of a radio receiver. The fact that they could still hear the radio signal after the shell landed puzzled the listeners. The matter was cleared up within ten days by the discovery that the ruggedness of the elements tested and the sensitiveness of the receiver were such that the oscillator could be heard half-buried in the ground. When seven 5-inch shells were fired at full velocity at Dahlgren, Virginia, on May 8, over water, Tolman, Lauritsen, and Tuve, listening in a boat, were able to hear signals from two, and possibly three in flight, as they passed overhead.

The success of these tests, and the progress being made in designing successful circuits, led the late Captain S. R. Shumaker, then Director of the Research and Development Division, Bureau of Ordnance, to request that Section T place a first priority on the development of a radio proximity fuze for shells.

Meanwhile, in November 1940, Dr. Alexander H. Ellett of the University of Iowa had come to Washington at Tolman's request, and after working for ten days with Tuve's group had organized at Tuve's suggestion another NDRC group to work on proximity fuzes for bombs and rockets at the Bureau of Standards. This group started work on both radio and acoustic fuzes, but dropped the latter in April. At first the roar made by the target plane seemed an obvious and easy target for an acoustic proximity device. But the more closely they investigated the problem, the greater loomed the difficulties caused by the noise the projectile itself made in its flight through space. Measured at the projectile, in which the proximity fuze would have to be installed, this "self-noise" was louder than that from the more distant target plane.

The development of a radio proximity fuze for bombs at the Bureau of Standards had meanwhile progressed rapidly. Section E's first model, fixed at the top of an 84-foot radio tower at the field station of the Bureau of Standards at Camp Springs, Maryland, indicated the passage of planes which came within fifty feet of the fuze. Other tests were conducted with the model carried in tethered meteorological balloons which were then shot down with a rifle. At the Naval Air Station at Lakehurst, New Jersey, fuze models were suspended beneath a blimp and the wave-form of the fuze signal as shown on an oscillograph was photographed as fighter planes dived past. After two earlier tests in February and March at the Naval Proving Ground at Dahlgren, six bombs containing fuzes of a new model were released separately on April 26, 1941, by a plane flying at 3000 feet. All six functioned properly at heights of from 150 to 300 feet over the water, which corresponded closely to their predicted performance as indicated by the previous laboratory tests of the responsiveness of the fuze. A few weeks after this outstanding success, Section E began work on similar fuzes for rockets.[1]

By May 1941 Section T had achieved a basic design for a radio proximity fuze for shells, which separated the components into an oscillator and amplifier circuit, battery, safety device, and detonator. The pressure from the Navy for this fuze had grown so great that it was decided to

---

[1]Section T had dropped a bomb equipped with a radio proximity fuze at Dahlgren on December 10, 1940, after earlier ground tests on October 31.

Recovery field testing; the proximity fuze

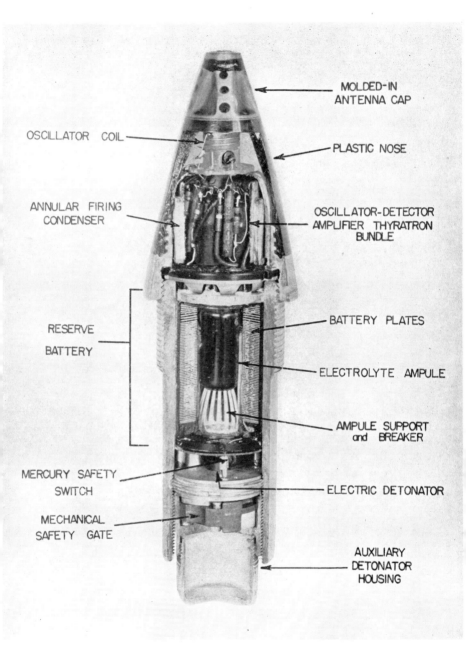

MOLDED-IN
ANTENNA CAP

OSCILLATOR COIL

PLASTIC NOSE

ANNULAR FIRING
CONDENSER

OSCILLATOR-DETECTOR
AMPLIFIER THYRATRON
BUNDLE

RESERVE
BATTERY

BATTERY PLATES

ELECTROLYTE AMPULE

AMPULE SUPPORT
and BREAKER

MERCURY SAFETY
SWITCH

ELECTRIC DETONATOR

MECHANICAL
SAFETY GATE

AUXILIARY
DETONATOR
HOUSING

A proximity fuze

confine all of Section T's attention to it, and to transfer all work on fuzes
for bombs and rockets to Ellett's section. L. R. Hafstad's group working
on photoelectric fuzes consequently moved from the Department of Terrestrial Magnetism to the Bureau of Standards in July. By October the
photoelectric fuze they had developed for rockets was superior in many
respects to their successful fuze of that type for bombs. They had been
aided in both developments by information concerning previous British
efforts.

The transfer of their own work on fuzes for bombs and rockets to
Ellett's Section at the Bureau of Standards enabled Tuve's section to
drive ahead faster with their program of radio proximity fuzes for shells.
It gave them more space for their work at the Department of Terrestrial
Magnetism, just at a time when progress in the development of rugged
components permitted their project to gain speed.

It was one thing for a physicist or engineer to produce a handmade
tube at a laboratory bench, and another thing to teach unskilled women
the art of assembling small rugged tubes on a pilot line or large-scale
assembly line. Since the circuits called for four or five tubes, and the
failure of any one would destroy the usefulness of the whole system, a
standard of 98 per cent performance was indicated. The first attempts
to produce the tubes by assembly-line techniques at Sylvania led to a
marked drop below this standard, till a campaign of instruction and inspection restored the quality to the required level. This story repeated
itself again and again in the production of VT-fuzes, indicating the
necessity of "follow through" from the laboratory to the last step in
large-scale manufacture. No matter how perfect the laboratory models
might be, the whole effort would have come to naught without mass
production of a usable device. And never, perhaps, in the history of
assembly-line methods, have the standards of performance been more
difficult to meet.

These requirements of extreme ruggedness applied not only to
vacuum tubes but to batteries, condensers, resisters, and the setback
switches which kept the dry-battery voltages from the components until the shell was fired. It proved necessary to assign a large part of the
staff of the Section to the problem of developing suitable batteries and to
maintaining satisfactory standards of quality once they were placed in

production. The first approach was to develop a miniature dry battery able to stand the shock of being fired from a gun. With the collaboration of members of Section T, work on this project was begun at the Cleveland laboratories of the National Carbon Company in November 1940. The first completely assembled batteries, in essentially the same form still used for the Navy's Mark 32 fuze, were delivered on June 20, 1941.

Two limitations on the effectiveness of this battery forced Section T and the National Carbon Company to a more radical approach to the problem. The first was its short shelf-life, limited to six to twelve months under normal conditions or to three to four in the South Pacific. The second was the difficulty in making dry batteries still smaller for use in smaller shells. Extraordinary ingenuity and long periods of experimentation were required to overcome these major difficulties.

Long shelf-life, possibly reckoned in terms of years, could be obtained if one could eliminate the dry-battery "mix" and substitute a liquid electrolyte stored in a suitable container, such as a glass ampoule, to be released at the time of use. The problem was to get an ampoule strong enough to withstand the shocks incident to normal handling of the fuze yet not so strong that it would fail to break when the shell was fired. The spin of the rotating shell would spread the electrolyte after the container was broken, and the short delay before the battery began to deliver power would constitute an additional safety factor. The road to success was almost as long and as difficult as that leading to satisfactory rugged tubes, but the efforts of National Carbon Company engineers and production men and Section T personnel were at last crowned with success, for both 2-inch and 1.5-inch models. Special studies were required to find an electrolyte satisfactory at low temperatures.

When the first complete fuzes were tested over water at Dahlgren during the late summer, much trouble arose from prematures and duds. This difficulty kept Section T members under heavy pressure throughout the autumn, during which the Erwood Company of Chicago undertook the production of experimental models of fuzes and components, and Sylvania and RCA were brought into the tube program. In August, Bush suggested to J. D. Hunsaker, then Co-ordinator of Research and Development at the Navy Department, that since "it certainly appears that the radio proximity fuze will probably be successful and important," the time had come to place production orders, even though the device had not been fully devel6ped and tested. In November 1941 Captain Shumaker concluded a development contract with the Crosley Corporation for pilot production of radio proximity fuzes and for preparation for full-scale production.

When the Japanese fliers scored nineteen torpedo hits on our stricken fleet at Pearl Harbor and two days later sank the *Prince of Wales* and the *Repulse*, the sense of urgency which spurred the members of Section T increased. The fuze, which its advocates hoped would improve anti-aircraft fire certainly by a factor of three and possibly by a factor of thirty, was desperately needed. On December 10 and 11 the Navy renewed the pressure on NDRC to expedite to the utmost the work of Section T. Already priorities of need had been established for these fuzes which put the United States Navy first, the British Navy second, the United States Army third, and the British Army fourth.

Captain Shumaker had set the goal of a 50 per cent score at a Dahlgren firing test, using material manufactured by pilot plant workers, as the signal for full approval for large-scale production. His conditions were fully met in tests held on January 29, 1942, when 52 per cent of the units assembled with Erwood components functioned properly. Shortly afterwards the Navy committed $80,000,000 for manufacture of these fuzes.[2]

Now that the Navy had decided on full-scale production, requiring a large extension of Section T's efforts to follow through from the laboratory bench to the last stage of manufacture, Tuve insisted that the Section be expanded and moved to quarters larger than those available at the Department of Terrestrial Magnetism. After a thorough study of the problem by Conant as Chairman of NDRC and then at his suggestion by an NDRC reviewing committee, it was decided to detach Section T from Division A, place it directly under OSRD, taper off the contract with the Carnegie Institution of Washington, and conclude a new management contract with Johns Hopkins University, as of March 10, 1942.

Under the new arrangement the Bureau of Ordnance transferred $2,000,000 to OSRD for expansion of the research on proximity fuzes for shells and assigned Commander (now Rear Admiral) W. S. Parsons,

---

[2]Up to this time the research undertaken by Section T had cost a little over $1,000,000.

U.S.N., to act as special assistant to Bush in charge of Section T activities.[3] Tuve continued as chairman of the Section, reporting to Bush through Parsons, with Hafstad as vice-chairman. D. Luke Hopkins of Baltimore, Vice-President of the Maryland Trust Company and a Trustee of the Johns Hopkins University, became the representative of the University to supervise the administrative details of the contract. Through his efforts a garage building was acquired at Silver Spring, Maryland, converted, and expanded as needs developed. Known as the Applied Physics Laboratory of the Johns Hopkins University, and guarded with every precaution the Navy and the contractor could devise, it provided almost ideal working conditions for a staff which grew from less than 100, in April 1942, to over 700 two years later. Tuve, Hafstad, Hopkins, Parsons, and his relief, Tyler, constituted one of the ablest and smoothest working teams which ever sought to translate new scientific ideas into mass-produced devices for combat use. Their drive, enthusiasm, and ability to inculcate team play, secrecy, and standards of highest quality pervaded not merely the central laboratory but the fifty allied establishments, academic and industrial, that shared in this great work.

The independent atmosphere provided for Section T permitted wide scope for the imagination of the talented group assembled there. One of the important tasks of management was to persuade manufacturers already heavily engaged in producing high-priority devices whose success was assured to take on contracts of so novel and difficult a nature as those for components of the VT-fuze.

The Navy-OSRD-Johns Hopkins team enjoyed many advantages. It was able to attract well-qualified technical men for the work, and maintain flexibility of assignments within the group, thanks to freedom from civil service requirements. Purchase of technical equipment and materials could be made without the delays inherent in government purchasing methods. The Bureau of Ordnance not only furnished funds and distinguished personnel but permitted prompt and full access to all necessary information. Thus the technical staff of Section T was kept currently posted as to the immediate needs of the Fleet.

A milestone in ordnance history was passed in April 1942 at the Marine Corps base at Parris Island, South Carolina. Here a Taylor cub plane covered with aluminum gauze was suspended from a Navy kite balloon

[3]He was relieved in November 1942 by Commander (now Captain) C. L. Tyler, U.S.N.

in such a way that it would swing with the wind through an arc of perhaps a hundred feet in the course of a minute. Against this target were fired 182 5-inch Navy shells with reduced charges equipped with standard VT-fuzes, made by factory methods. These tests, under conditions approximating service use, were highly encouraging. But before more elaborate tests could be undertaken from a ship at sea much hard work was required on safety devices, over and above those normally provided for the conventional time and contact fuzes.

The reader would not care to carry a loaded revolver in his pocket if there were no safety device incorporated in the weapon. It is a simple matter to equip small arms with such a mechanism, which is released when one cocks the revolver; but the problem of safety devices for the proximity fuze proved stubborn. A single burst of a VT-fuzed shell close to the muzzle in the early days of the project would quite likely have meant the end of the research as well as the death of some or all of the gun crew. Tuve figured that if personnel and equipment were to be reasonably safe, muzzle bursts should not occur more than once in a million rounds. To get this degree of safety, the fuze had to be provided with both mechanical and electronic safety devices, all subject to severe limitations of space and requiring a high degree of ruggedness.

The safety devices, incorporated in a separate unit known as the rear fitting, went through a long and difficult evolution. The natural attack was to start with the standard clockwork time fuze, and adapt parts of it to the VT-fuze. This was done with shells, but the clockwork mechanism proved too bulky for smaller projectiles. For these a switch was eventually developed consisting of two chambers separated by a porous diaphragm. In the inner chamber mercury maintained an electric short which acted like the safety mechanism of a revolver. When the shell was fired the spin of the projectile forced the mercury out of the inner chamber through the porous diaphragm into the outer chamber, removing the short so that the primer could fire. By this means the fuze was "armed," just as a pistol is made ready to fire by cocking. A wealth of ingenuity was lavished on this device, which represented, in its later models, the highest degree of control yet achieved in the field of powder metallurgy.

A further safety device is incorporated into the auxiliary detonator at the base of each VT-fuze, in which the rotation of the shell is relied on to move misaligned explosive charges into alignment. Another highly ingenious device, known as the reed spin switch, serves as a safety device prior to firing the gun, and provides a means of self-destruction for the projectiles that miss their target. A vast amount of effort on these safety features was expended by the personnel of Section T and of various sub-contractors. And to such good purpose that the VT-fuzes have been the safest ever furnished the armed services.

Satisfactory progress with safety devices paved the way for the first tests of the VT shell fuzes under conditions essentially like those of battle. These took place on the cruiser *Cleveland* in Chesapeake Bay on August 10 and 11, 1942, with spectacular results. Shells fitted with fuzes produced by Crosley, Sylvania, and Erwood were fired against drones (radio-controlled target planes) which were knocked down one after another with an expenditure of a very few shells. These results gave a great impetus to the work, and increased the desire of the Navy for fuze deliveries in quantity at the earliest possible moment.

By September production had reached 400 per day. As rapidly as possible 5000 rounds of VT-fuzed ammunition were accumulated at the Mare Island Ammunition Depot, from which samples were flown daily across the country to Dahlgren to make sure that nothing had gone wrong in transit and loading. By the middle of November 4500 shells were on their way across the Pacific, and by Admiral Halsey's orders they were distributed at Nouméa to the ships most likely to see early action.

On January 5, 1943, four Aichi 99 dive bombers attacked an American task force, scoring two near-misses and a hit on a cruiser. One pilot, thinking he was outside effective antiaircraft range, flew in a straight path long enough to give the *Helena's* after 5-inch battery a perfect setup. Two twin mounts opened fire with VT-fuzes, and on the second salvo the Japanese plane crashed in flames.

From that moment a great increase in the safety and mobility of our sea forces was assured, provided Section T and its contractors and the companies working on Navy production contracts could solve the problems of large-scale manufacture. Here American industry came through as superbly as in the production of radar and the atomic bomb. Before the war began the nation's entire tube output had amounted to no more than 600,000 a day. Before it ended, Sylvania alone, which was producing 95 per cent of the miniature rugged tubes, was turning out a total of more than 400,000 a day in 23 different plants.

At the peak, over 10,000 persons were engaged in rugged-tube production. Every tube manufactured was spun in a centrifuge to an acceleration of 20,000g and hundreds of thousands of them were shot from guns in tests designed purely to control quality. By the end of the war more than 130,000,000 tubes had been produced, and the cost had dropped to less than that of many commercial standard tubes. Similar triumphs in the production of rugged reserve-type batteries were achieved by National Carbon, Eastman Kodak, and the Hoover Company. At the peak of production, with 300 different companies and 2000 different plants at work, nearly 2,000,000 fuzes were manufactured each month. Large-scale production had reduced the cost per fuze to between $16 and $23, depending on the type.

The great secrecy required created many problems. Even after contracts were negotiated only top personnel in the key companies were given basic information. Few subcontractors knew anything important about the project. Fuzes transported by rail from assembly plants were kept under Marine guard. Upon arrival in port, no one was permitted to leave a transport until every VT-fuze on board had been accounted for and turned over to the proper authorities.

When the fuzes simplified so greatly the work of the men behind the Navy's 5-inch guns, the desire of the Army for prompt deliveries naturally grew more intense. Proximity fuzes appealed to the ground forces not merely for antiaircraft fire, for which the targets were less numerous than formerly, but primarily for howitzer fire against troops on the ground. It had long been realized that air bursts would inflict many more casualties on troops in trenches and foxholes than would shells fuzed to explode on contact. The difficulty was to set time fuzes with sufficient accuracy to ensure bursts at the exact range and height desired. It was hard to time, precisely enough, a projectile traveling several hundred feet in a tenth of a second. Shells fitted with radio proximity fuzes could deliver uniform bursts at the preferred height regardless of variations of terrain, bad weather, or darkness. Tests against targets placed in deep and shallow trenches indicated that the VT-fuze, triggered by reflection from the ground, could improve the efficacy of howitzer fire against personnel by a factor of ten for long-range fire. With the VT-fuze, air bursts "follow" the terrain, bursting at the same height from the ground over a hill as they do over a valley. To the ground forces the new device seemed a heaven-sent means to open holes in the German lines for our advancing troops.

The danger, however, was that, despite the self-destroying features incorporated in the VT-fuze, the Germans might recover a dud, and prove able to duplicate the fuze in time to use it against us. If they did, they might blast the 8th Air Force and the R.A.F. from their skies. If they gave their discovery to the Japanese, it was possible that we might lose one of our greatest advantages. So, though the Navy began production of fuzes for the British and United States Armies in November 1943, the Combined Chiefs of Staff maintained the rule that VT-fuzes could be fired only over water, where there would be no risk of compromising the device.

The arrival, in the autumn of 1943, of secret intelligence that the Germans were preparing to use robot bombs against London and the ports in Southern England, where the forces destined to invade Normandy would eventually be gathered, threatened the success of the great cross-Channel operation. Activity in OSRD reached fever heat. With the co-operation of Allied intelligence services, a Section T member brought back from London detailed information concerning the buzz-bomb, six months before the first of them was launched at England. A complete mock-up of the robot bomb or V-1 was hastily constructed, and was suspended between the two towers on the Section T proving ground operated by the University of New Mexico group near Albuquerque. Full-scale tests proved that the buzz-bombs would trigger the VT-fuzes and indicated which model of proximity fuze would function best against them. Under the compulsion of necessity the Combined Chiefs of Staff relaxed their security restrictions to permit the use of VT-fuzes against the new German menace. Three months before the first buzz-bomb fell on British soil a shipment of VT-fuzes arrived in England.

When the problem of hitting these robot missiles, traveling at 350 miles or more per hour, first presented itself, the first reaction was to assume that the gunner's eye would have to play the largest part in such difficult shooting. Before the study was completed the solution reached was to rely as little as possible on the gunner's skill of hand and eye, and instead to trust the accuracy of the new devices which had been developed for antiaircraft fire. The laurels went to three new weapons, all developed by NDRC, and all manufactured in the United States. They were the SCR-584 radar, the M-9 electrical predictor, and the radio proximity fuze.

As all three were used in combination, and none would have been so effective without the others, it is impossible to divide the credit, which was won in abundant measure by all. When General Sir F. A. Pile, Chief of the British Antiaircraft Command, sent a copy of his report on these celebrated operations to Bush, he wrote on the cover: "With my compliments to OSRD who made the victory possible."

It was an extraordinary story. When the V-1 bombs were first launched against London on June 12, 1944, the antiaircraft played at first a minor role and interceptor planes carried the chief burden of defense. During the second week of July a large concentration of antiaircraft guns was effected on the Channel coast where the duds and the early bursts from VT shells would not be dangerous to civilians. This concentration included large numbers of British 3.7-inch guns and five battalions of 90-mm. guns, all under the command of General Pile and all equipped with SCR-584 radar, the M-9 predictor, and the VT-fuze, described in Army parlance as the T-98 or Pozit fuze. In the four closing weeks of the eighty days of V-1 attacks the shooting steadily improved. In the first week, 24 per cent of the targets engaged were destroyed, in the second 46 per cent, in the third 67 per cent, and in the fourth 79 per cent. On the last day in which a large quantity of V-1's were launched against British shores, 104 were detected by early warning radar but only 4 reached London. Some 16 failed to reach the coast, 14 fell to the R.A.F., 2 crashed thanks to barrage balloons, and antiaircraft accounted for 68.

Although the Combined Chiefs of Staff had released VT-fuzes for the defense of the artificial harbors constructed as if by magic on the Normandy beaches, and of Cherbourg as well, the expected German air attacks did not materialize. No release of VT-fuzes for general use over land was permitted at this time, for fear of duds which might reveal the secret to the enemy. General Lear, Chief of our Army Ground Forces, who regarded the VT-fuze as "the most important innovation in artillery ammunition since the introduction of high-explosive shells," pressed strongly for release. Careful estimates had been prepared as to the shortest possible time in which Germany or Japan might duplicate the fuze, for it would have been a most formidable weapon indeed against our planes in bomber formations. Finally on October 25, 1944, the Combined Chiefs of Staff agreed to its release for general use, on a date which was later fixed as the sixteenth of December.[4] Great credit is due to Admiral King for his ability to see the war as a whole and his readiness to expose one of the most closely guarded of Navy secrets in order to help our ground forces over the hard sledding ahead.

Bush visited General Eisenhower's headquarters for conferences on the introduction of the new fuze into general Army use. On December 16 Von Rundstedt launched the last great German drive of the war. The VT-fuze did deadly service that day against German planes and two days later was first used in howitzers to stem the German advance toward the Meuse and the threat to Liège. Observers close to the scene of action agreed that "the terrific execution inflicted and the consternation resulting from night and day bombardment" had contributed materially to halting the advance and hastening the reduction of the salient. Prisoners of war characterized our artillery fire as the most demoralizing and destructive ever encountered. General Patton wrote to General Levin Campbell, Chief of Ordnance, on December 29: —

The new shell with the funny fuze is devastating. The other night we caught a German battalion, which was trying to get across the Sauer River, with a battalion concentration and killed by actual count 702. I think that when all armies get this shell we will have to devise some new method of warfare. I am glad that you all thought of it first.

The VT-fuze proved its worth repeatedly in the days that followed, notably in the crossings of the Rhine and in the defense of the all-important Allied base at Antwerp, against which the Germans laid down a heavy barrage of V-1 bombs. It was used with great effect in the Mediterranean theater and in the heavy fighting on Okinawa and Luzon. Although the Navy continued to control the procurement of VT-fuzes and on December 1, 1944, took over the Johns Hopkins contract from OSRD, by far the largest share of production since the close of 1943 has gone to the United States Army.[5]

[4]The date, originally set for December 24 or 25, was changed to December 16 because of the German breakthrough.

[5]Of the 8,301,000 radio proximity fuzes produced in 1944, 61 per cent were for the United States Army, 6.7 per cent for the British Army, 5.6 per cent for the British Navy, and 26.8 per cent for the United States Navy.

The successful development of proximity fuzes for the defense of ships against planes introduced a new factor into the fire-control problem. Because fewer rounds per bird were required, several targets might be engaged simultaneously. Where three or more planes were in range, centralized fire control became inefficient as compared to local fire control, since, because of the much greater probability of hitting, fewer guns needed to be engaged per plane. The reader who has fired into a covey rise of quail knows the importance of picking an individual target.

Studies at Michigan on damage probability had made it clear that the effective use of proximity fuzes could be greatly enhanced by adoption of local fire control. Instead of a few large heavy directors, what was needed was a great number of lightweight directors to permit more accurate fire against a larger number of targets. The full potentialities of the VT-fuze would not be realized unless the Fleet were equipped with local-control gun directors and unless each of these was provided with less cumbersome, more versatile radar equipment to permit blind firing.

In the autumn of 1943 the Bureau of Ordnance asked Section T to undertake the development of both manual and power-driven gun directors for local control of fire with proximity fuzes. In these systems radar is used for blind tracking, range, and range rate. Lead angles from the above-deck components are transmitted to a below-deck computer for combination with director position angles to give the final angles for positioning the gun.

The highly successful manual Gun Director Mark 57, whose development was pushed rapidly at Eastman Kodak Company, was issued to the Fleet late in 1944 and proved of much assistance in improving gunfire against kamikazes. Prototypes were installed on the *Missouri* and the large cruisers *Alaska* and *Guam* and production models later on many other vessels. They are known to have accounted for many a suicide plane, with an astonishing economy of ammunition.

Parallel with this development, but at a somewhat slower tempo, was the work of Section T on the power-driven Mark 61 director for use with either 40-mm. or 5-inch guns. The first of these was shipped in November 1944 to the University of Virginia, for tracking and stabilization tests on a roll-and-pitch platform. This development, though complete, was not achieved in time for use in the Fleet during the war.

The detonation of torpedoes upon proximity to the underhull of a ship had long been a desired aim. Since the underhull is the most vulnerable part of a ship, a proximity exploder might greatly increase the effective target area and break the ship's back. The major navies, including our own, had expended lavish efforts on the development of magnetic exploders for torpedoes, but had found the problem a difficult one because of premature firing when the torpedo rolled, pitched, or yawed. When the United States Navy invited its assistance in 1943, Section T proposed a new line of attack, which eventually provided a solution for the earlier difficulties. The proposed basis of operation made the exploder insensitive to minor changes caused by the roll, pitch, and yaw, but on the other hand it called for a much more delicately balanced device.

To solve this problem OSRD concluded a separate contract with the University of Washington for the establishment of an Applied Physics Laboratory to work in close liaison with the central laboratory of Section T at Silver Spring. To make the design usable in all marks of torpedoes, the most difficult case of all was attempted first, that of the aircraft torpedo Mark 13, which was more subject to roll, pitch, and yaw than the larger submarine torpedoes and had to withstand impacts of the order of 300g from airplane drops.

The Mark 9 Torpedo Exploder, which resulted from these studies, was successfully adapted to aircraft- and submarine-launched torpedoes, both steam- and electric-driven. It utilizes highly sensitive electrical components, and parts developed for the rugged VT-fuze. The unit is equipped with an anti-countermine switch which prevents premature firing by protecting the device from the mechanical shock resulting from the detonation either of other torpedoes in the salvo or of enemy countermine charges. Designs were "frozen" in November 1944, and production was entrusted to the International Harvester Company. This device was ready for use when the Japanese surrendered.

In addition to its huge purchases through the Navy of radio proximity fuzes for shells, the United States Army had several important projects of its own under way at the Bureau of Standards, under the guidance of Alexander Ellett's Section E, which in December 1942 became Division 4 of NDRC. Proximity fuzes for bombs and rockets were easier to develop than those for shells, because little or no setback was involved. But they had difficulties of their own, in that they had to operate at wide ranges of temperature including the extreme cold encountered at high altitudes. In rockets the residual unburned powder, which fizzles and stews after the main burning is over, tends to ionize the air behind the rocket, and to make it act like an antenna of varying length, thus triggering the fuze.

One of the basic problems in designing fuzes is to devise a satisfactory system for "arming," which is the equivalent of slipping the safety catch on a revolver and cocking the trigger. If the bomb exploded just after it left the bomb bay it would destroy the plane. The normal solution is to equip each bomb with a small vane which begins to turn when the bomb starts to fall through the air. After the vane has turned a certain number of times the bomb has traveled a definite distance away from the bomb bay and is now ready to fire, like a cocked revolver.

This use of a wind-driven propeller for what is called "air travel arming" suggested to the scientists at the Bureau of Standards the application of a similar device to produce the current required in the fuze and eliminate batteries. This would include in a pocket-size radio fuze not merely a miniature radio station, equipped for sending and receiving, but a power station as well, complete with dynamo, rectifiers, and a means of controlling voltages. They finally developed a satisfactory electrical generator, driven by a tiny propeller in the airstream, but the road they traveled was a rocky one. To produce the necessary current, these generators required speeds up to 50,000 revolutions a minute, or four times as great as that of high-speed machine tools. Such high speeds produced vibrations which, added to the vibration inevitable in a falling bomb, constituted the chief stumblingblock in the manufacture of bomb fuzes. To surmount it required the production of miniature radio tubes relatively insensitive to vibration, and the development of a turbine-driven generator so smooth-running and compact that it reduced not only the vibration but also the over-all length of the fuze.

In May 1942, the Army Ordnance Department requested Section E to develop a proximity fuze for a new Army 4.5-inch airborne rocket, the M-8, to be used by fighter planes against the then all-powerful *Luftwaffe*. With the guidance of the group at the Bureau of Standards, the National Carbon Company developed a satisfactory miniature dry battery, and Globe-Union, Inc., of Milwaukee, produced an effective safety switch. Section E made a double-barreled attack on the rocket problem, developing both photoelectric and radio proximity fuzes. In the first of these two developments great assistance was obtained from Bell Telephone Laboratories. The Signal Corps, which handled the procurement of the rocket fuzes and of part of the bomb fuzes which followed, set up a laboratory for quality control at Belmar, New Jersey, in November 1942, but transferred this activity in August 1943 to the National Bureau of Standards. About 400,000 each of these radio and photoelectric proximity fuzes were manufactured. Further work on photoelectric fuzes was discontinued as the radio proximity fuze gave definitely better results.

Although the original purpose of these rocket fuzes was for plane-to-plane use, the interest turned to ground targets as the number of German bombing missions declined and the weight of Allied bombardment of enemy-held territory increased. Tests of rockets with radio fuzes in 1943 indicated that they would produce on the average 5.2 times as many casualties among ground forces as did contact-fuzed rounds. The heights of the bursts averaged sixty feet. Although these results were extremely encouraging, the Allied High Command feared what might follow if the Germans captured one of these fuzes and succeeded in duplicating it.

This did not prevent the development of successful generator-powered fuzes for the Navy 5-inch AR and HVAR rockets in air-to-ground and air-to-air versions. These met all service requirements and were placed in production in April and July, 1945. VT-fuzed 4.5-inch rockets were used by fighter aircraft against ground targets with success in the European theater, and in the Mediterranean theater they played a ground-to-ground role. Impressed with the success of NDRC's development of the rocket fuze, the Ordnance Department in January 1943 requested Division 4 to develop a similar bomb fuze for air-to-air attacks on enemy bomber formations. As the *Luftwaffe* declined in strength, the possibilities of air-to-air bombing declined with it, and interest shifted to the bombing of enemy ground forces and installations. The superiority of air bursts for these purposes had long been realized, but it was first placed on a scientific basis by the important studies of blast effect made by

A conventional 5-inch cathode ray oscilloscope and a subminiature radio
tube of the type used in the proximity fuze

Official Photo U. S. Army

105-mm. proximity-fuzed shell bursting over hill

Official Photo U. S. Army

Air bursts of 155-mm. proximity-fuzed shell

Division 2 of NDRC. As these studies showed how to calculate the best height for air bursts to demolish buildings, they increased the demand for proximity fuzes of the right sensitivity to produce bursts at the height desired.

Exhaustive tests in 1944 indicated that the superiority of air bursts over contact bursts would be five to one under certain conditions and twenty to one in others, against troops who had taken cover in foxholes and trenches. The radio proximity fuzes functioned satisfactorily on bombs of all sizes from 100 to 4000 pounds, and were first used with great effect by bombers of the 7th Air Force against Iwo Jima in February 1945. They were reported as having paralyzed antiaircraft fire on this and other occasions in the Pacific, European, and Mediterranean theaters. VT-fuzed general-purpose, fragmentation, and "gel-gas" bombs were used with deadly effect by the 12th Air Force in Italy against personnel and matériel shielded from ordinary ground bursts by walls, revetments, or foxholes. In the strikes by the Third Fleet against the Japanese mainland from July 10 to August 15, 1945, about one third of all bombs dropped by the carrier planes had VT-fuzes.

The last big program undertaken by Division 4 for the Army was the development of a radio proximity fuze for the 81-mm. mortar to reach the Japanese in foxholes. These 8-pound shells are so small that fuzes of the size of those used for bombs and rockets would spoil the flight of the projectile. Where the rocket fuzes had to withstand a shock 100 to 1000 times the force of gravity, a mortar fuze must withstand 10,000g. At the same time the size of the fuze must be reduced by two thirds. Preliminary design work began in the late spring of 1944, and the Army gave the project top priority early in 1945. A highly ingenious system of manufacturing circuit components, such as condensers and resistors, and the connections between these, by new techniques developed in the field of ceramics by Globe-Union, permitted considerable saving in space. By V-J Day an Army production program of 100,000 mortar fuzes per month was getting under way, and would shortly have been quadrupled but for the Japanese surrender. It was believed that these fuzes would have increased the effectiveness of mortar fire by from ten- to twenty-fold.

If one looks at the proximity fuze program as a whole, the magnitude and complexity of the effort rank it among the three or four most extraordinary scientific achievements of the war. Towards the close of hostilities it monopolized 25 per cent of the facilities of our electronic industry and 75 per cent of the nation's facilities for molding plastics. The job never could have been done without the highest degree of co-operation between American science, American industry, and the armed services. That it was done at all borders on the miraculous. The results are writ large in the story of the war on land and sea and in the air.

CHAPTER XVI

DUKW AND WEASEL

T HE TWO sections of Jewett's Division of NDRC concerned with transportation, which were later combined as Division 12,
made their great contributions in the field of amphibious warfare.
Hartley Rowe, the Chief Engineer of the United Fruit Company, who
headed the Division, had behind him years of experience in handling
cargoes on difficult shores. He gathered around him a small but extremely
able group of yachtsmen and engineers to whom difficulties were cock-
tails and time-saving a passion.

In the fall of 1941, NDRC undertook, at the suggestion of individual
officers in the Corps of Engineers, the conversion of the 1/4-ton 4 × 4 GP
(general-purpose) truck known as the jeep into an amphibian designed
for a speed of five miles an hour in water. The chassis, power plant, transmission, differential, and wheel components were unchanged, but the
body was a waterproofed hull of welded steel with a propeller mounted
in a tunnel at the stern. A marine rudder interlocked with the wheel
steering system.

This project, formalized by a directive from the Quartermaster Corps,
was not "thought all the way through to the stage of tactical use" as was
the later Dukw. The amphibious jeep was too small to be of much use
logistically. Liaison with the services was inadequate. The Army Service
Forces ordered 6000 of the vehicles and later increased procurement, but
failures in production and testing developed and the drivers received no
special training. Some of them did not know that they had to install
bilge plugs before entering the water. Others took off with the forward
hatch or air intake open, and spray drowned the motors out. Still others
tried to go through heavy surf, for which the vehicle was not designed.
After 13,000 amphibious jeeps had come off the line, production was
shut down.

Norway offered tempting possibilities to Allied strategists, including
a blow at the power plants which, it was believed, were producing heavy

water for German scientists working on an atomic bomb. On May 1, 1942, General Marshall asked Bush to develop a snow vehicle which could be carried by gliders or heavy bombers, and could convert snow from a barrier into a highway. The mission which the British Prime Minister had dispatched to Washington reported that Mr. Churchill, confident that "you Americans can do anything," expected that a vehicle able to traverse snow, dry land, mud, rocks, and water should be delivered in 180 days for the training of troops to undertake an airborne invasion early in 1943. It must be able to travel 25 miles an hour with a pay load of 1200 pounds, climb a 30-degree slope in soft snow, and stand being dropped by parachute onto bare lake ice.

Division 12 members pointed out that in the automobile industry it normally took 140 days to tool up for production and a year to get a new model from the drawing board to the consumer. But they took the job, once assured of top priorities, and moved with astonishing rapidity.

Palmer Cosslett Putnam, a human dynamo of Division 12, left by plane that afternoon with Major Wedderburn of the British mission for Mount Rainier. Tests there and at Soda Springs in the high Sierras of California proved that no existing snow vehicle could turn the trick. Most of them had been designed for sport or for rural mail delivery. Those with air propellers could not climb steep grades, travel over bare rock or through the woods. Those driven by Archimedean screws lacked speed over bare rock and on roads and required excessive beam or profile dimensions. Vehicles with very large balloon tires failed on mild slopes in powder snow, and steered badly. All those with forward skis were unable to make turns at high speed, particularly when running downhill over undulating snow. It was clear that a snow vehicle should be supported entirely on its driving members and that the location of the center of gravity was a critical factor.

To get more data on snow and its shear strength scientists flew to Alaska and Chile on vain quests. The testing ground finally selected was on the Saskatchewan Glacier in the Columbia Ice Fields, about 60 miles north of Lake Louise.

Meanwhile Roderick Stephens of the New York firm of naval architects, Sparkman and Stephens, Inc., was busy with designs of a track-laying vehicle which Division 12 christened the Weasel. The Studebaker Corporation began work on the designs on May 17 and completed an amphibious pilot model in 38 days. Work on a shorter and more compact model began on May 25. Goodrich and Firestone worked on the rubber tracks, which proved to be a very difficult problem.

This first amphibious model had no difficulty in traversing marshy ground and a weedy lake but would not steer on dry ground. Four non-amphibious models, completed in 35 to 55 days, were tested first in Indiana sand and then in Canadian snow, for speed, maneuverability, resistance to rolling, and hill-climbing ability.

In these tests the nonamphibious model T-15, later standardized as the M-28, proved able to climb 20-degree grades in $1\frac{1}{2}$ to 2 inches of powdered snow and 25-degree grades in 7 to 8 inches. On dry turf it successfully climbed 45-degree grades. Its top speed on the level in $1\frac{1}{2}$ to 2 inches of snow was approximately 20 miles per hour. In sidehill travel it traversed a 16-degree slope successfully at an angle of 3 degrees. On the level and up easy grades it towed 16 skiers and hauled a sledge loaded with 2000 pounds. It got across ditches with 50-degree sides and went up 12- to 15-inch steps. It could knock down most trees up to 5 inches.

Finally on October 14, 15 and 16, 1942, before a galaxy of top-ranking American and British officers, the weasel snowed its stuff, competing against every other snow vehicle that could be assembled. Many times a weasel was sent out to rescue one of its competitors which had been stalled in a snowdrift. In a tactical test, a whole pack of weasels was used in a mock-invasion maneuver: the invaders raced across the snow, blew up Quonset huts temporarily posing as Norwegian power plants and then roared back to their rendezvous, pursued by an "enemy" ski battalion. The skiers, given the advantage of an 1800-foot schuss, came whizzing down the slope, but they had no chance to catch the invaders, who finally turned around, picked up the exhausted "enemy" and brought them back to headquarters for hot coffee.[1]

Then the Combined Chiefs of Staff called off the proposed airborne operation in Norway, and entrusted the attack on the power plants to saboteurs. This decision freed the Weasel project of some of the original pressure. Still the first production models were completed in 205 days — or 25 days after the date originally set by the Army.

On the basis of tests and trials a complete redesign of the Weasel was

[1]"Project Weasel," *Saturday Evening Post,* February 9, 1946, p. 50. This colorful article was written by Milton Silverman, the historian of Division 12.

shortly undertaken to make it more suitable for use in swamps and in mud. The new model, the T-24 or M-29, embodied changes aimed to give increased life, reduced rolling resistance, more satisfactory cooling to facilitate operation in the tropics, increased trackage in contact with the ground, better spring suspension, more satisfactory performance in hill climbing, and increased cargo capacity.

Field tests on the redesigned Weasel, which began early in March, 1943, showed that the new vehicle actually achieved nearly all of these ends. It had the engine in front and the track drive in the rear. It could climb about 20 per cent better in snow than the T-15 and travel about 12 per cent faster on hard ground. Production of the M-29 began on August 30, 1943, with an order for 1000 vehicles, which nine months later had been increased to over 4000.

The secret of the ability of the M-29 to perform in mud and swamp where other vehicles bogged down lay in its low ground pressure, 1.9 pounds per square inch. In comparison, the ground pressure of a fully equipped soldier is about 7 pounds per square inch and of a standard Army truck 12 pounds per square inch.

The next step was to convert the M-29 into a self-propelled amphibious vehicle which could operate in deep water and could also, if need arose, rescue airplane crews forced down in swamps and other inaccessible areas. The Studebaker Corporation in co-operation with Sparkman and Stephens undertook the adaptation.

After considerable experimentation they came out with the M-29C, which was equipped with special cells to give added buoyancy, and with rudders, skirts, and other devices to assist water propulsion by means of its own tracks. It could achieve a speed of 4 miles per hour in water and 36 miles per hour on land. It could also negotiate snow, mud, and other difficult terrain as well as any of its predecessors. Production began on May 25, 1944, with an order for 3400 vehicles. Eleven months later this had been increased to a total order of 19,619.

The M-29 had a varied operational career. Like the T-15, it was used in training and in patrol and rescue work along the air route from the United States to Siberia. In Europe it made its operational debut on the Anzio beachhead, where it rescued $2\frac{1}{2}$-ton trucks mired in Italian mud, and then took part in the assault on Mount Cassino. Later it participated in the D-Day landings at Utah Beach in Normandy. Throughout the

Supplying the invaders: a Dukw returns to the ramp of an LST for
another load

An M 29–C Weasel climbs out of a swamp

Transporting blood and penicillin by Dukw

winter campaigns in Italy, France, and Germany, medical units found it particularly useful in getting over snowdrifts and over mines buried in frozen ground. In fact, it was sometimes used specifically for detonation of anti-personnel mines. By walking twenty or thirty yards behind and by using light ropes attached to the steering levers, operators drove vehicles equipped with rollers over mined areas. It was frequently used in shallow water and across swamps to move supplies and to evacuate wounded. Once in the Hurtgen Forest, it got casualties out when it had been thought that no motor vehicle could negotiate the terrain. The Signal Corps used the M-29 widely for wire laying, as well as for reconnaissance and message carrying. And in China-Burma-India, on Leyte and Okinawa and Iwo Jima, Army and Marine medical groups rarely had enough M-29's for their needs.

Like the M-29, the amphibious M-29C was particularly useful in evacuating wounded over difficult terrain. In this role it saw action in the invasion of Walcheren Island and in the crossing of the Rhine. It was also employed in large fleets with excellent results on Iwo Jima, Leyte, and Okinawa. At Bougainville it towed guns through obstacles that hopelessly mired other vehicles. It, too, was widely used for cargo carrying and for wire laying, when a single vehicle had to negotiate mud, water, and hard roads. And since it could be waterproofed and blacked out for night operation, it often carried over inaccessible terrain vehicular radios and radio teams, which normally required a $\frac{1}{4}$-ton 4×4 truck and a trailer.

As defeat followed defeat in the grim months following Pearl Harbor, the shipping shortage assumed more and more menacing proportions. The Axis Powers had put clamps on the Sicilian war channel, forcing the Allies to supply their ships and troops in the Middle East and Eastern Mediterranean by the long route around the Cape of Good Hope. The U-boats were taking a heavy toll on our Eastern seaboard and in the Gulf of Mexico and the Caribbean. With shipping so scarce in proportion to our vast needs it was infuriating to learn of vessels lying off the ports of Africa or the Persian Gulf for months on end, unable to discharge their cargo.

Hartley Rowe had discussed with Bush before the war the necessity of discharging cargo directly across a beach. His colleagues Putnam and

Stephens came up with a solution. "If we could get an amphibian that could take cargo from a ship lying out in the harbor and bring it right to railroad sidings, it would speed up shipping so much that it would be just as good as adding millions of tons to the Allied merchant fleet." In amphibious operations, moreover, which would soon be necessary on an unheard-of scale, there would be no harbors or piers ready for use after Allied bombings and gunfire and enemy demolition. A vehicle that could operate on both land and water, over reefs and sandbars, would prove invaluable in keeping cargo moving rapidly across the landing beaches.

The first question to be settled was whether to design a boat and put wheels on it or to convert a truck, already in large-scale production, into an amphibian. The latter solution offered many advantages. One started with a vehicle which existed in quantity in all theaters, so that spare parts were available, if need be by "cannibalizing." And the "bugs" had already been eliminated. For these reasons Divison 12 decided to start with the Army's celebrated $2\frac{1}{2}$-ton 6 × 6 truck and wrap a watertight hull around it. In the terminology of the engineering department of General Motors, to whom NDRC turned for assistance, D stood for the year 1942, U for utility, K for front-wheel drive, and W for two rear driving axles.

By April 24, 1942, just a week before General Marshall's directive for the development of the Weasel, the General Motors Corporation Truck and Coach Division had begun engineering and experimental shop work for the Dukw. Sparkman and Stephens took the contract for the naval aspects of the problems, solutions for some of which had already been solved in the conversion of the $\frac{1}{4}$-ton jeep. The top levels of the Army Service Forces were hostile. The Dukw looked to them like just another special vehicle, of which they thought they had too many already. Bush launched the project on his own initiative and obtained General Somervell's O.K. to proceed on one pilot model only by agreeing to cancel the other three.[2]

The first pilot model of the Dukw was completed in 38 days and was

[2]Division 12 had some encouragement from Colonel R. R. Robins, Chief of the Development Section, Army Service Forces, and from Colonel E. B. Van Deusen, who had suggested that General Motors build four pilot models; from Brigadier General T. H. Dillon of the Transportation Corps; and from General Jacob Devers, then the Chief of the Armored Forces, who was looking for a way to get his tanks ashore.

demonstrated at the General Motors Proving Ground, Milford, Michigan. In its first water tests on June 3, it carried 63 people at a speed of $5\frac{1}{4}$ miles per hour. Despite its good performance and apparently favorable reception, the Army was little interested. After another demonstration at Fort Belvoir, the Chief of the Corps of Engineers indicated that there was no need for such a vehicle.

On June 24, Colonel (later Brigadier General) A. C. McAuliffe of General Somervell's office lunched with Putnam and Rowe at the Metropolitan Club in Washington to discuss the problem of unloading ships on the French coasts. When they argued that the Dukw was just what he needed, he asked if the wheels would not get stuck in the sand.

"Look here," said Rowe. "My business is landing cargo. I've been landing cargo and picking it up on the beaches of South and Central America for more years than I'd like to count. I can assure you, Colonel, that a wheeled vehicle like ours will cross ninety per cent of the beaches in the world. Don't worry about sand. If you keep the tire pressure high for hard roads, but keep it low for sand, you'll be all right."[3]

McAuliffe, convinced, telephoned Putnam the next morning that the Quartermaster Corps had been authorized to order 600 Dukws for delivery by December 31, and procurement was soon increased to 2000.

Though the Dukw improved its performance during the summer, Army circles remained cool and the Navy would have none of it. There was a widespread feeling that other vehicles could do all that the Dukw could do and do it better. Division 12 banked heavily on tests to be held in December 1942 at Provincetown on Cape Cod, with Dukws manned by specially trained men from Brigadier General (later Major General) Daniel Noce's First Engineer Amphibian Command.

Four days before the demonstration, a Coast Guard patrol boat with seven men went ashore at night on Peaked Hill Bars in a full gale, and the Coast Guardsmen found conditions too severe to effect a rescue either by surf boats or by a breeches buoy. Putnam, Stephens, and two Coast Guard officers headed a Dukw straight into the surf, cleared the breakers, reached the wreck a quarter of a mile off shore. In six minutes they had rescued the seven Coast Guardsmen whose ship vanished dur-

[3]Milton Silverman, "Three Men in a Dukw," *Saturday Evening Post,* April 20, 1946, p. 141. General McAuliffe will be long remembered for his remark "Nuts," in the Battle of the Bulge.

ing the night. When the Dukws were demonstrated four days later, 86 top-ranking officials hailed them with enthusiasm. For ten days the Dukws demonstrated their capacity to unload cargo and to land 105-mm. guns through surf from three to six feet in height. Largely because of intensive training the program went off without a mishap. In this sense it was too successful since the impression was gained that the Dukw was a foolproof vehicle which could be operated under any conditions by troops with very little training.

The War Department ordered 100 Dukws to be distributed among four theaters. They were sent out without trained drivers, and as a consequence were at first pronounced unseaworthy. Personnel of OSRD had to go overseas themselves to prove the value of the vehicle.

The Dukw could make about 5 knots in smooth water and 50 miles per hour on good roads and could carry 10 tons in the water and 4 tons on land. Each of them had a remarkable centrifugal bilge pump, operating from the propeller, with a capacity of 260 gallons per minute[4]; but even in the roughest seas they shipped little water unless holed by enemy shells. The motor was so fully protected from spray that it would operate satisfactorily if a fire hose were played directly on it.

The most important improvement incorporated in later Dukws was the central tire-control system which will inflate or deflate the tires on all wheels at the same time while the vehicle is stopped or in motion. This control, which is found on all Dukws after the first 2005, enables the driver, without leaving his seat, to vary the tire pressure to that required by the terrain, whether hard roads, coral, or very soft sand. The area of ground contact of a tire deflated to 12 pounds pressure is approximately four times that of the same tire inflated to 40 pounds. The deflated tire tends to travel over the sand, while the highly inflated tire digs in. No wheeled vehicle, however, will operate satisfactorily in soft mud.

For its role as a cargo carrier, personnel of OSRD developed special techniques to enable the Dukw to discharge loaded vessels efficiently and to dump cargo quickly on land. OSRD personnel also had a hand in developing methods for ferrying tanks, trucks, and airplanes, and in devising accessory equipment, such as pallets and A-frames for handling heavy cargo. An A-frame mounted in a Dukw was an amphibious crane, which could be landed during an assault long before truck-mounted

[4]On the first 2005 Dukws, 160 gallons a minute.

cranes. It was usual for one Dukw in five to erect an A-frame at a shore dump and unload other Dukws as they drove in.

In all major operations towards the end of the Pacific War 105-mm's were loaded in Dukws, brought ashore, and then unloaded by Dukw A-frames in battery position. Once a Dukw equipped with an A-frame was at a battery position, it was possible to unload a howitzer and have it ready for operation in 75 seconds. Filled with specially designed 120-rail 4.5-inch rocket launchers, Dukws also introduced beach barrage rockets in the Southwest Pacific.

Not only did members of Division 12 contribute to the development of amphibious doctrine, they did a superlative job in training Dukw personnel. Roderick Stephens and Roger Warner trained in Scotland the crews of the British Dukws which landed in Sicily in July 1943. Putnam and Dennis Puleston served with Lord Louis Mountbatten in the Southeast Asia Command. Eventually OSRD personnel staged demonstrations in nearly every combat theater.

At the end of the war there were about 76 U.S. Dukw companies of 50 Dukws each, manned by approximately 13,000 United States Army and Marine Corps troops. Schools under OSRD supervision at Provincetown, Massachusetts; at Fort Story, Virginia; at Fort Ord, California; at Charleston, South Carolina; at Waimanalo on Oahu; and at Mumbles, Wales, had trained about 75 per cent of these men. Personnel of OSRD had likewise trained British troops in Scotland, England, and India. After training Dukw drivers in the Pacific, India, and England, and establishing the Dukw school in Hawaii, Puleston when the war ended was about to set up a new one on Okinawa to train drivers for landings on the main Japanese islands. By August 15, 1945, over 21,000 Dukws had been produced.

The Dukw was not without its weaknesses. It was small, it was difficult to unload, it performed poorly in mud, it was slow in water. Despite these shortcomings it proved a huge success, long-lived and marvelous in surf. The persistent efforts of OSRD, continuing beyond research and development into salesmanship, training, and tactical doctrine, gave the Allies a priceless vehicle which played a role of the first importance in the greatest amphibious operations in history.

Part Three: Chemistry and the War

CHAPTER XVII

NEW EXPLOSIVES AND PROPELLANTS

To BE successful a military explosive must meet many requirements. It must be capable of production in large quantity, it must be reasonably safe to handle and easy to load into shells, and it must not deteriorate too rapidly or be unduly affected by changes in temperature. At any given time there will be explosives known which are more powerful than those in wide use, but they will be too sensitive or deficient in other respects. Much of the work done in this field consists of taming and improving these black sheep of the family rather than giving birth to new ones.

Thanks to the progress of science the best explosive of one war may become a second-rater in the next. For two decades after the Peace of Versailles the man in the street thought of TNT as the last word in destructive power. Veterans of the First World War were conscious that they themselves were slowing up and that the next war would be fought by younger men, but they did not realize that the most devastating high explosive of the war they had fought would be esteemed in the next war less for its power and brisance than for those steady dependable qualities we associate with middle age. Trinitrotoluene is a very stable, pale yellow solid which is not usually exploded by the impact of a rifle bullet. It is less powerful than several of its competitors, but its stability and sure response to detonation have made it an explosive of the first importance, used the world over mainly as a bursting charge in shells, bombs, and mines.

The great American producers of explosives, du Pont and Hercules, had acquired consummate skill in the manufacture of TNT. They were the giants in the field, not only in the size of their facilities and staff but in accumulated experience. They were skeptical of the possibility of developing a better high explosive, justly proud of their "know how," and disinclined to admit that chemists from the academic world, without previous experience in the explosives field, could enter it safely and with hope of success.[1] Army Ordnance felt the same way.

From the first days of NDRC, however, Conant had felt certain that academic scientists could find useful roles to play in the development of explosives. As Chairman of Division B, he stressed the importance of a positive program in this field. There were very few academic chemists in the country with a knowledge of military explosives, but with the help of his vice-chairmen, Roger Adams and W. K. Lewis, Conant recruited a very able group of organic and physical chemists, which was organized as Section A-1 of Division B with Dr. Tenney L. Davis of the Massachusetts Institute of Technology as chairman. When Davis's health failed in January 1941 he was succeeded by G. B. Kistiakowsky of Harvard.[2]

In conferences with representatives of Army Ordnance and the Office of Production Management, Conant learned in the autumn of 1940 that until the shooting began the Army proposed to concentrate its manufacture of explosives on TNT and smokeless powder, the Navy on ammonium picrate. Within a year, it was hoped, there would be sufficient toluene production from a million pounds a day of petroleum to provide high explosives in an amount which was believed sufficient for an army of two million men.[3] Smokeless-powder production was estimated at the same figure. Since toluene would, for a time at least, prove a bottleneck, OPM was interested in possible substitutes.

As soon as it was decided to embark on an extensive program of fundamental studies of explosives, Division B needed to create a sizable laboratory for the purpose. By an arrangement concluded in October 1940 the

[1]Du Pont and Hercules played a most helpful part in the later work of Division 8.

[2]On the formation of OSRD in June 1941 Section A-1 became Sections B-1 under the chairmanship of Kistiakowsky and B-2 under the chairmanship of Dean F. C. Whitmore of Penn State, who was succeeded by Ralph Connor of the University of Pennsylvania in August 1942. When NDRC was reorganized in December of that year, these two sections were merged in Division 8, with Kistiakowsky as chief. When he joined the Manhattan Project in February 1944, Connor took his place.

[3]Thanks to the prodigious efforts of American industry, and further improvements of methods of manufacture, our production of toluene from petroleum was developed to a point where we could produce 4000 tons of TNT per day, though it did not prove necessary to produce such large amounts.

Explosives Research Laboratory was set up at the experimental station of the Bureau of Mines at Bruceton, Pennsylvania, some fifteen miles from Pittsburgh, and was operated jointly by the Bureau of Mines under a transfer of funds and the Carnegie Institute of Technology under a direct OSRD contract. Here, under the direction of Kistiakowsky, until December 1942, and then under L. P. Hammett of Columbia, was the principal seat of NDRC activity in the explosives field. Work of great significance, however, was also done at the Underwater Explosives Research Laboratory at Woods Hole, Massachusetts; and on rocket propellants at the Allegany Ballistics Laboratory at Cumberland, Maryland, and at the California Institute of Technology. Some of the best theoretical work was done at Cornell, Harvard, and Princeton. Great advances were made in the measurement of blast effect in air and water, the theory of detonation and shock waves, and methods of testing. Before the Second World War it had been possible to calculate in advance the explosive power of a suggested substance; now the theory had advanced to a point enabling one to predict the velocity of detonation. What actually happened in an explosion had been all too little understood. Flash photography, with exposures of a millionth of a second, made it possible to study shock waves traveling at 5000 feet a second.

Although there were many skeptics in Army Ordnance as to what NDRC could accomplish in the explosives field, the British strongly encouraged this wholly civilian effort. The Tizard Mission brought in its black box some information about an explosive called RDX, which had been known since 1899 but had proved too sensitive and too expensive to win favor. They had developed at Woolwich a method of manufacture and means to desensitize the product by mixing it with beeswax. In the summer of 1941, five members of the Explosives Section, Kistiakowsky, R. C. Elderfield, Hammett, D. P. MacDougall, and E. B. Wilson, Jr., visited England and returned with many new ideas concerning both propellants and high explosives.

As things turned out the only "new" chemical high explosive developed in the United States during the war was EDNA or Haleite, patented as an explosive in 1935 by Dr. C. G. Hale of the Picatinny Arsenal at Dover, New Jersey. In power and brisance it surpasses TNT but is slightly inferior to RDX. Like the latter it is too sensitive for use in large munitions except in mixtures with other high explosives or with desensitizing agents.[4] Division 8 played an important role in the development of Haleite, both by finding adequate materials and by improving methods of manufacture. In June 1943 Major General Levin Campbell, Chief of Ordnance, congratulated NDRC and its contractor, the du Pont Company, on their success in reducing the cost of manufacture of the intermediate, ethyleneurea, to one fourth of that by any other method. "This work," declared General Campbell, "has unquestionably brought 'EDNA' into the realm of practical military explosives of high power." After this success at the pilot plant stage, du Pont erected a $5,000,000 plant for Army Ordnance with a capacity of 15 tons a day. Its product, however, did not get into combat use before the war ended.

Far more important was the development of RDX. This powerful explosive had been tested by Picatinny Arsenal in 1923 and rejected as too sensitive and too costly. Though the service interest at the time was nil, three outstanding organic chemists, one at Cornell, one at Michigan, and one at Penn State, were assigned the problem in November 1940. None of them had hitherto worked in the explosives field. Roger Adams's brief letter of instructions is a model of the decentralized system employed by Division B. He explained that at a conference with British and Canadian representatives it had been learned that RDX, or cyclonite, was an extraordinarily interesting and important explosive. The British were making it at Woolwich by direct nitration of hexamine. Another process had recently been devised at McGill University which involved the treatment of formaldehyde with ammonium nitrate in the presence of a dehydrating agent.

Conant felt that at least two or three laboratories should engage on the problem. Each of them, however, was free to select its own method of attack. Bachmann, the Michigan scientist, whose "heart sank" when Adams first suggested he work in this field, wrestled with the problem in his laboratory daily from 8 A.M. to midnight or later. By January he had hit on a new idea combining the Canadian process with direct nitration. The result was a huge success, obviating the enormous nitric-acid requirements of the Woolwich process and requiring much smaller amounts of the dehydrating agent than did the McGill process. The high yields possible by this combination method were most encouraging.

By the time Conant returned from England in April 1941 the success

[4]Because it is less sensitive than RDX, Haleite can be press-loaded into small shells.

of the new process seemed assured, but Army Ordnance evinced no interest, having frozen its program on TNT. He nevertheless set up an RDX committee composed of three Americans, three Canadians, and an Englishman which met on telegraphic notice for "golf at Ann Arbor," and wired for "100 pounds of golf balls" when RDX was required for experimental purposes. Meanwhile important further contributions to the new method were made at Michigan, at Cornell, and at the University of Toronto.

During the spring and summer of 1941 the British were active in Washington trying to persuade the Army and the Navy to go in for RDX for American and British use. Conant and his associates were also active protagonists of an RDX program. The log jam was broken by Admiral Blandy, Chief of the Bureau of Ordnance, who became convinced of the great possibilities of RDX, especially for use in mines and torpedoes. If we take 100 as the measure of TNT's explosive power in air, RDX's was 150. Under water the factor of superiority was even greater. In an underwater explosion one pound of the RDX mixture, Torpex, was equal to more than 1.5 pounds of TNT. By volume the superiority of Torpex approached two to one, for its density was slightly greater. Admiral Blandy's request that Army Ordnance procure RDX for the Navy brought the American services into the picture.

To meet the Navy requirements and a request from the British for 220 tons per day,[5] Army Ordnance contracted in December 1941 with du Pont for the construction of the huge Wabash River Ordnance Works with a capacity of 50 tons per day. As the Woolwich process was adopted, this involved the construction of the largest nitric-acid plant in the world.

It was not yet clear that the United States Army would procure RDX for its own use as well as for the Navy and the British. That Bachmann's combination process was brought into the picture was owing to the persistence of NDRC and the imagination and courage of a few highly placed officers and civilians in Army Ordnance. Everything depended on the tests of the new method in the three pilot plants for which NDRC had contracted with the Western Cartridge Company, du Pont, and the Tennessee Eastman Corporation, a subsidiary of Eastman Kodak. Progress was slow in the first two plants, but Tennessee Eastman hit the jackpot. This company had had no previous experience in the explosives field

[5]British production amounted to 70 tons per week.

but their engineers and production men took to it with extraordinary success. When four of them spent the night in St. Louis after their first visit to Ann Arbor, two of them sat up all night discussing the combination process and devised a scheme for continuous production instead of the batch method. They soon had a design for the required apparatus, found hearty agreement at Michigan with their new suggestion, and were off to a flying start. This was but a single illustration of the qualities that made the pilot stage of the combination method a brilliant success, and the great Holston Ordnance Works, built and operated by Tennessee Eastman, a model of perfection. Its first assignment was the production of 170 tons of RDX per day.

Years ago a farsighted east Tennessean, J. Fred Johnson, distressed at the lack of opportunities for advancement for the hill folk among whom he lived, had called on George Eastman, who had made Kodak a household word, and persuaded him to build a great plant in the valley of the Holston. The Tennessee Eastman Company, in developing plastics and acetate fabrics of great beauty, had brought prosperity to the men and women of those mountains. This company was a natural choice to develop the combination process, for it had become the world's greatest producer of the dehydrating agent which was required, acetic anhydride. On a 6800-acre plain in the Holston Valley near Kingsport, there sprang up ten lines of production for RDX, widely spaced and provided with every safety precaution known to the explosives industry. Many of the employees were women, whose husbands were fighting for their country overseas. Working alongside of men they helped to handle almost every stage of the production process. Clad in white with white caps, mixing TNT and RDX in huge kettles or boxing the cooled product, they might be taken for girls working in the familiar Fannie Farmer candy kitchens. Their product, though candylike in appearance, was one of the most powerful explosives known to man.

So capable were the workers and so skilled the engineering that the time was cut on almost every stage of the operation and production mounted from 170 tons to 220 tons per day. The great advantage of the combination process was not so much in reducing the cost per pound, which was only two cents higher at Wabash, thanks to improvements made by du Pont in the Woolwich process, but in the lessened cost of plant. To get 220 tons a day of RDX by the Woolwich process, even as improved at Wabash, the Holston plant would have had to cost not $70,000,000, but $170,000,000.

When the Army stepped up the order in June 1943 to 340 tons per day, the demand was met by further reductions in the time of operation and by lengthening the "jeeps," which were the heart and circulatory system of the continuous process. On that scale of production, the saving to the Government in plant cost alone was over $200,000,000. This involved not only money but critical materials. Compared with this huge sum it is interesting to note that the research at Michigan, Cornell, and Penn State cost $45,000 and the pilot plant stage of development cost less than half a million.

RDX is too sensitive to be used alone. As all the bees in the world would not produce enough beeswax to desensitize the huge quantities of it now desired, an effective substitute was developed from petroleum at the Explosives Research Laboratory at Bruceton. In the latter days of the war this found wide use in other explosives required by the Navy. The most important use of RDX was in a mixture with TNT and aluminum known as Torpex for mines, depth charges, and torpedo war heads. The latter were so much superior to earlier war heads that when first available for use in the Pacific they were issued to commanders with the highest score of kills. RDX mixtures were also used in bombs, including the 12,000-pound "Tallboys" used on the German submarine pens and in the sinking of the *Tirpitz*. For one of the RDX compositions, Tennessee Eastman developed an ingenious method of pouring and cooling on a stainless-steel conveyor belt. The product, resembling maple sugar, was known at Holston as Jap Kisses.

If a flat charge of high explosive is detonated in contact with a metal surface, damage will be done to the metal. If now another charge of the same weight of the same explosive is arranged so that it presents a concave instead of a flat surface to the metal, this second charge on detonation will do greater damage to the metal. In particular, the penetrating power of the second charge will be greater than that of the first, sometimes as much as fifteen times greater. This effect, discovered by C. E. Munroe in 1888, is known as the Munroe effect, and charges of this type are known as shaped charges or hollow charges. Such charges serve to focus part of the energy of the explosion in a limited area.

Practical military applications of the Munroe effect were not made until World War II. Probably the first, and certainly the best known, application by our services was the bazooka. This weapon, taking advantage of the penetrating power of the shaped charge, enables an infantryman to stop a tank — a job that, before the advent of shaped-charge weapons, required the artilleryman's high-velocity armor-piercing shells. NDRC work with shaped charges was along three lines: studies of the factors affecting the performance of shaped charges; the development of shaped-charge weapons; and theoretical studies of the Munroe effect. The last-named studies are too highly technical for discussion here and security regulations do not permit a discussion of specific weapons, but an indication of the lines of development of the work on the factors affecting performance may be given by pointing out that the performance of shaped charges can be reduced to that of ordinary charges by poor design and manufacture.

The night actions in the Pacific in the late summer of 1942 had shown the need for a propellent powder for Navy 6-inch and 8-inch guns that would not blind those directing the fire. The Bureau of Ordnance on December 12, 1942, requested that NDRC undertake such a development on a high-priority basis. According to this letter, flash reduction to the point of hiding the location of the guns was not deemed necessary. Rather, the desire of the Bureau was "to have powder charges for these guns that will permit night firing without interfering with the fire control of the ship." The British propellant Cordite N was flashless, but did not meet with favor on this side of the water because it contained nitroglycerine. It was a tradition in the American service, whose magazines are ventilated, to oppose the use of any powder containing nitroglycerine because of the risk that this highly volatile substance might separate from the powder and cause an explosion.

A quick solution to the problem of obtaining flashless performance on a basis satisfactory to the Navy was to develop a modified Cordite N, replacing the nitroglycerine by a nonvolatile explosive plasticizer. Many compounds were investigated as possibilities and the most promising candidate was selected after firing trials. This compound, known as DINA, had been prepared on a test-tube scale in Canada a year or two earlier. It proved possible to develop satisfactory manufacturing procedures, and to incorporate the new plasticizer in a powder which was named Albanite. Extensive tests on proof lots of this powder prepared in the NDRC pilot plant showed that it matched the ballistic behavior and flashless qualities of Cordite N. Complete engineering data were obtained in the pilot plant to permit the full-scale manufacture of Albanite, and just prior to the end of the war a contract was let by the services to procure 4,000,000 pounds per month to meet in a large measure the requirement for flashless powders in all major-caliber Navy guns.

It is of interest that about the middle of 1944 the problem of flashlessness had become so important that the Navy actually procured from Canada a considerable amount of Cordite N for use as an interim measure, pending the complete development of Albanite by NDRC. It is probable that the decision to issue Cordite N to the Fleet, in spite of its nitroglycerine content, was hastened considerably by the prospects of obtaining within a reasonable time a product more satisfactory to the Navy.

A large part of the work of Division 8 was devoted to finding better propellants for rockets and guided missiles. The story of rocket development, related in an earlier chapter, made clear that double-base powders could not be produced by the wet-extrusion process commonly used in the United States with a web much greater than three eighths of an inch.[6] By the dry-extruded process adopted at the California Institute of Technology, Lauritsen's group could produce grains of ballistite up to six inches in thickness. Using this method, applied to trench mortar sheets available in large quantities, they carried the Navy-OSRD rocket program from one triumphant success to another.

From the outset the possibility of developing wholly new rocket propellants was held in view, even though they might be available in sufficient quantities only near the end of a long war. Chemists, it will be recalled, when they use the term "double-base powders," do not mean powders with any two bases, but those made from nitrocellulose and nitroglycerine. Division 8 engaged in a long hunt for suitable alternatives to double-base powders and found a way to produce "composite propellants" in granulations even larger than could be attained with dry extrusion of double-base. This could be done by molding large grains under pressure from mixtures of solids held together by a plastic binder,

[6]See above, pp. 202–204.

or devising a technique by which the powder could be cast, producing grains of great strength and any desired thickness.

On their visit to England in 1941 Kistiakowsky and Hammett had learned that the dry-extruded Cordite used in the British rockets had some serious disadvantages, particularly because of its insufficient mechanical strength at high temperatures. Moreover neither the heavy and complicated machinery required for dry extrusion nor the technical personnel skilled in this art was available for immediate production in this country. NDRC consequently set up a project at Bruceton for the study of rocket propellants other than double-base powders, and by contract with the Monsanto Chemical Company arranged for work at its Central Research Laboratories in Dayton, Ohio, under the supervision of the director of those laboratories, Charles A. Thomas. This Monsanto group, chosen for their wide knowledge of the field of plastics, collaborated so closely and so effectively with the investigators at Bruceton that the two teams may be considered as one.

By April 1942 it was clear that a large variety of plastics could be employed as binders for a mixture of sodium nitrate and ammonium picrate that could be prepared in an edge-runner mill or a roll mill, and molded by compression in automatic mechanical presses like those which had been perfected for molding metal powders. The resulting pellets could be cemented together to form a rocket-propellent grain of any desired length and adequate mechanical strength. As an alternative method of forming grains it appeared possible that a screw extrusion press like those used in the plastics industry might prove satisfactory.

Compositions of this sort could be obtained which burned smoothly in parallel layers, had reproducible burning rates, and yielded a specific impulse of about 80 per cent of that given by double-base powder. Because of greater density they compared more favorably in terms of impulse per unit of volume. Their great advantage over double-base powder lay in the fact that their behavior was less affected by changes of temperature.

To develop such composite propellants a pilot plant was constructed at Dayton between July and November, 1942, with a capacity of 500 pounds per 8-hour shift. The first of these powders, known as Composite Propellant 218, consisted of equal parts of finely divided sodium nitrate and ammonium picrate with 5 per cent binder. It offered great advantages in stability of operation and simplification of motor design.

Because of the complete novelty of the process and the need for prolonged investigations to develop suitable methods of control, the pilot plant stage of development was slower than had been hoped. It took over a year to demonstrate that a product of completely reliable properties could be obtained under economically feasible conditions. There were many hard nuts to crack in developing satisfactory processes for the milling, the molding, and the curing, the cementing of the molded pellets, provision against fracture of the grains from mechanical shock and against harm from conditions of high humidity, and the development of procedures for testing. No ignition took place in any other stage of the process than the milling in the whole course of the development, but three explosions destroyed the mill before a satisfactory technique was finally discovered in September 1943.

After much experimentation with plasticizers, Composite Propellant 218 was superseded in the pilot plant stage by 218-B, which performed with complete reliability at all temperatures under the normal operating conditions of 2000 pounds per square inch or less. Rocket motors filled with this propellant not only will withstand violent vibration and severe jolts, but can be dropped eleven feet onto solid concrete without injury to the grain.

By this means as great a projectile velocity can be obtained in a given rocket motor as with ballistite. Since the temperature coefficient is only one third that of the usual double-base powders, a motor containing this composite propellant is a less sensitive and more stable performer. The major defect of these composite propellants is the production of large amounts of white smoke. This has prevented their adoption for rockets fired from the ground but is not an obstacle to use in rockets fired from aircraft.

Propellants suitable for the assisted take-off of airplanes require grains of large diameter. With the 325-ton press available at Bruceton satisfactory grains of 8.5 inches diameter were produced by the end of 1943. The growing interest in jet-propulsion devices led Bush to appoint a special committee to investigate the problem. Its report coincided with a new request from Wright Field and led to an expansion of the Dayton pilot plant to permit experimentation with a 600-ton press. Composite Propellant 404 developed in this project proved entirely satisfactory.

The decision of the Army Air Forces to produce 1000 "Chinese copies" of the German V-1 flying bomb at the Ford Motor Company gave top priority in large-grain work to the development of a perforated grain for use in the launcher. The Bruceton-Monsanto team solved this problem in a few months by producing Composite Propellant 492 with grains of 8.5 inches diameter weighing 24 pounds each, five of which, cemented together, formed a unit of 120 pounds. The loaded motors were delivered to Wright Field as early as October.

The successful launching of the JB-2 robot bombs with four units (480 pounds) of this new propellant led the Ordnance Department to place a contract with Monsanto for the construction and operation of a plant with a capacity of 1,000,000 pounds a month at Karnack, Texas, which was known as Longhorn Ordnance Works No. 2. This led in turn to considerable Navy interest in Division 8's composite propellants.

Another Bruceton group had started work in August 1943 on the development of what has been called a hybrid between solvent-extruded double-base powder and the previously developed composite propellants. They hoped to combine the low temperature coefficient of the latter with the toughness and ease of manufacture of the former. There was a large capacity in the United States for the production of solvent-extruded powders which might be utilized if success were attained.

The line of attack was to introduce into a colloid of the double-base powder type various mixtures of finely divided solids which were insoluble in the nitrocellulose-nitroglycerine colloid. Within a month it was found that filler mixtures of potassium perchlorate and carbon, potassium perchlorate and nitroguanidine, potassium nitrate and ammonium picrate, and potassium nitrate and carbon, all gave satisfactory results. They had the good qualities of molded composite propellants, but were much tougher mechanically, and could be produced in existing plants built for the manufacture of double-base powder. By October 1943 it was seen that one of these hybrids, named EJA, was of extraordinary promise. Although it produced much smoke its temperature coefficient was low and its power was greater than the hottest double-base powder in use. Another variety, EJB, produces less smoke, but still too much for ground use.

Out of the work on these hybrids came a development of great importance for the future of the bazooka. This valuable weapon had serious drawbacks in operational use because of poor precision at low temperatures and the expulsion, under those conditions, of powder residues which injured the gunner. Even if he were equipped with a mask he found the particle blast hard to stand up to. Division 8 eliminated these serious hazards by the development of a solvent-extruded composite propellant known informally as BBP (blastless bazooka powder), which was adopted for service use in 1945. Its temperature coefficient was only half that of standard double-base bazooka powder, the smoke produced was not sufficient to be a serious disadvantage, and production could be carried out in existing plants without modification.

The increased interest in assisted take-off, robot bombs, and guided missiles led to great emphasis on the production of large grains. Here a notable advance was scored at Bruceton in 1945 in the development of a process for casting large charges of double-base powder. In this process for casting, small granules of powder containing nitrocellulose and nitroglycerine are mixed with a liquid composed of nitroglycerine in an organic solvent. The pourable slurry which results can be cast in any desired form. When heated at 60° C. for one or two days the mass sets to a tough, homogeneous product with satisfactory burning properties.

The spectacular successes scored by Division 8 in the development of high explosives and propellants were paralleled by work on a variety of projects on a smaller scale which together might compare in importance with the work on RDX, rocket propellants, or flashless powder. To take but a few examples, methods of analysis developed by Linus Pauling and his group contributed to a better understanding of the stability tests used for explosives and propellants. Work done at the Explosives Research Laboratory on detonation led the Navy to change the method of exploding the 5-inch 38-caliber antiaircraft shell. Members of Division 8 preached the gospel of aluminized explosives to good effect and carried out at Bruceton and Woods Hole experiments which demonstrated conclusively their advantages for use in aerial and depth bombs. The Division's solution of the problem of gassing of aluminized explosives in torpedo war heads was simple, spectacular, and successful. In co-operation with Division 19 and the Office of Strategic Services an explosive was developed which could be smuggled to Chinese saboteurs behind the Japanese lines. Because it looked like the flour with which it was mixed and could actually be used to make biscuits, this successful mixture was known as Aunt Jemima.

CHAPTER XVIII

WHY NOT GAS?

$\mathbf{A}$LL OF THE great powers engaged in the world conflict made very extensive preparations for the use of poison gas. These preparations included the manufacture of new devices for using the familiar gases of the last war, the synthesis and manufacture of new gases, and the large-scale provision of protective equipment. Despite enormous expenditures on the part of all nations concerned, gas warfare was not used except for instances which seem to have been unplanned if not wholly accidental. What is the answer to this riddle?

Moral considerations seem to have played a prominent role in the rejection of gas warfare, at least by Great Britain and the United States. In a war which was marked by repeated bombings of civilian populations, unprecedented destruction of great cities by incendiaries and high explosives, and use of the atomic bomb, it seems strange that moral objections should have weighed so heavily against a weapon used in World War I when moral standards were, if anything, higher than today. Was it logical to rule out gas on ethical grounds while proceeding to cook people alive with flame throwers and incendiaries? Indeed, carbon monoxide generated by burning flame-thrower fuel is one of the common causes of death from these weapons; yet this was not considered to be chemical warfare. It must be concluded either that poison gas had been subjected to peculiarly effective propaganda or that gas warfare was considered by experts not to be effective enough to warrant risking the opprobrium which would have been heaped on the country which initiated it.

Most civilians and most soldiers have an almost superstitious fear of gas, despite the evidence that few gas casualties are permanently disabled, whereas high explosives cause loss of legs and arms, and other permanent disfigurement. This fear might be overcome by education. Nevertheless, the mysterious character of gas, its difficulty of detection, and the complications ensuing from its use all tend to make this weapon disliked by the majority of military men.

Individuals who have spent years developing and studying a certain weapon often become apologists and propagandists for it. The full effectiveness of gas, compared to other weapons, will only be known if it is used on a large scale in modern war. There seems to be little doubt that the use of gas on cities, particularly an initial use if surprise could be achieved, would cause widespread casualties and confusion. No one knows how rapidly a population would develop protective measures and rally sufficiently from the confusion to render gas of no greater value than other weapons. Since history shows that recovery from shock of a new weapon is usually rapid, it is probable that many of the advantages attributed to gas would be lost within a short time. After this initial period a careful comparison of gas and other weapons would have to be made. Since gas is primarily an anti-personnel as distinguished from an anti-matériel weapon, elimination of all prejudice in assessing its usefulness would be difficult. In any case, gas would complicate considerably the services charged with fire fighting and rehabilitation.

It would complicate, too, the conduct of an offensive. New kinds of munitions would have to be supplied to forward areas, new and more complicated protective equipment, which would cause discomfort to the wearers, would have to be made available, and new types of training would be required. Since transport was usually critical in planning operations, presumably gas munitions and protective equipment could only have been supplied as substitutes for other items.

The question of whether to use gas or not presented itself differently to Great Britain, the United States, Japan, and Germany. Great Britain, like most of the nations of the world except the United States and Japan, had renounced gas warfare by signing the Geneva Protocol of 1925. Her population was largely concentrated in great cities within easy reach of the *Luftwaffe*. Her thinking about gas warfare was fundamentally defensive, but she was wise enough to realize that the best defense against German gas attacks was the power to retaliate. While issuing gas masks to her entire civilian population, she prepared vigorously for offensive chemical warfare in the event that Germany should repeat her tactics of 1915 and spring a surprise gas attack. From the British standpoint, preparations for gas warfare would be crowned with success if they deterred the Germans from using gas.

The United States, unlike Great Britain, had not signed the Geneva

Protocol and was free to resort to gas warfare. Here, as in other English-speaking countries, there was a general repugnance to the use of gas, though the wide expanse of the Atlantic and Pacific rendered us relatively safe from retaliation. There were phases of the war in the Pacific in which the idea of smothering the Japanese in their strongly defended island caves to save time and American lives had an appeal to many. Yet if the Japanese had used mustard gas to defend their beaches, it would have taken a heavy toll of American attackers, especially in hot and damp climates where men sweat freely. And if we had used gas, the Japanese might in retaliation have used it against the Chinese, who were the least prepared to defend against it. Although the step seemed inadvisable to many specialists in chemical warfare, it is not surprising that President Roosevelt and Prime Minister Churchill both announced that they would use gas only if their enemies used it first. Their large-scale preparations for gas warfare were primarily designed to deter the enemy from gas attacks.

If Japan had been adequately prepared to use gas and to defend against it, she might well have been more inclined to resort to it than Germany, Great Britain, or the United States. She had never renounced the use of gas and indeed had used it occasionally during the earlier years of the war in China. Against the unprepared Chinese it was a weapon of tremendous potentialities. But such small islands as Saipan, Guam, and Iwo, so essential to her defense, were vulnerable to a drenching gas attack, and the Japanese High Command knew that whatever initial advantage she might gain through gas, its use in the end would be to the advantage of the Allies. Japan lacked a great chemical industry as a basis for gas warfare. And from what we now know of her unpreparedness for it, the reasons for her abstention are clear.

For Germany the problem had many angles. Her method of conducting hostilities did not lend color to the argument that moral considerations weighed heavily in any of her decisions. Germany felt no more compunction about starting the unrestricted bombing of cities than had the Italians in using gas in their undeclared war against Ethiopia. It may be true, as has been suggested, that Hitler had a particular aversion for gas, growing out of his experience in the First World War. Early in the Second World War he let his readiness be known to honor Germany's signature to the Geneva

Protocol against gas warfare, but this was not to be counted on.

During the war in Europe, significant enemy stocks of gas were not captured until the Allied armies crossed the Rhine. It was suspected that the Germans had stocks of odorless blister gases, known as the nitrogen mustards, but these gases are not very effective and the stocks were very small. They also improved their protective equipment during the war. Occasional statements by prisoners of war and in military intelligence reports served to keep the subject alive. The German official radio talked of a secret weapon but in language which seemed to apply better to bacteriological or atomic warfare than to gas.[1] When the Allied forces entered Central Germany and Austria the extent of enemy gas-filled munitions, the extent of enemy productive capacity for war gases, and the new gases he had developed and manufactured all came as surprises. Germany's readiness was such that the initiation of gas warfare might have caused some embarrassment to the Allies, except for the fact that Germany had lost control of the air.

The statement recently made before a Senate subcommittee investigating the I. G. Farben chemical industry that Germany had "the deadliest poison gas in the world," of a type "unknown to the military authorities of the Allied nations and which could have penetrated any gas mask in existence," has been denied by Major General Alden H. Waitt, U.S.A., the new Chief of our Chemical Warfare Service.

In reality [says General Waitt], the new German gas is good but not revolutionary. In some respects it is superior to mustard gas; in others it is of less value.

Perhaps its greatest advantage is that it is difficult to detect and very small concentrations in the air will blind a man for forty-eight hours. Higher concentrations, if breathed, will kill. A few drops on the bare skin will cause severe casualty. However, it cannot penetrate the American mask, nor can any gas developed up to this time.[2]

East of the Rhine the Allied forces found a quarter of a million tons of Nazi toxic munitions and bulk agents. The proving ground and testing installation of the German chemical warfare service at Raubkammer[3]

---

[1] Bacteriological Warfare research was conducted by the War Department and received little help from OSRD.

[2] See his interesting article, "Why Germany Didn't Try Gas," in the *Saturday Evening Post*, March 9, 1946.

[3] *Ibid.*

covered fifty square miles. In view of the immensity of these preparations, to which were devoted huge amounts of manpower and materials
sorely needed in other fields of the war effort, it is hard to believe that
the High Command thought gas to be ineffective, and permitted the
proponents of gas warfare to go so far just to keep them quiet. Nevertheless the evidence does not warrant a categorical statement that the Germans intended to start gas warfare in Europe.

During the early days of the war and until Allied air superiority made
itself manifest, the Germans may have believed that they did not need
to resort to gas warfare. Fear of retaliation may have been important in
these days because, as far as we know, the German civilian population
was not adequately provided with gas masks as were the British. At the
time of the fall of France in 1940, the Germans obtained from the French
all reports and documents concerning research and development work
by the British Empire and by the French on the subject of gas warfare.
The information obtained in this way seems to have led them to believe that German preparations were inferior to those of the Allies.
There is some further evidence that the Germans believed the Russians
to be well prepared for gas warfare. On the other hand, statements by
certain prisoners of war as late as 1945 indicated a fairly good knowledge on the part of the Germans of the extent of Allied preparations.

There were at least two, and perhaps four, occasions on which the
use of gas by the Germans might have been a very material help to them.
One of these occasions was at the time of the siege of Stalingrad. There
seems to be no reasonable doubt that the extensive use of mustard gas on
Stalingrad by the Germans would have enabled them to take the city.
Whether the capture of this one city would have had enough long-range
effect on the course of the war to make the use of gas desirable cannot,
of course, be stated, but rumor has it that the German General Staff
felt this to be the case. Use of gas on the Anzio beachhead would also have
been of considerable value to the Germans.

General Waitt has expressed the belief that heavy gas attacks on the
Allied beachheads in Normandy "might have delayed our invasion for
six months and made later landings at new points necessary."

Such a delay [he says] could have given the Germans sufficient time to
complete new V-weapons, which would have made the Allies' task all the
harder and England's long range bombardment considerably worse. True,

we could have replied manifold, for we were prepared to deal a terrific gas blow. But the question poses: Would the delay of six months in our invasion have been worth it to the Germans? As things turned out I think it might have been but they didn't dare grasp the opportunity.

It is true that no stocks of gas-filled German munitions were captured in France, and it seems that in June 1944 such stocks were well in the rear and probably located in Central Germany. Therefore, gas-filled munitions to be delivered on the beachhead would have had to be transported considerable distances. Perhaps the Germans were unable to use gas during the invasion owing to loss of control of the air.

Gas might have been of material assistance to the Germans at the time of the crossing of the Rhine, or more particularly during the period when the Allies were preparing for that crossing. There were large concentrations of personnel and of matériel, and the situation for the use of gas was almost ideal. Hitler may have decided again through personal prejudice not to permit the use of gas at this time, but lack of transport and fear of retaliation probably were the decisive factors. Stocks of gas munitions would have been strategically placed for use during this period if the Germans had really intended to take advantage of this weapon.

Mutual distrust and a fear that chemical warfare might introduce a decisive factor into the war caused all nations to expend an enormous effort on research, development, and production. This effort was most deleterious to those countries with the least manpower and resources. In this sense, the Allies won the gas warfare of 1939–1945. If, in addition, the Allied effort caused the enemy to be afraid to initiate a type of warfare which might have delayed the final victory, the gas warfare victory may have been notable even though not glamorous.

The contributions of the National Defense Research Committee to this victory of sheathed swords were important. Much that was done must, of necessity, be withheld from publication for the time being, but enough can be told to make a quite complete story. The NDRC aided in solving both offensive and defensive problems of gas warfare. This work was centered in Division 9, of which Walter R. Kirner was chairman, and in Division 10, though a few projects found their way into Division 11, whose successive chairmen were Robert P. Russell, Earl P. Stevenson, and Harris M. Chadwell.

In 1939, chemical warfare activities were centered at Edgewood

Arsenal. The Naval Research Laboratory had been active in developing oxygen masks for ship rescue work, but in 1940 that laboratory received authorization to work on chemical warfare subjects. A small but very active group was started in 1941. Prior to 1939, appropriations in both services for chemical warfare had been small and much of the effort had of necessity been devoted to improvement in protection. However, the airplane had been recognized as an important vehicle for spreading gas, and some work on bombs and spray tanks had borne fruit. The mortar, developed by the Chemical Warfare Service, was an outstanding weapon for short-range delivery of gas by ground troops. Nevertheless, it is safe to say that the fundamental basis for the offensive use of gas had shown little real advance since the war of 1914–1918.

Preparations for offensive gas warfare are in three stages: (1) Search for new compounds followed by manufacture and purification for those adopted; (2) Development of weapons and munitions for delivering the gas on the enemy; (3) Study of the field behavior of the agents and weapons.

To be useful as poison gases, chemical compounds must have the desired effects on man: lachrymatory, vesicant (that is, produce blisters), sternutatory (sneezing), or lethal as the case may be. But that is not all. They must be stable in storage so that they may be transported to the front and they must not be destroyed by the munitions used to deliver them on the enemy. The tests to which chemical compounds must be subjected before they can be accepted as usable war gases are numerous and are laborious and time consuming.

The main war gases available toward the end of the last war were phosgene (a lethal coughing gas), mustard gas, and lewisite (both blister gases). A few others had been used from time to time but were relatively unimportant. All nations, Allied and enemy alike, had continued the search for new war gases, but at the start of this war, the United Kingdom and the United States had not found any deemed sufficiently good to warrant manufacture. Indeed, lewisite, which was never really used during the last war, was discarded during this war as being not good enough.

The search for new gases was accelerated following 1939 and Division 9 carried most of the burden of this program. Thousands of compounds were made and tested, but while several had real promise, none was considered sufficiently outstanding to warrant full-scale manufacture. It may be worth noting in passing that the British also had tested several thousand compounds and had arrived at a conclusion similar to that just stated. Two gases discarded during the war of 1914–1918 were resuscitated because ways of stabilizing them were found, but essentially the Allies ended this war with the gases which were used in World War I.

The Germans uncovered some new war gases, at least one of which was produced in large quantities. They are more toxic than any manufactured by the Allies, and, when absorbed in small doses, cause contraction of the pupil of the eye, with consequent impairment of vision. This effect lasts a few days or weeks. While these German gases may have some advantages over the stand-bys of the last war, none of them is sufficiently awe-inspiring to change our fundamental ideas of the effectiveness of gas warfare.

The improvements in manufacturing and purification processes for agents old and new were part of the programs of Divisions 9 and 11. The purification of mustard gas was extensively investigated. Division 11 did pilot plant work on several methods, but the final process developed was based on a chance observation made by Dr. C. C. Price's group in Division 9 at the University of Illinois. According to this observation, water-washed impure mustard gas of the type manufactured by the Chemical Warfare Service could be vacuum distilled with better results than unwashed material. The vacuum distillation process was developed and put through the pilot plant stage by the Chemical Warfare Service, and large quantities of impure mustard gas would have been purified by this method had the war lasted much longer.

The NDRC entered the weapons and munitions picture only in 1943, and none of the new developments were in the field at the close of the war. The Chemical Warfare Service developed spray tanks, bombs, shells, and rockets for dispersing gas. While many of these munitions were far from perfect, by and large they were adequate for use as contemplated, namely overwhelming the enemy with massive attacks. Division 10 had one development which looked promising and which would have increased the effectiveness of mustard gas for "surprise" — that is, for giving a heavy dose before protective devices can be put on.

The third stage in studying gas for offense involves finding out how the agents, the weapons, and the munitions actually behave in the field.

The fuzing must be proper to prevent the munitions from burying themselves in the ground with consequent crater loss, the bombs must burst in such a way that the agent is properly distributed, and the burst of the bomb must not burn up the agent. These and many other factors concerning the functioning of the munition must be observed. Equally important is ascertaining what concentrations can be obtained, how many munitions must be placed on the target to get the desired effects, what effect wind speed, temperature, and other meteorological factors have on the behavior of the agents as well as on the susceptibility of men exposed to them. Without giving any more detail, it can be appreciated by the casual reader that these studies are very complex, that they are costly because they involve bodies of troops, airplanes, and artillery as well as numerous devices for measuring concentrations over a big area. It is sometimes necessary to expose men as well as animals in order to be able to ascertain exactly what can be expected.

This kind of large-scale field experimentation was started in the United States at Dugway Proving Ground, in Utah, during 1942, and has been continued by the Dugway Proving Ground Mobile CWS Unit, located in Florida, and by a large project located in the Republic of Panama. At all of these stations NDRC personnel worked hand in hand with the Army both in developing methods for carrying on these studies and in aiding in the studies themselves. In this case, perhaps, the co-operation of the NDRC with the Army was more intimate than in any other field.

In addition to these American stations, there were several stations located throughout the British Empire: in the United Kingdom, in Canada, in Australia, and in India. In 1944 it was decided that some central Allied agency should examine critically the data from all of these stations and try to derive the best conclusions possible. The Project Co-ordination Staff was started at Edgewood Arsenal in March 1944 with representation from the NDRC, from the various Divisions of the Chemical Warfare Service, and from several countries in the British Empire. This staff analyzed the field data and published several reports, among which was one summarizing the best considered conclusions on the field use of chemical warfare material. In a sense, this report is the climax of a large amount of effort expended not alone by the United States but also by British agencies.

So much for the offensive use of chemical warfare. The defensive end is equally important, since no army would knowingly send its own troops into battle to use munitions against which they are less well protected than the enemy. The essential parts of protection consist of the gas mask, clothing, and ointments. Research and development on these items centered at Edgewood Arsenal and at the Chemical Warfare Service Development Laboratory at the Massachusetts Institute of Technology for the Army and at the Naval Research Laboratory for the Navy.

The gas mask should protect against gases and vapors as well as against toxic smokes, it must be comfortable, and it must be serviceable in all climates. The requirements for a good gas mask are stringent since it must protect against any unknown gas which the enemy might use without warning.

The Army and Navy gas masks of 1939 were good, indeed they compared favorably with those of other armies, but they had certain weaknesses which could be and have been remedied. In a wet climate the charcoal takes up a lot of water and in so doing it loses much of its ability to take up other gases. In wet climates like those in the Southwest Pacific and in parts of Italy the mask was almost useless against certain gases which the enemy might have used. The protection against toxic smokes was far from good, especially in wet climates.

The NDRC was given the job of improving the protection of the mask against gases, vapors, and smokes, particularly with a view to making that protection universal against all types of compounds and in all climates. This was accomplished in co-operation with the Chemical Warfare Service and the Navy and all gas-mask canisters shipped overseas toward the end of the war had charcoal and filters resulting to no small extent from the work of Division 10.

The most effective gas used in World War I was mustard gas and it was known that the enemy possessed large stocks of this compound. This "gas" produces blisters when either the liquid or its vapor comes into contact with the skin. It is also very bad in its effects on the eyes when breathed. The liquid could be kept off the skin by an impermeable suit, but no soldier could stand such a suit for long, at least in warm climates. Hence it was imperative to have clothing impregnated with chemicals which would destroy mustard gas, and an ointment which could be used either for protection or to rub on any droplets as a decontaminant.

The Army had an ointment at the beginning of the war, but, as someone said facetiously, the ointment was so irritating that it was hard to tell which would be worse: an ointment burn or a mustard-gas burn. The problem of producing a nonirritating ointment is not an easy one because powerful chemicals are necessary to destroy mustard gas, and such chemicals are apt to be irritating to the skin.

The Naval Research Laboratory was very active in the search for better ointments and developed two new chemical compounds, one of which, when incorporated in ointment, was better than that used by the armed services in any country. Division 9 formulated and developed the ointment itself, and was subsequently very active in the testing program. The final ointment was adopted by both the Army and the Navy and was available overseas at the close of the war.

The impregnation of clothing with chemicals which would destroy mustard gas is also a difficult problem, particularly since the clothing must be nonirritating in hot weather, and must be stable in storage. While the Army had a reasonably satisfactory impregnation process before the war and U.S. soldiers were better protected than those of any other army against mustard gas, the fabrics disintegrated very badly under storage, particularly in hot and humid climates. Division 9 made notable contributions to increase the stability of impregnated clothing and the clothing issued by the close of the war was considerably better than that which had been available earlier.

The impregnated clothing standardized by the Chemical Warfare Service was useful only against lewisite and other agents of the mustard type, and was relatively ineffective against other persistent agents. In 1941, the British started to develop a type of clothing which would protect against the vapors of all agents of this type. This development was continued by Division 9, and by the end of the war very useful clothing of this type was in prospect. In view of the fact that the chemical warfare of the future may rely on many other agents than mustard gas, this development is particularly significant.

If gas warfare had started, the problem of supplying enough clothing to troops in the field would have been a very serious one indeed. Simplification of the process particularly so that it could be used near the front was essential. Small impregnation sets for buckets and even for steel helmets were developed largely with the aid of Division 9, and both the Army and the Navy had field impregnation sets available in theaters of operation before the close of the war.

The tangible things produced as a result of NDRC efforts form only one chapter of the chemical warfare of nerves. All countries, both Allied and enemy, made a practice of examining material received either voluntarily from allies or by capture from the enemy. An examination of enemy protection might afford clues to the gases which he expected to use. The game of espionage and counterespionage, the spreading of rumors, and a little plain braggadocio all served to confuse the issue, to cause wastage of effort, and to render life miserable for those charged with the responsibility of preparing for eventualities.

Some of the items developed by the NDRC contributed their share in causing anxiety to the enemy. We have already mentioned that two gases known in the last war were revived during the present conflict because means of stabilizing them had been found. One of these was apparently considered very carefully by the Russians and caused the Germans to modify the filling of their gas-mask canisters. The other was manufactured by the United States and caused the Germans to modify further the filling of their gas-mask canisters. As might be expected, the United States ensured protection of its own troops by modifying the filling of its own canisters, beginning in 1943. The Germans tried to duplicate this filling as soon as they learned of it through capture of U.S. Army canisters in Italy. It is interesting to note that in spite of nearly two years' effort on this subject, the Germans failed, and that after V-E Day prominent Germans were quoted as saying that they considered the United States canister to be the best that they had ever examined.

Similar tales could be told on the subject of impregnated clothing and ointments. The Germans never succeeded in producing satisfactory impregnated clothing in quantity, although evidence indicates that they spent enough time on this subject. Moreover, shortly before V-E Day, they captured the most recent American ointment and decided that it was better than anything the German Army had available. There was insufficient time after this capture and before V-E Day for them to have made any real progress in duplicating this ointment.

So much for the reason why gas was not used and so much for a brief survey of NDRC contributions to the subject of toxic-gas warfare. Some attention might be paid in conclusion to the relationships of NDRC to the Army and to the Navy with special emphasis on the Chemical Warfare Service, since that service carried the major share of the responsibility for preparing the country for this type of warfare.

No two organizations, either large or small, ever got along with each other without points of friction, and the relationships of NDRC to the Chemical Warfare Service proved no exception to this rule. The Chemical Warfare Service had existed since the last war, it had research groups at Edgewood Arsenal, and a laudable *esprit de corps*. It was inevitable that the NDRC would be regarded with suspicion since it was an independent agency free from Army control. On its side the NDRC was bound to regard the Army as set in its ways, as unco-operative, and as unwilling to accept new developments which it had not originated itself. The competition which existed between the two organizations led inevitably to duplication of effort and wastage of time.

In view of numerous possibilities for misunderstanding, it is gratifying to state that by the close of the war there existed the closest co-operation, intermingling of personnel, and mutual tolerance, even though not always mutual affection. The NDRC had numerous academic men in its organization, many of whom could be classified as strong individualists who had had little experience in working in large organizations. Moreover, the NDRC had little or no knowledge at the start of the problems which confronted the armed services. Indeed, the latter were often unable to state their needs clearly and precisely because new and unforeseen problems were being encountered.

During 1940 and 1941 NDRC received the greatest aid and stimulation from colleagues in the United Kingdom and in Canada. The latter had begun thinking of war problems several years earlier. They gave freely of their ideas, their results, and their time. It is safe to say that the delay in the effectiveness of NDRC was considerably lessened by this aid received from our Allies.

During World War I, all scientific work on the subject of chemical warfare had been centralized in and around Washington. NDRC operated in an entirely different fashion for a variety of reasons. It was believed in the first place that existing laboratories throughout the country should be used wherever possible with consequent avoidance of a new building program and the acquisition of laboratory apparatus difficult to obtain in wartime. In the second place, it was also considered advisable for academic institutions to retain as much as possible their normal functions in training of scientific personnel. For these and other pertinent reasons, NDRC operated by placing contracts in academic and research institutions as well as in industry. This decentralization of the research work imposed a severe burden on those in the Washington office from the standpoint of co-ordination. The problem of keeping the armed services informed of developments was a serious one. This difficulty contributed in no small measure to misunderstandings which arose between the users and the research workers. The chemical divisions alone had several hundred contracts in more than 100 different laboratories and this will give some small idea of the difficulty in maintaining a co-ordinated program, but it is reasonable to believe that the advantages of this system far outweighed the disadvantages.

The early contacts between the NDRC and the Chemical Warfare Service were maintained by occasional visits by key personnel to Washington and through technical aides stationed in the Washington office. These contacts were probably not sufficiently intimate to overcome the main sources of friction, and it was felt by the NDRC that its developments were not receiving careful consideration by the Chemical Warfare Service. On the other hand, the NDRC did not always adhere to military channels, and all too often it tended to indulge in a sales campaign for items not fully developed and not ready for adoption.

As an experiment, in the summer of 1942, one representative of Division B, NDRC, was placed in the Office of the Chief, Technical Division, Chemical Warfare Service, to represent those sections which were later to form Divisions 9, 10, and 11. This NDRC representative was treated in every way as a member of the CWS and was shown every courtesy and facility in performing his functions. Nevertheless, during the next few months some exceedingly troublesome problems arose. To aid in co-ordinating the entire effort, there was established a CWS-NDRC Technical Committee responsible directly to the Chief, Chemical Warfare Service, with Colonel (later Brigadier General) W. C. Kabrich as chairman, and consisting of Colonel M. B. Chittick, Dr. J. B. Conant, Dr. Roger Adams, Dr. W. A. Noyes, Jr., and Major F. B. Stewart as secretary. Later Dr. W. R. Kirner and Lieutenant Colonel G. C. White were added to this Committee and Colonel M. B. Chittick resigned when he assumed other duties. Lieutenant Colonel (later Colonel) George W. Perkins, Chief of Field Requirements Division, and Colonel C. P. Rhoads, Chief of Medical Division, both CWS, also met with the Committee in the discussion of problems of particular interest to their Divisions. This Committee dealt with some of the most difficult problems, and gave an orientation to the research program of both the NDRC and the CWS. It gradually ceased to function as the co-operation of the two organizations improved, and by the end of 1944 it had become largely inoperative.

In November 1942, the Office of the Chief, Technical Division, Chemical Warfare Service, moved from Washington to Edgewood Arsenal and simultaneously a reorganization of that office was effectuated. The Chief of Division 10, and shortly thereafter the Chief of Division 9, were added to the staff of the Chief, Technical Division, and acted in his name to co-ordinate and to a large extent direct certain phases of the research and development programs both of the NDRC and of the Chemical Warfare Service. In this way, almost complete co-operation between the two organizations was obtained and duplication of effort avoided. This arrangement continued until the spring of 1944 when several events conspired for its termination.

During the latter part of 1942 Dr. Duncan MacRae of the technical staff at Edgewood Arsenal was transferred to Evanston, Illinois, where he made his headquarters with the Division 10 laboratory at Northwestern University. He acted in a liaison capacity between NDRC contracts and the Chemical Warfare Service and was very instrumental in educating NDRC personnel on the ways and problems of the Army.

The Project Co-ordination Staff was started in 1944 to analyze data from Field Testing Stations and to make recommendations for testing chemical warfare items so that the best ways of using them could be ascertained. This Staff was responsible to the Chief, Chemical Warfare Service, United States Army, and to corresponding authorities in the United Kingdom, Canada, and Australia. Its reports were approved by the Committee on the Effectiveness of Gas Warfare Material, which itself had representatives of the various parts of the U.S. Army, the U.S. Navy, NDRC, and the various nations of the British Commonwealth.

The Director of the Project Co-ordination Staff came from NDRC, and its personnel consisted of Army officers, of civilians, and of representatives from the British Commonwealth. The close harmony which always existed on this Staff indicated as well as anything possibly could the degree to which the distrust and animosities of the early years had been replaced by mutual respect and tolerance.

In pure research, in the solution of practical problems on Army Posts at home and abroad, and even in the direction of the effort, the dividing line between the NDRC and the Army had all but disappeared by the close of the war. When one adds to this co-operation the most cordial relationships developed and maintained at all levels with the United Kingdom, with Canada, and with Australia, it would probably be difficult to find a parallel case of effort united in a common cause.

CHAPTER XIX

SMOKE, INCENDIARIES, AND FLAME THROWERS

WHEN THE surprise landing on the Anzio beach spent its force before the vital German communication lines could be cut, the invading forces came near being thrown back into the sea. Their tenuous hold on their beachhead, against which the Germans massed artillery and bombing planes, depended, as had the British hold on Malta two years earlier, on the use of smoke screens.

The use of smoke screens on a large scale for military purposes seems to have originated with the navies. Black smoke produced by burning oil with insufficient air in the furnaces of oil-burning vessels was employed in World War I to protect convoys and capital ships against submarine attack and against fire from naval artillery. Such screens were effective for obstructing horizontal vision, that is between ship and ship or between shore and ship, but the problem of screening objectives from aerial observation is quite different. Indeed it is often desirable to afford protection against air attack without at the same time reducing visibility on the ground to the point of confusing and obstructing traffic.

The rapid development of the bombing plane has called for new means for screening tactical and strategic objectives from aircraft. Although the type of camouflage used in the First World War was revised and improved, it was inadequate against newly devised methods of locating targets. Smoke screens therefore attained an importance in World War II beyond all expectation.

Soon after the outbreak of war in 1939 the factories in industrial regions of the United Kingdom were instructed to emit as much smoke as possible when air attack was imminent. The problem was of such importance that Winston Churchill in 1940 requested the British Admiralty to develop a method of screening harbors and industrial areas.

The Chemical Warfare Service, U.S. Army, assigned to the newly formed National Defense Research Committee during the summer of 1940 the general problem of studying smokes. This group made important contributions to the production of better smokes and to their operational use.[1]

The smokes available in the early part of the war were mostly chemical. None of them was adequate for the conditions of World War II because they were either poisonous, or corrosive, or liable to explosion in the process of manufacture, or produced from materials which were in short supply. The Germans used chlorosulphonic acid in screening the battleships *Gneisenau* and *Scharnhorst* at Brest, and the British used a hexachloroethane type of smoke at Malta. Something better was needed.

Oil smokes had been considered during the last war. When Prime Minister Churchill requested the British Navy, in May 1940, to develop a method of screening factories and harbors, the Admiralty Fuel Experimental Station at Haslar developed the first oil-smoke generator which was used on a large scale. This consisted essentially of a vertical oil furnace into which water was injected near the top to quench the flame and yield a brownish smoke cloud. This generator was large, cumbersome, and very inefficient. Moreover, experience proved, as we shall see later, that a white smoke is usually preferable to a colored smoke.

The Chemical Warfare Service, U.S. Army, had standardized an oil-smoke pot, referred to as the M-1. This smoke pot resembles the smudge pots so familiar in the orange groves of California: it gives a black smoke which teaches the inhabitants of the neighborhood a new and largely unprintable vocabulary. Nevertheless these pots were installed in large numbers around the Panama Canal and certain strategic targets in the United States, particularly along the Pacific Coast, during the days just before and just after Pearl Harbor when air raids were feared in this country.

The attack on this problem by Section L-1 is a beautiful example of the solution of a practical war problem by principles established through fundamental research. Irving Langmuir, a former Nobel Prize winner, at the General Electric Company, and Victor LaMer at Columbia University, working independently under NDRC contracts beginning in September and October, 1940, threw fresh light on the problem of aerosols — that is, the suspension of particles of liquids or solids in air.

---

[1] Section L-1, whose chairman was Professor W. H. Rodebush of the University of Illinois, was created during July 1940 to undertake this assignment. This section later became Section B-5 under Division B, and finally, in December 1942, was incorporated in Division 10.

The theory of light scattering had been developed by Lord Rayleigh half a century ago. This theory led to the conclusion that light is scattered more if its wave length is short than if its wave length is long, and showed how this scattering is related to the size of the smoke particles and to the physical properties of the material from which the smoke is made. In order to scatter visible light, the particles must have the proper size to scatter the parts of the light which are predominant. At Columbia University laboratory methods were developed for producing smokes which had particles of uniform diameter. These uniform particle smokes yielded spectral colors at various angles even though they were made of transparent materials.

The problem of what a screening smoke ought to do is partly psychological, partly physiological, and partly optical. A homely example will help to explain it. Baseball players sometimes "lose" the ball in the sun. Nothing is placed between the eyes of the player and the ball, but the eyes are so blinded by bright light that they are unable to focus properly.

The question may be asked, therefore, whether it is necessary for the screening smoke to cut off all of the light, or whether it might not be used merely to confuse the vision. In the latter case less smoke might be necessary than in the former.

Let us imagine an object covered by a smoke screen and illuminated by the sun. A bombardier in a plane located above the target and above the screen is trying to focus his eyes on the target so that he can drop his bombs with high precision. The light from the sun strikes the smoke and some of it is scattered — that is, it is reflected from each little smoke particle. This scattered light travels in all possible directions and some of it gets back to the eye of the bombardier. Some of the light goes on through the smoke without being scattered and is reflected back by the target. This is the light which the eye of the bombardier must use to see the target. In coming back through the smoke some of this reflected light will be scattered. When the bombardier tries to look at the target, he sees the scattered light along with the light from the target itself. Now if the scattered light is much more intense than the light from the target, his eye will be confused and unable to focus on the object he is trying to see. He is, in effect, blinded just as a person is blinded in approaching the bright headlights of a car. But what is the difference if

A generator from an LST belches smoke to screen the assault on a
Pacific island

An amphibious tractor throwing flames into a Jap cave on Peleliu

the smoke is made of colored materials? Instead of scattering the light, the smoke is now absorbing a lot of it. Hence there will be less of it to confuse the eye.

One of the most difficult practical problems connected with screening smokes is in ascertaining just how good they really are. When a smoke screen is set up in the open, it varies from point to point, and about all one can use as a criterion is the opinion of some observer in a plane. From a scientific standpoint, this is not quantitative and not very satisfactory. In order to obtain a better idea of just what is wanted, extensive experiments were carried out at the General Electric Company in boxes where the smoke could be maintained as a stratified layer at definite concentrations and where various lighting effects could be studied. The floor of the box could be raised and lowered so that the thickness of smoke necessary to produce obscuration under various conditions could be ascertained.

Thus independently at General Electric Company and at Columbia University the optimum size of particle for light scattering was determined. If a "good" screening smoke is obtained, the sun's disk will appear red when viewed through it. We have also seen that usually a white smoke will make a better screen than a smoke made from a colored substance. Theoretical predictions were verified in practice. Indeed the practical difficulties of measuring the usefulness of a smoke are so great that theory turned out to be more useful than observation as a means of deciding what smoke to use.

Under certain conditions, colored smokes may have some advantages. Since white smokes reflect brilliantly, they are easily seen, and unless they are properly used, they may serve merely to indicate the general location of the target. The screen should be considerably larger than the target; otherwise it may be a disadvantage rather than a help. A colored smoke, however, may blend into the surroundings and be very difficult to detect. In this sense, it acts as camouflage rather than as a screen. For moonlight nights, a brownish smoke over a city may be very effective indeed, but it should be kept in mind that if the enemy planes drop any flares, the visibility through such a brownish smoke may be very good.

Having determined the particle size and the fact that the smoke must be white, the next step was to make a smoke generator. Interest in the problem was heightened when American consuls returning to Washington from Germany reported to NDRC interviewers in June 1941 that the Germans had developed a screening smoke which was used in congested factory areas on the approach of British aircraft. Water fogs are good screens but water evaporates so rapidly on a dry day that the fog disappears as it is carried away by the wind. Oils with low vapor pressures offered much more promise. The early experiments at General Electric were made with oleic acid, but the final generators all used high-boiling fractions of petroleum.

Langmuir had proved that it was essential to produce myriads of small droplets and blow them apart fast enough so that they would not bump into each other and coalesce. If a heavy oil is boiled, the vapor condenses to form droplets when it comes out into the cool air, like steam from a teakettle. If cooling is rapid the droplets will be small, and if there is enough turbulence at the jet to suck air into the stream and produce rapid dilution, they can stay small for long periods of time.

By the late fall of 1941 Langmuir had produced a small generator based on these principles and had operated it on the roof of the General Electric Laboratory at Schenectady. This caused considerable commotion as it made enough smoke to stop transportation around the plant and bring out the local fire department. Subsequent tests were made in a near-by quarry until Langmuir discovered an excellent test site thirty-five miles away in the Schoharie Valley, where a promontory called Vrooman's Nose overlooked a broad plain. Here were tested on June 24, 1942, before a group of Army and Navy officers, Langmuir's experimental model and others developed on his principle by the Servel Corporation and the Standard Oil Development Company. One of the main contributions of the latter company consisted of applying well-known petroleum distillation methods to the design of a unit which could produce the desired Langmuir type of oil smoke continuously over long periods of time without the formation of coke and tar and with no danger of spontaneous ignition of the oil vapors.

The Chemical Warfare Service, which was charged with the responsibility for smokes, had had little experience with mechanical devices of the type developed by Standard Oil Development Company. These generators had gasoline engines to operate blowers and pumps, coils in which oil and water are evaporated, and burners using fuel oil to heat the coils. They resembled in no way the type of chemical-smoke device to which the Chemical Warfare Service had been accustomed. Therefore, there was considerable resistance to the adoption of this new idea. But the demonstrations at Vrooman's Nose were so conclusive that procurement was ordered, and the Esso generator was standardized by the Chemical Warfare Service as the M-1 Mechanical Smoke Generator.

The M-1 Mechanical Smoke Generator was manufactured by the Heil Company at Milwaukee from the Standard Oil Development Company design as a unit which could be transported in trucks or standard Army trailers. Although it was later found in the field that a lighter unit would be more desirable, the Esso generator was procured by the thousand and successfully used overseas. It probably saved the Anzio beachhead, and was mainly responsible for the ability of the Allies to maintain regular supply routes to certain ports in North Africa. The artificial harbors used for landing supplies on the Normandy beaches were screened regularly at certain times of day by these generators.

The United States Navy asked the Besler Corporation to engineer a generator along the same general lines. Two different generators resulted, both of which were procured and used. The DeVilbiss Company, operating under a Section B-5 contract, also developed a satisfactory generator which was procured by the Navy. All three of these generators weighed less than half a ton. However, a really lightweight generator was badly needed. The Besler Corporation completed the development of a lightweight generator weighing about 165 pounds and called the M-2 Mechanical Smoke Generator. This generator was procured in large numbers and used overseas, and despite several defects played an important part in many developments following the invasion of Normandy.

In a combustion-type generator, hot gases from burning fuel are used to vaporize the oil as well as to carry along the oil vapor with the high velocity necessary to successful operation. A generator developed under a Columbia University contract was submitted to York-Shipley, Inc., of York, Pennsylvania, for engineering, and although it was rejected by the Chemical Warfare Service, it was adopted by the U.S. Navy and gave very satisfactory service.

Thus we see that the original theoretical developments led to a variety of smoke generators, large numbers of which were used by both the British and the U.S. Armies overseas. The culminating use of smoke screens occurred during the preparation for the crossing of the Rhine in the late winter and spring of 1945. While men and matériel were being assembled for that crossing, a huge smoke screen prevented the enemy from observing what was going on. All Allied armies on the Western front made extensive use of mechanical smoke generators to screen airfields, bridges, troop concentrations, ports, and railways. The development was extensive and the work of Section B-5 saved literally millions — even billions — of dollars of shipping, supplies, and planes, not to mention human lives.

Since the extensive use of screening smoke was essentially a development of World War II, studies had to be made of the best way to use these generators. The operational use of smoke falls under two main headings — the protection of strategic targets, usually of considerable size, and the still more difficult task of screening tactical operations, where the targets are often in movement and it is essential to confuse the enemy without at the same time confusing friendly troops. As the two bodies of troops may be separated by only a few hundred, or at most a few thousand yards, wind direction and persistence of the smoke may determine entirely whether or not its use would be more of a help than a hindrance. Smoke-filled artillery and mortar shells are useful in blinding an enemy but cannot be used to lay down screens for friendly troops because of the risk of casualties. Smoke laid by planes from spray tanks can be used to protect strategic targets, but it is blown away by the wind. The maintenance of such screens over large areas for long periods of time might thus necessitate the use of a prohibitive number of aircraft. The most useful devices for screening strategic targets are smoke pots and smoke generators placed on the ground and replenished as need arises.

In collaboration with the Chemical Warfare Service and the Navy, members of Division 10 played an important part in experiments on the operational use of smoke, the development of the doctrine, and the preparation of smoke manuals. The Chemical Warfare Service had a large installation of Esso smoke generators to protect the locks of the canal at Sault Ste. Marie. Extensive tests were made of these generators during the winter of 1942–1943 and were witnessed by Section B-5 personnel. During the spring of 1943, Division 10 personnel collaborated with the Chemical Warfare Service under Brigadier General E. F. Bullene at Camp Sibert, Alabama, in carrying out an extensive series of tests with Esso generators. These tests were designed to show how many generators had to be placed along a line to give adequate screening of a strategic target. Since many important targets were placed near shore-lines, the behavior of smoke at ocean-land boundaries was important, and this problem was investigated by a Division 10 group at Browns-ville, Texas, during the spring of 1943. The largest series of tests, and by all odds the most important, was conducted by the Navy at Fort Pierce, Florida, during 1944. Several CWS officers collaborated in these tests, and several members of Division 10 were also present. As a result of these studies at Fort Pierce, definite conclusions were drawn as to the best type of smoke munition and the general rules for the use of smoke during amphibious operations. However, practical experience overseas by the using branches of the service powerfully influenced the way in which smoke devices were used in practice. The officers in charge of these smoke operations probably know more about the subject in general than any group in the United States. However, it is only fair to say that in the Pacific war the use of smoke had not been fully appreciated even at the close of hostilities.

While NDRC chemists were developing better smokes and better methods for their use on the long roads to Rome, Berlin, and Tokyo, other members of the chemical divisions were hard at work on the in-cendiary bombs which burned out the heart of the Japanese industrial system and inflicted far more damage and casualties than any other munition. Around the relative merits of incendiaries and high-explosive aerial bombs raged one of the hottest arguments of the war. Members of Division 11 contended that it was futile to risk the lives of aircrews carrying loads of small high-explosive bombs and that incendiaries were a much more valuable bomb load. The findings of the United States Strategic Bombing Survey, after prolonged and careful study, bear them out. These show that the M-47 incendiary weighing 70 pounds was twelve times as effective, bomb for bomb, as the 500-pound HE bomb against targets classified as readily inflammable, and one and a half times as effective against targets classified as fire-resistant. The rela-tive value of these two munitions against urban areas is attested by all observers returning from the devastated cities of Germany.

Both the production and the evaluation of incendiaries are far more difficult than is generally realized. An incendiary bomb must have stability in the air and just the right terminal velocity. If the latter is too great, the bomb will shatter and fail to function; if it is too low, the bomb will not penetrate the structure. When it reaches its goal it must start a fire rapidly of such magnitude that it cannot be easily extinguished. In the early part of the war these difficulties were not fully appreciated and the awkward problem of evaluating different incendiaries under simulated conditions had received inadequate attention.

When NDRC launched a study of incendiaries in the summer of 1941 the incendiary bomb was a relatively new weapon. Its only extensive use had occurred during the blitz on England, and the Germans had fortunately not realized its full measure of effectiveness. American incendiary bombs available at this time were the M-50, a 4-pound magnesium bomb which was a copy of the principal British incendiary bomb, and the M-54, a 4-pound thermite bomb, intended as a substitute. The serious shortage of magnesium led General H. H. Arnold to write Dr. Bush in September 1941, urging that the development of substitutes be pushed more vigorously. The program was formalized by a letter from the Chemical Warfare Service on October 7. The Harvard group led by Dr. Louis Fieser, already hard at work on the problem, shifted their efforts to a study of organic incendiary materials, and NDRC concluded a contract with the Standard Oil Development Company for a small incendiary bomb filled with a petroleum product.

Both the Harvard and the Standard Oil Development groups recognized the importance of thickened or jellied gasoline as an incendiary material because of its easy ignition, high heat of combustion, and controlled burning rate. The British had made jellied gasoline with rubber, but Japan's bewilderingly rapid conquests had slammed the door on that line of development at the same time they made the development of a practical incendiary more important than ever.

The Harvard group, reinforced by members of the staff of Arthur D. Little, Inc., investigated the potentialities of aluminum naphthenate as a thickening agent, and in January 1942 hit on the idea of adding the aluminum soap of coconut acids. This new material, christened Napalm, was destined to play a great role in the war both in incendiary bombs and in flame throwers. Important contributions to its development were made in the next few months by the Nuodex Products Company. The addition of aluminum oleate and the development of a coprecipitation process gave a dry granular soap powder capable of producing a gasoline jelly by simple mixing at ordinary temperatures.

The principal application of gasoline jelly at this time was in the M-47, 70-pound incendiary bomb being developed by the Chemical Warfare Service. This was a bursting-type bomb operating by means of an impact fuze and a central burster tube. During the spring of 1942 the Harvard group developed an improved burster for this bomb, consisting of an inner core of TNT surrounded by white phosphorus instead of the conventional black-powder burster.

Meanwhile the Standard Oil Development Company was testing various mechanisms for incendiary bombs against specially designed targets simulating attics. These experiments led to the important conclusion that the radius of effectiveness of the incendiary material in a small bomb was quite limited unless a means could be found to project the material over a wider portion of the target. A tail-ejection bomb was conceived, consisting of a hexagonal steel container, $2\frac{7}{8}$ inches in diameter and $19\frac{1}{2}$ inches in length. This was filled with gasoline jelly, and provided with a delay fuze which would permit the bomb to take a horizontal position after penetrating a roof, and a powder charge to ignite the incendiary material and eject it through the tail. Another novelty in bomb design was the substitution of cloth streamers for the conventional rigid metal tail. Successive experimental lots of the new gasoline-gel bombs were made during the spring of 1942. These were exhaustively tested in a wind tunnel to fix the terminal velocity at the value necessary to penetrate roof structures, as determined by firing from mortars at appropriate targets with varying striking velocities. This was a difficult undertaking, for the roof structures we desired to penetrate ranged from the lightest of Japanese through medium industrial roofs. The figure arrived at determined the strength that had to be built into the bomb and the amount of drag to be imposed through the tail streamers.

Tests of the various gasoline-thickening agents in May 1942 indicated that an isobutylmethacrylate material produced by du Pont was the most satisfactory, but by 1943, when Napalm had been improved and its manufacture standardized, it replaced the du Pont product for filling both the M-47 and the new Standard Oil Development bomb. Both of these bombs were available by the summer of 1942 in sufficient quantities for airborne testing against condemned farm buildings at Jefferson Proving Ground, Indiana. These tests showed the superiority of the TNT-white phosphorus burster over the old burster for the M-47, and the outstanding advantages of the new gasoline-jelly bomb over the other small bombs tested. This was standardized as the M-69 and the Chemical Warfare Service put it into production. The TNT-white phosphorus burster was turned over to the Chemical Warfare Service for final development and production, and was eventually standardized as the M9-M13 burster-igniter, which was used extensively in the bombing of Germany and Japan.

As production got under way on the M-69 bomb in the winter of 1943, the Standard Oil Development group began work on a modification containing a small tetryl charge, a heavy nose for production of fragments, and a variable time delay. This bomb, which showed great promise as an incendiary and anti-personnel weapon, unfortunately did not get into production until March 1945.

The tests of the M-69 bombs against farm buildings at Jefferson Proving Ground had been challenged vigorously by those who contended that these structures were easier to set afire than German or Japanese buildings. To meet these objections, the Standard Oil Development group, using plans developed by a former German architect, constructed full-scale sections typical of German urban and industrial structures which could be used as targets for incendiary bombs fired from mortars to simulate bombs dropped from airplanes. These tests led to the drawing up of plans for typical German and Japanese houses with the help of architects who had practiced for years in Germany and Japan. In March this project was turned over to the Chemical Warfare Service, but the Standard Oil Development group retained an important role as architect-engineers. Ground was broken for these structures at the Dugway Proving Ground in Utah on March 29, and by May 15 twelve two-family Japanese houses and a block of six German houses were ready for testing. This period of seven weeks was one of feverish a tivity. The Hawaiian Islands and the West Coast were ransacked for Japanese straw floor mats and other house furnishings, and authentic German and Japanese furniture was manufactured in New York.

Tests held at Dugway from May 17 to July 16, 1943, produced convincing evidence of the superiority of the M-69 over other available small incendiaries, and foreshadowed the terrible conflagrations it would cause in a country of crowded cities with a high percentage of wooden construction. Following these tests the first plans for the incendiary bombing of Japanese cities were drawn up by the Air Force in the fall of 1943, with the assistance of NDRC personnel.

During the same autumn, the Air Force imposed a new requirement on incendiary bombs. Small bombs released from clusters immediately below the plane dropping them constituted a major hazard to formation flight, and in addition were adversely affected in their aim by wind condition. All incendiary bombs were henceforth required to be produced in aimable clusters, which fall unopened with the same trajectory as a large demolition bomb until they are within a few thousand feet of the target, at which time the cluster bursts open, scattering a shower of small bombs. CWS and the Standard Oil Development group both carried on development work on aimable clusters, and the final model adopted combined features from both development groups. In the late fall of 1943, the Air Force requested rush production of 10,000 aimable clusters for use by the 20th Bomber Command in China. In co-operation with CWS, the Standard Oil Development group assumed full responsibility for supervising the production and inspection of this order and met the deadline for delivery. These clusters were subsequently sent to China and were used in bombing operations there. During 1944, large-scale production of aimable clusters was initiated, and by the end of the war approximately 30,000,000 M-69 bombs had been produced.

The first important operational use of the M-69 bomb was in March 1944 when the 7th Air Force attacked the town of Ponape on Ponape Island, producing extensive fire damage with about 20 tons of bombs. The first M-69 bombs dropped on Japan fell on January 6, 1945, when Nagoya was attacked by the 21st Bomber Command with 138 tons of bombs. By March the 21st Bomber Command based on Guam, Tinian, and Saipan was ready for large-scale incendiary attacks, which were inaugurated by the historic attack on Tokyo on March 9, 1945. This attack, carried out by 279 B-29 bombers with 1753 tons of M-69 incendiary bombs, destroyed about 15 square miles of the center of the city, an area almost four times that destroyed by the atomic bomb attack on Hiroshima five months later. Significantly enough the area destroyed in this attack was

almost exactly the same area that was destroyed in the earthquake and
fire of 1923. This highly successful attack was followed in quick succession by four major attacks on Nagoya, Osaka, Kobe, and a repeat on
Nagoya, during March 11 to 18. These attacks exhausted the supply of
incendiary bombs in the Marianas, so that it was possible to make only
two more attacks during the ensuing two months. Finally sufficient
stocks of bombs arrived to permit regular attacks to be resumed on May
15. During the next two months a series of heavy incendiary attacks
effectively destroyed all the major cities of Japan, except Hiroshima,
Nagasaki, and Kyoto. In these attacks about 50 per cent of the total
weight of bombs dropped were M-69 bombs, the other 50 per cent being
made up of other types of incendiary bombs, demolition bombs, and
fragmentation bombs. This air offensive was a major factor contributing
to the surrender of Japan in August. If the enforced delay in the incendiary bombing offensive from March 18 to May 15 had not occurred,
the war might have ended even sooner.

Prior to World War II flame throwers had been little used in warfare
and were generally considered by military men to be weapons of minor
or negligible importance. Although the Chemical Warfare Service had
asked NDRC as early as February 1941 to study flame throwers from the
point of view of fuel composition and nozzle design, neither the Army
nor the Navy was much interested until some months after Pearl Harbor; and the fundamental NDRC studies of projection of liquid jets at
M.I.T. and of nozzle design at the Associated Factory Mutual Fire Insurance Companies progressed slowly. The impetus to more rapid progress came from the discovery of Napalm and from the information received early in 1942 as to the intensive development of flame throwers
by the British Petroleum Warfare Department.

In March 1942 NDRC contracted with the Standard Oil Development Company and the Gilbert and Barker Manufacturing Company
for the development of large long-range flame throwers suitable for
mounting on tanks or other fighting vehicles. And the tests of fuels
thickened with Napalm by the M.I.T. group a month later showed a
phenomenal increase in range over ordinary fuels. To speed the development Bush appointed in May an *ad hoc* reviewing committee composed
of representatives of NDRC, CWS, the Infantry, the Armored Force,

Making it hot for the enemy on Okinawa

Firing thickened fuel at a range of eighty yards; an E14–7R2 mechanized flame thrower

Tank Destroyers, the Corps of Engineers, the Navy, and the Marines, which reported in July that portable flame throwers were definitely required but that the need for long-range mechanized flame throwers was problematical. A joint CWS–NDRC Committee appointed by Brigadier General W. C. Kabrich, Chief of the Technical Division of the CWS, in August, undertook to adapt the standard M-1 portable flame thrower for the use of thickened fuels. The Standard Oil Development and Factory Mutual groups solved this problem within a month, and the improved M1A1 flame thrower was subsequently produced in large numbers.

Despite the striking effect of thickened fuel on the performance of the portable flame thrower, its adoption in the theaters of war was slow. Unthickened fuel made a great show. The weapon was fearsome, and there were many who believed that almost the sole effect of the portable flame thrower was psychological. This was in fact the case with old-style fuel, producing as it did a range of but 20 yards with delivery of less than 10 per cent of the fuel at the end of the trajectory. Slowly, however, the marked superiority of thickened fuel began to be recognized. A range of two to three times that of old-style fuel, a capacity for delivery of up to 90 per cent of the fuel *at* the target, an aimability far superior to the old fuel — these new characteristics finally caused recognition of the effectiveness of the new weapon for burning out underground emplacements and cave defenses, and helped make possible our tortuous advance from Guadalcanal to Okinawa. The back-borne flame thrower in the hands of our troops in the Pacific was truly a lifesaver.

By December 1942 the Standard Oil Development group had designed, built, and tested a practical large flame thrower, which was improved during the production stage and eventually became a standard and highly successful weapon.

Since the summer of 1942 the British had been adapting flame throwers to their best tank, the Churchill. The most modern of the American tanks, however, were in such great demand by field commanders that our Army designated the M5A1 light tank as the fighting vehicle to which mechanized flame throwers should be adapted. By the time this problem was solved, few theater commanders had much interest in so light a tank. Some of these tank flame throwers were sent to the Philippines and saw action at Balete Pass in April 1945.

Tests of flame against models of Japanese fortifications built by the

Corps of Engineers at Fort Belvoir and Fort Pierce in the summer of 1943 stimulated interest in the Navy and the Marine Corps and led to the development by the Standard Oil Development Company of a flame gun, fuel tanks, and controls in a self-contained armored unit which could be placed in the cockpit of any small landing craft and used for attacks of beach fortifications. Twenty of these Mark I flame throwers were rushed to completion by the M. W. Kellogg Company by March 1944. They did not reach the Marianas in time for use in the invasion of Saipan and Guam, as originally intended, but they were used very effectively in September 1944 in the invasion of Peleliu, mounted in LVT-4 amphibious cargo tractors. At long last in 1944 the Army ordered 20, later 620, flame-throwing tanks of the M-4 or Sherman model and LVT-A1 amphibious tanks, but none of them reached the Pacific theater in time for action. They would probably have seen extensive use if the invasion of Japan had materialized.

Although production of long-range flame throwers in the United States was initiated too late for significant use in the war, a somewhat parallel development of mechanized flame throwers at Pacific Ocean Areas headquarters in the Hawaiian Islands was notably influenced and expedited by the development work in progress in the United States. At the request of the Commanding General, U.S. Army Forces in the Central Pacific, NDRC sent two technical advisers on flame throwers to the Central Pacific in June 1944. One of these men was from the Shell Development Company group and one from the M.I.T. group. During the summer and fall of 1944 these men worked effectively with CWS and other Army personnel in the Hawaiian Islands in the design and production of about 60 tank-mounted flame throwers in local and Army and Navy shops. Many ideas and design features developed under several NDRC contracts in the United States were utilized in this development. These mechanized flame throwers went to Iwo Jima with the Marines and to Okinawa with the Tenth Army, and played an important part in these campaigns. The Seventh Army in its march across France and attack on the fortifications of the west wall made repeated and effective use of large mechanized flame throwers borrowed from the British.

Though less familiar to the public than the triumphs of the physicists in radar, rockets, the proximity fuze, and the atomic bomb, the contributions of American chemists to the war were of extraordinary variety and importance. For many of them, such as the notable work of NDRC in the improvement of hydraulic fluids, adequate space is lacking in this volume. Chemists played roles of the first importance in the production of the atomic bomb, insecticides, and penicillin. They gave our fighting forces explosives of unexcelled power, screened them with new and better smokes, and equipped them not merely with flame throwers of fearsome range and power but with more deadly incendiary bombs. These had turned Japan's major cities into infernos weeks before the first atomic bomb was launched over Hiroshima.

Part Four: Military Medicine

CHAPTER XX

ANTIMALARIALS

W HEN THE Office of Scientific Research and Development was organized in July 1941 there was established within it a Committee on Medical Research, whose function it was to initiate and support a research program "for the national defense." The membership of this Committee was composed of representatives of the Surgeons General of the Army, Navy, and Public Health Service and of four civilians appointed by the President: Dr. A. N. Richards, of the University of Pennsylvania, Chairman; Dr. Lewis H. Weed of Johns Hopkins University, Vice-Chairman; Dr. A. R. Dochez of Columbia University, and Dr. A. Baird Hastings of Harvard University. In contradistinction to NDRC, with which the previous chapters of this book have been concerned, it was the purpose of this Committee to save the lives of our troops; directly by improving methods for treating the sick and wounded, indirectly by preventing disease. In theory this function was easier of fulfillment than that of NDRC, for the prevention and cure of disease was a peacetime occupation of medical research. In practice the quantitative shift of emphasis, the dislocation of interest, was so great that much of the research had to be conducted practically *de novo*. The control of disease-bearing insects or even of malaria, for example, had been rather academic insofar as the health of the United States was concerned. It now became of controlling importance. Similarly the necessity of flying aircraft at unprecedented heights and at unprecedented speeds introduced quite new problems.

There was grave need for the establishment of such an official agency as the CMR. For more than a year, since war had seemed possible and more than possible, committees of the Division of Medical Sciences of the National Research Council had been meeting in Washington to answer questions posed by the Army and Navy and to recommend procedures to them. In July 1941 there were 41 such committees, each composed of eminent men in the medical and surgical specialties, but many of the questions put to them could not be answered from existing knowledge and many of the procedures recommended were obviously susceptible of improvement. On both accounts research was essential but, aware as the committees were of this necessity, there were no funds at their disposal with which to conduct investigation. The Committee on Medical Research was able to implement with Government funds the research programs which these committees had planned. It continued throughout the war to utilize their advice upon proposals for specific investigations. Upon its own initiative and upon advice of its service members the Committee amplified these programs and extended them into other fields, utilizing its knowledge of the investigative and personnel resources of the country to do so. It was never hampered by lack of funds. It was hampered by the lack of a considered national policy to maintain highly trained technical personnel in their proper sphere: the laboratory and hospital. During its existence the Committee expended some $24,000,000 — a sum which would have supported our share in the war for only four hours — in approximately 600 contracts with 133 universities, foundations, and commercial firms. Over 1500 doctors of medicine, science, and philosophy and 4000 other laboratory personnel were engaged in these researches on scores of subjects.

From these subjects, five have been selected for description in the subsequent chapters of this book: research upon malaria, transfusions, penicillin, insecticides, and aviation medicine. They were selected because they lend themselves to nontechnical exposition better than do many of the others. Each of them in its own fashion contributed to winning the war. In each it will be observed that one or several years intervened between recognition of the problem and the discovery and development of its solution. This lag in time is unavoidable because the problems are complicated ones. If these chapters carry any moral it lies in this very observation: the time for the conduct of research in military medicine is before and not after the war starts.

"Malaria is an acute and chronic febrile disease, its onset often marked by chills, which is present in countries lying between 45° North and 40° South latitude." There are several million GI's who would have found that statement not only meaningless but uninteresting four years ago. Today the sentence does not seem meaningless to them. Either from their own experience or from the recollection of their friends the word "malaria" means chills and fever and sweating in bashas or tents pitched in far places. They are wise in the habits of mosquitoes, in the use of repellents and mosquito bars, in the types of Plasmodium, and the color of atabrine.

Maps designed to show the distribution of malaria picture a black band of heavy incidence round the belly of the world. A grayish mottling in the southern part of the United States indicates our light infestation. But North Africa and Sicily are in black, and India and all of Burma and Southern China are in black, as are the West Pacific islands and Panama. In these areas and in the regions of Western Africa and South America where malaria is common, it is estimated that there are 300,000,000 cases a year and 3,000,000 deaths. These were the areas to which, in December of 1941, it became clear our armies must go.

MALARIA

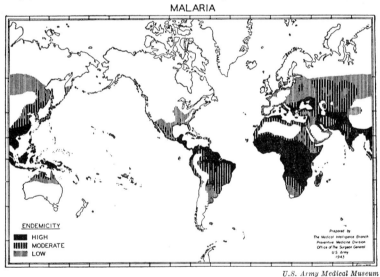

U.S. Army Medical Museum

MAP SHOWING MALARIAL ENDEMICITY

At the outbreak of the war, although not one out of a hundred of the doctors who were to enter the services had seen a case of malaria, they were familiar with the essential features of the disease: that it was caused

by organisms called Plasmodia, that it was spread by mosquitoes, that
its acute symptoms were relieved by quinine. All of these points had
been known for many years. In point of time, the discovery of quinine
had come first. Back in 1638 when the Spanish Count Cinchon was
Governor of Peru, his wife, falling sick of an "intermittent fever," was
treated with brew made from the bark of a native tree and promptly
recovered. In recollection of this Countess, the tree was named cinchona
and when one of the bark's active principles was isolated in 1820 it was
called quinine. Taken to Europe and known there as Jesuit bark because
of its use by the monks, it provided the first rational and specific treatment of an acute disease. For a long time of course it was not clear why
certain cases of fever were cured by quinine and others unaffected by
it. The mystery was only partly solved by calling those which were
cured malaria, only completely solved in 1880 when the Frenchman
Leveran demonstrated organisms which he called Plasmodia in the red
blood cells of patients infected with the disease. These organisms were
absent from the blood of patients with other fevers, they could reproduce the disease when they were injected into other patients, and they
disintegrated and disappeared under treatment with quinine. As the
name of the disease implies it had been attributed to "bad air" or, more
specifically, to noxious vapors, miasmas, arising from swamps in the evenings. This conception was a little fuzzy but fundamentally sound. It
became more precise in 1898 when the Englishman Ross proved that
mosquitoes, rather than air, arising from swamps in the evenings transmitted the disease. He demonstrated Plasmodia in mosquitoes and showed
that men develop malaria when bitten by them. By the turn of the century the fundamental information was thus in hand.

The information has been amplified. It was found that only the
Anopheles mosquito transmitted malaria, indeed only some 60 of its
200 species which have been recognized in various parts of the world.
The Plasmodia spend a portion of their life cycle within the stomach
wall of these carrier-species and then migrate to the salivary gland where
they are in an ideal position for transmission to man when the mosquito
bites. In man the Plasmodia grow in the tissues for from seven to fourteen days and then, reaching the blood stream, produce an acute attack
of the disease. When the structure of the Plasmodia was studied as they
developed in the mosquito stomach and in human blood, it was found

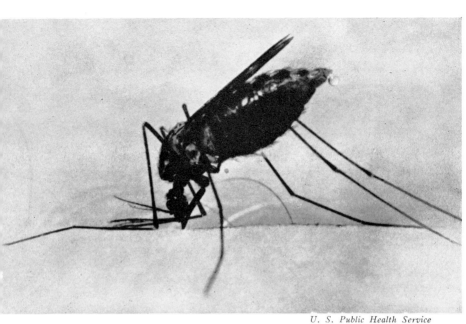

How malaria is spread: Anopheles mosquito biting a man's arm

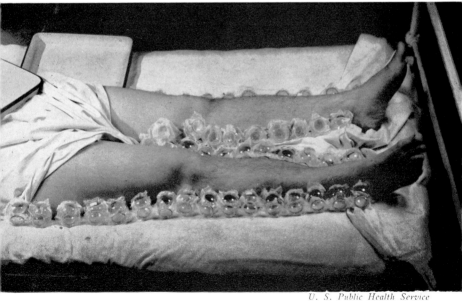

Malarial research: infecting mosquitoes by allowing them to bite an
infected patient

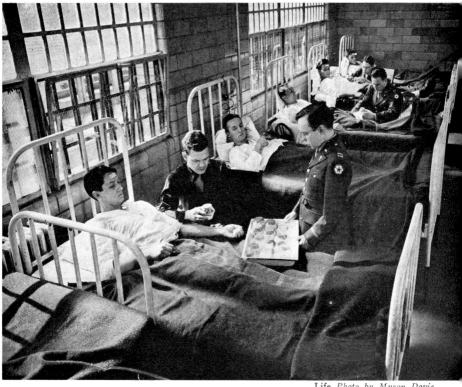

Malarial convicts contribute to knowledge of the disease

that they were not all alike but had to be divided into four species, anatomically distinguishable one from the other. This species difference explained the different clinical types of malaria which had already been observed, for a different Plasmodium was found to be associated with each type of the disease. Only two species are sufficiently common to warrant mention: *P. vivax*, which produces *vivax* malaria (synonym benign tertian), and *P. falciparum*, which produces *falciparum* malaria (synonym malignant tertian, subtertian, estivo-autumnal). A great majority of cases in the African theater were to be of the *falciparum* type; in the Pacific and CBI theaters distribution between the two was to be nearly equal. The two types of malaria are not unlike in their clinical onset. In both instances, approximately two weeks after being bitten by an infected mosquito, the patient begins to feel ill, usually quite suddenly. He develops chilly sensations which may increase to a bed-shaking chill and within a matter of hours his temperature has risen to $102-105°$. His head aches, his back aches, he is nauseated, he feels sick, he looks sick, he is quite uninterested to hear that he will be better in a day or so. In both instances, if the patient receives no treatment, the disease will last for from several weeks to several months, gradually subsiding as he gains some immunity to the infection. In both instances, though more commonly in the *vivax* type, if the patient is treated and recovers from his initial attack he shows a tendency to relapse: some weeks or months later another attack of the disease occurs and these relapses may follow each other, at intervals of a month or more, for from two to twenty times with gradually decreasing severity. As long as the patient remains in a malarial area it is not possible to distinguish these relapses from reinfections caused by being bitten again by an infected mosquito. When they occur after removal to a nonmalarial region or when they occur in malarial regions in seasons when there are no mosquitoes abroad, the distinction is clear. They are relapses. Relapses were to occur in about two thirds of cases in the Pacific theater, in about one third of cases in the African and C.B.I. theaters. *Falciparum* malaria differs from *vivax* in the severity of the acute attack, the temperature being more sustained than in the characteristic forms of *vivax*, and the patient more prostrated. It differs too because, in occasional cases of *falciparum* malaria, blood vessels in the brain become blocked by Plasmodia or by their products and the patient may gradually or suddenly sink into coma or develop any one of an amazing assortment of paralyses, from the partial paralysis of a single muscle of one eye to the complete paralysis of an entire half of the body. This is the so-called "cerebral" malaria and has a mortality of approximately 20 per cent even in well-treated cases.

The importance of malaria from the military point of view was expected to lie in its frequency rather than its mortality. In the civilian populations of tropical countries, mortality was said to be of the order of one per hundred. Since the majority of these patients had received little or no treatment it was reasonable to think that the mortality of our troops would be far less than this. It turned out to be only one per two thousand. It was important to have an effective treatment for acute attacks of malaria so that the illness might be as brief and the deaths as few as possible. But it was even more important to be able to prevent the attacks. We were to send, say, 3,000,000 troops into malaria-infested regions within the next two years. At a conservative estimate and in the absence of effective measures for prevention, one half of these troops would become casualties in the first mosquito season. A malarial casualty is not hospitalized as long as a wound casualty but, during his hospitalization, he is just as absent from duty. It was relatively unimportant that a million and a half cases of malaria would overtax any practicable hospital facilities. It was enormously important that 50 per cent of the effective strength of combat and service troops would be inactive for a period of two weeks or longer; not only once during the malarial season but repeatedly, as relapses from the initial attack or reinfection from a second bite occurred. This might, without a single fatality, lose the war and would at best inactivate forces for a considerable portion of the year. The prevention of malaria was a *sine qua non* for fighting in the tropics. The more successful the prevention, the better the chance of our winning the war. There could be no mistaking that.

The measures which were available to the services in 1941 to fight malaria fall into two categories: mosquito control, measures calculated to kill the mosquito or prevent it from biting the soldier; drug control, measures calculated to prevent the disease or to treat it after the biter had bit.

The possibility of preventing malaria by the control of mosquitoes was implicit in Ross's discovery that the disease was mosquito-borne.

The aim of this control must be to kill all mosquitoes in the area. It is true that only between one in three and one in a thousand *Anopheles* are infected. It is true that many species of *Anopheles* and all other types of mosquitoes do not carry malaria. That is why there is as large a degree of luck in acquiring malaria as in being hit by a bullet; in the one case the mosquito must have a Plasmodium, in the other the bullet must have a name on it. But the distinction requires a microscope. It cannot be made on the wing and the aim must be to kill all mosquitoes. The traditional way of doing this was to abolish or poison the stagnant or slowly moving, fresh or slightly salty water where mosquito larvae develop. This could be done by drainage. It could be done by spreading a film of kerosene or fuel oil over the water, or by blowing powdered arsenic on the surface to kill them. These methods had proved successful in mosquito-control projects before: notably during the building of the Panama Canal and in the Pontine marshes outside Rome. But the difference in scale between such projects and those imposed by our necessities was enormous. Those projects had been concerned with a few hundred square miles. We were concerned with draining and oiling a large part of the uncivilized world. Paddy fields are purposely and tediously constructed with the very design of holding water. The ground vegetation or water in thick jungle country cannot be sprayed even from the air.

In addition to possibilities of drainage and oiling which were to be the province of the theater or section malariologists, there were the antimalarial precautions which could be exercised by the individual soldier. He would be instructed by moving pictures, by placards, by lectures, to keep his sleeves rolled down and his trousers tucked inside his socks after dusk. He would be told to sleep under a mosquito net and to make sure that it was well tucked in and free of holes. He would be issued mosquito repellent and told to apply it to his hands and face if he went outdoors in the evening. He would be issued insecticides and told to spray his quarters with them. Attempts would be made to screen his quarters or to line them with Hessian cloth so as to prevent mosquitoes from entering. There could be no doubt about the effectiveness of these antimalarial precautions if they could be perfectly executed. If personnel, after dusk, would really stay in screened, sprayed quarters and sleep under mosquito nets there should be no malaria at all. But this was to idealize the situation. Men having such quarters would not stay in them after dusk, and, going outdoors, would be much less well protected by clothing and repellents. Nor would the majority of troops have such quarters. As conditions become more and more rugged with actual combat as the end point, these methods would have to be abandoned one by one. Neither mosquito nets nor jungle hammocks nor, eventually, mosquito repellent could or would be carried in a pack. The usefulness of individual precautions, like those of drainage and oiling, would be a factor of the circumstances under which the unit functioned. It did not seem possible in 1941, nor did it prove possible after the introduction of DDT and other improvements, that these methods would provide complete control of malaria. Given a relatively small area, with a stable population, an adequate supply of native labor, well-disciplined troops, a great deal could be accomplished. Given troops on the move or in actual combat, in jungle or swampy country, the proposals were not even germane. Guadalcanal and Northern Burma were to bear witness. Something more was needed.

The other weapon which the services could employ against malaria was drugs: quinine, plasmochin, atabrine. Quinine had been used to control acute attacks of malaria for three hundred years. There was no doubt of its effectiveness. Within forty-eight hours after beginning proper dosage of the drug the vast majority of patients have no fever and, though they must continue to take medication and feel some residual effects for several days, they are substantially recovered. This effect is so constant that the abrupt termination of an acute febrile disease following the use of quinine is strong presumptive evidence that the disease is malaria, though the demonstration of Plasmodia in a drop of blood is required for absolute diagnosis. This control of the acute attack cannot be defined as a cure. The occurrence of relapses in a considerable proportion of both *vivax* and *falciparum* infections proves that sufficient Plasmodia have survived the action of quinine to multiply and reproduce the disease. Quinine is similarly imperfect in the prevention of malaria. Given in daily dosage of 0.3 gram to travelers in malarial areas, to British troops stationed in India, it had usually prevented acute attacks while its administration was continued. But when its administration was stopped both *vivax* and *falciparum* infections frequently developed. Its action is therefore suppressive rather than truly preventive. It can suppress the development of Plasmodia. It is not able to prevent the infection and, its suppressive action being removed, the Plasmodia develop and produce the disease. It fulfills the acute and immediate needs of a military campaign. It is not the perfect drug, in theory or practice. Its prolonged use as a suppressive has also the disadvantage of producing ringing in the ears, blurring of vision, nausea, symptoms that are a source of discomfort to anyone and of danger to aviators.

These imperfections of quinine, understood in a general way in 1941, were to become clearer and more precise as the OSRD research program defined them. Despite their existence, the long experience with quinine, the familiarity with its potentialities and limitations, would have made it the first choice for therapy by the services in 1941 had it not been for the alarming fact that the available supplies were inadequate. The shortage existed because the cinchona tree had been found to grow particularly well in the East Indies, and at the outbreak of war over 95 per cent of the quinine requirements of this country were met from that source. This supply was obliterated at a blow when the Japanese turned southward. Plantations in South America, where the tree was native, had been abandoned in the nineteenth century. It would have taken years to re-establish them. The daily use of quinine by large bodies of troops as a means of suppressing malaria could not even be considered. Three million soldiers receiving 0.3 gram a day per man would consume thirty tons of quinine a month. At that rate we could not have fought the war for four months. The deficiency of quinine seemed of vital importance and dominated all thinking at the time. Some substitute would have to be used. The picture was not bright. The only bright spot, the spot that eventually covered the entire picture, was atabrine.

The Germans had been preoccupied with the idea of finding substitutes for quinine since the First World War. Their access to it lost by the Allied blockade, they experienced a shortage of the drug and encountered grave difficulties with the Macedonian campaign in consequence. In methodical fashion they set about testing thousands of new compounds synthesized by their dye industry, I. G. Farbenindustrie. In 1924 they found a substance which they called plasmochin. The drug could kill Plasmodia but its toxicity in man was so considerable that it did not of itself provide a practicable treatment for acute attacks of malaria. The form of the organism against which it was particularly effective was not responsible for symptoms of the disease in man but for its transmission to the mosquito. There was some evidence, obtained by the British in India in 1930, that the incidence of relapses could be decreased by giving small doses of plasmochin concurrently with quinine in the treatment of acute malaria. This was an important observation if true, but its demonstration was not absolute. On the whole it did not seem likely that the drug would prove very useful.

Atabrine[1] seemed much more promising than plasmochin and fortunately so. In the absence of adequate supplies of quinine there was no alternative available. We were committed to its use though with considerable trepidation. The compound is a yellow dye, discovered in later course of the same investigations which had synthesized plasmochin. In the ten years intervening between its discovery and the outbreak of war it had been widely used in the tropics and many papers had been written about it. It was said to control acute attacks of malaria but there was no accurate information concerning its success as a suppressive. The consensus, in the months following the outbreak of the war, was that it would be a useful drug; but that it would be less effective than quinine in the treatment of acute malaria and would be too toxic to use as a suppressive over long periods of time.

The directive for treatment and suppression of malaria, issued by the Surgeon General of the Army in October 1942 after consultation with committees within the National Research Council, reflected the points of view which have been recited. The shortage of quinine made impossible its use as a suppressive. The impossibility of estimating the duration of the war, of determining whether there were to be 100,000 or 5,000,000 malarial casualties, made it seem wise to husband the stocks of quinine and not rely upon it for the sole treatment of acute attacks. Plasmochin might be valuable in the prevention of relapses. Atabrine appeared to be too toxic for routine use as a suppressive. The so-called QAP regime was therefore presented as the preferred method of treating acute malaria: two days of *q*uinine, five days of *a*tabrine, two days without medication, five days of *p*lasmochin. The minimum period of hospitalization was two weeks. Atabrine was recommended as a suppressive

[1]Atabrine is the trade name given this drug by the Germans and has been so commonly used that it is employed here. The official name in this country is quinacrine, in England mepacrine.

but was only to be given "when the need for emergency suppressive treatment exists." For this purpose two tablets were to be given twice a week. The directive was about the best that could be done with the knowledge then in hand.

New knowledge was to be acquired by a very extensive program of research sponsored by the CMR. The military importance of malaria and the desirability of investigations in this field had been pointed out to committees of the National Research Council by the Surgeons General in 1940. In July 1941 the Council called a Conference on Chemotherapy of Malaria at which a program of investigation in certain fundamental aspects of the disease was outlined. One of the first actions of CMR, formed later in the summer, was to approve this program and arrange for its support by OSRD funds. By June 1942 the nucleus of a more comprehensive and practical study had been established and, eventually, more than seventy investigations were being conducted for CMR by chemists, pharmacologists, biologists, and clinicians in universities and commercial firms throughout the United States. At first supervised by CMR and by the Conference on Chemotherapy of Malaria of the National Research Council, the studies were integrated in December 1943 by the establishment of an independent Board for the Co-ordination of Malarial Studies.[2] This Board was composed of four key investigators in the CMR program who were Chairmen of the National Research Council's panels on clinical testing, pharmacology, biochemistry, and chemistry, of official representatives of the CMR, and the Surgeons General of the Army, Navy, and Public Health Service. The presence of the service members enabled them to follow developments in civilian laboratories and, through their knowledge of problems in the field, to direct the attention of civilian research to particular problems that demanded solution. When developments in civilian laboratories reached a stage where field trials were warranted, the service members were able to arrange for such trials promptly and with a minimum of difficulty.

[2]A deliberate attempt has been made to omit names from the text of these chapters on the assumption that readers are interested in developments rather than personalities. It seems unrealistic, however, not to mention the civilian members of this Board who played such an important part in stimulating and ordering the malarial program. Its chairman was Dr. Robert F. Loeb and its members Drs. James A. Shannon, E. K. Marshall, Jr., Wm. Mansfield Clark, C. S. Marvel, and A. R. Dochez. Dr. George A. Carden, Jr., Chairman of the Malarial Division of CMR, served as its secretary.

Basic studies concerned with the fundamental mechanisms of malaria were initiated in the fall of 1941 and continued through the program. For their conduct, and for the investigation of new antimalarial drugs which was subsequently undertaken, it was necessary to import new species of Plasmodia in infected mosquitoes from Mexico and India and to establish colonies of these mosquitoes and of infected monkeys, chickens, canaries, ducks, and turkeys. These are the only laboratory animals in which malaria can be reproduced. The colonies were established and investigators examined the life cycle of Plasmodia in several types of avian malaria, determined their nutritional requirements, made chemical studies of their metabolism. It was always possible that general studies of this sort would have practical application. In one instance, a study of the life cycle of Plasmodia in avian malaria, the results had important implications. The various stages of development carried on in the stomach of mosquitoes had always been available for examination and these pages of Plasmodial life were an open book. But there had been little knowledge of what occurred during the two weeks between injection of the organism into the skin by a mosquito bite and its reappearance in the blood stream. Periodic examination of the skin of chickens and canaries at the site of mosquito bites disclosed that Plasmodia undergo repeated changes of form within tissue cells during this period. The fact that Plasmodia are actually inside tissue cells at this time suggested that they might be unresponsive to the ordinary antimalarial drugs. This proved to be the case. These intracellular forms were unaffected by concentrations of quinine and atabrine which killed Plasmodia in the circulating blood. Presumably, though the demonstration has not yet been made, these same intracellular forms exist within the tissue cells of man and show a similar resistance to antimalarial drugs. Here, without much doubt, lies an explanation of the relapses which occur in *vivax* infections and the incomplete success of preventive treatment.

In the emergency posed by inadequate stocks of quinine all possible efforts were made to assure diversion of existing supplies into proper channels. In March 1942, when the War Production Board sought advice from the National Research Council on the impending shortage of drugs, a Committee on Drugs and Medical Supplies was formed which made the conservation of quinine its first concern. On recommendation of this committee the War Production Board undertook to forbid the use of quinine in hair tonics and bromoquinine tablets and to obtain the excess stocks of pharmaceutical houses and drugstores for the services. This was a useful step though palliative by definition. There was a little more quinine to treat acute malaria. There could not be enough for suppressive treatment. An attempt was made to augment the supply of quinine by encouraging the Office of Economic Warfare to harvest bark from the wild cinchona forests in Central and South America. This bark was known to be low in quinine content but to contain other quininelike alkaloids which might prove useful against malaria. The point had been previously explored with indecisive results. It was thoroughly re-examined by CMR investigators and these other alkaloids proved definitely effective. This had the important result of providing a supply for civilian use at a time when other antimalarial drugs were being diverted to the services. It did not sensibly affect the military problem because the amounts were insufficient and the findings too delayed.

The ability to suppress, or better still to prevent, acute attacks of malaria was to be the crux of maintaining an effective fighting force in malarial areas. The fear that atabrine was too toxic for such a use was of controlling importance during nearly two years of war and had the unfortunate effect of sharply limiting the use of the drug. It was the first important practical subject upon which CMR investigators focused. The fear of atabrine toxicity had a triad of bases. In part it was a fear of the unknown, a perfectly proper reluctance to give to millions of troops and for a long period of time a relatively new drug about which relatively little information was at hand. The variable degree of yellow skin discoloration which it produced might reflect progressive liver damage. There might be some basis for the rumor that it affected virility, always a sensitive point to GI's. No one knew what obscure lesion of brain or kidney or stomach prolonged and daily administration of the drug might produce. In part the fear was a natural result of observing the definite, sometimes severe, gastrointestinal disturbance which the drug produced: pain, nausea, vomiting, even prostration from the ingestion of two tablets. This was noted in the States, it was noted in the Pacific early in 1942, and later that year in Africa. It was sufficiently marked so that soldiers displayed a very widespread reluctance to take the drug. Nor were their commanding officers or medical officers sufficiently convinced of its usefulness to take necessary disciplinary action, though their co-operation was essential to enforce regular administration. It seemed to a commanding officer, understandably, quite as undesirable to have his men incapacitated by atabrine as by malaria. The final basis for this fear lay in the fact that it was being made in the United States for the first time. All of the drug heretofore used in this country had been made in Germany. The American firm which held the patents had served merely as a distributing agent for the I. G. Farbenindustrie. The shortage of certain chemicals required for synthesis according to the German patent required the development of new methods before it could be produced on a large scale. This change of method might have led to the manufacture of a different compound. The severity of gastrointestinal symptoms being encountered so far exceeded that described in prewar literature that it was even suggested, and seriously suggested, that the patent contained a flaw which had led to the production of a poisonous substance.

In the spring of 1942 it was a matter of first importance to confirm or deny this possibility that the American-made product was different from the German product. The question could not be answered by simply looking at the two specimens of yellow powder lying there on the table or by ordinary chemical analysis. A prolonged and careful chemical, pharmacological, and clinical comparison of the two drugs was therefore undertaken by CMR investigators. In its course the two compounds, their intermediate products, their unavoidable contaminants, the crystalline pure substances, were all examined. By the fall of 1942 it had been demonstrated on irrefutable scientific grounds that American- and German-made atabrine are identical compounds and that any adverse reactions encountered are due solely to the atabrine molecule itself and not to any contaminating or adulterating substance.

The yellow skin pigmentation proved due to the fact that atabrine is a dye with strong affinity for tissue proteins. Simply that and nothing more. The gastrointestinal disturbance was the direct result of gastric irritation. One could see the lining of a dog's stomach become red when atabrine was placed upon it. The disturbance became less as subjects continued to take the drug, and was minimal when one tablet a day was taken rather than two and when it was ingested with food rather than between meals. These observations were subsequently confirmed by experience with great masses of troops in the field, and, in the doses in which it was used, atabrine turned out to be a relatively nontoxic drug. Military practice eventually disclosed a number of cases of a skin disease called lichen planus and of psychosis which seemed definitely associated with atabrine if not actually caused by it. This association had not been suspected in the CMR experiments, but incidence of the complications was well below one per thousand and not sufficient to make them of quantitative importance. This evidence that atabrine could be safely used in the suppressive treatment of malaria was not all in hand by the fall of 1942, but it was apparent even then that the potential toxicity of the drug had been grossly overrated. It therefore became important to obtain accurate information concerning its clinical usefulness and deficiencies.

Information from troops in the field in 1942 indicated that atabrine was inferior to quinine in controlling acute attacks of malaria and was relatively ineffective as a suppressive. Was this irrevocably the case or would these defects vanish if a more precise understanding of the drug were obtained? The answer to this question, the second major practical contribution furnished by CMR investigators, was supplied by a study initiated in November 1942. The example of previous researches in the sulfonamide field was followed and methods were developed for the accurate measurement of atabrine concentrations in blood and urine and body tissues. These methods made it possible to follow the fate of the drug after its administration to animals and man; to determine the rate at which it was absorbed, excreted, and destroyed in the body; to establish its distribution between blood cells, blood plasma, and tissues after absorption. The development and employment of these methods allowed a scientific evaluation of antimalarial drugs for the first time. Not alone in the case of atabrine, but with the newer drugs which were subsequently synthesized and for which methods of analysis were developed, it became feasible to ascertain the precise plasma concentration necessary to control the Plasmodia and thereby to establish the relative antimalarial potencies of a series of compounds. It became practicable to determine how large and frequent dosage is necessary to produce these concentrations and whether inadequate absorption or excessive excretion is responsible for an inability to effect them. As far as atabrine is concerned several facts of major practical importance emerged from this study and from the extension of it, undertaken by the Army at Fort Knox, Kentucky, which confirmed its results and added valuable data concerning the effects of exercise, climate, and diet on the behavior of atabrine in the body.

In the treatment of acute malaria it was found that the plasma concentration of atabrine necessary to control the symptoms (30 micrograms per liter) is achieved only after several days, if the drug is given at the rate of three tablets a day as had been the custom. This slow achievement of an effective concentration accounts for what had been regarded as the inferiority of atabrine to quinine in the treatment of acute attacks. The inferiority disappears when larger doses of atabrine are given during the first twenty-four hours of treatment and the disease is controlled quite as rapidly by atabrine as by quinine. Not only is this true but atabrine, thus given, cures *falciparum* infections as quinine is unable to do. No relapses occur after treatment of *falciparum* malaria by atabrine though they continue to do so after *vivax* malaria. With this demonstration our services and the British promptly altered their directives. The quinine-atabrine-plasmochin regime was dropped in August 1943 and a course of atabrine alone was substituted for it. Plasmochin was omitted because of the toxic results which had been reported from its use in all theaters and the effect of this omission was to shorten the hospitalization by half, a matter of great military importance. Quinine was thereafter reserved for intravenous injection in severe cases of *falciparum* malaria in which immediate effects are desired or for the unusual patient who is unduly sensitive to atabrine.

In the suppressive treatment of malaria the CMR investigators demonstrated that six or seven tablets a week, rather than the four which had been previously recommended, are necessary to produce an effective plasma concentration of atabrine (15 micrograms per liter). The Surgeons General accordingly ordered this increase in dosage. No additional difficulties are imposed by the necessity of giving the drug daily, in fact rather the reverse, for it had always been difficult to decide which day was Wednesday or Saturday or even Sunday. The daily dosage allowed a routine to be established which worked satisfactorily in well-disciplined units under noncombat conditions and when the men were messing together. As usually carried out, a noncommissioned officer gave a tablet to each man at the noon mess, watched him swallow it, and checked off his name on the roster. Since, even with this increased dosage, the investigators found that three weeks were required to establish adequate plasma concentrations, it became the practice to commence atabrine administration several weeks before troops entered malarial areas. When this new suppressive regime was adopted and imposed by the Army it was found that, again in contradistinction to quinine, atabrine is a true preventive of *falciparum* malaria. This prevention does not extend to *vivax* malaria, which continues to occur in soldiers after suppressive treatment is stopped, but *falciparum* infections are as truly prevented by atabrine as they are truly cured. This difference between *falciparum* and *vivax* infections in response to atabrine, apparent both in treatment of the acute attack and in suppressive therapy, is taken to mean that intracellular tissue forms of the organism do not occur in *falciparum* malaria or, occurring, are sensitive to the drug. In theory the effectiveness of atabrine as a suppressive is absolute. In controlled clinical experiments it has been impossible to produce malaria in patients who are receiving atabrine even when they are bitten by infected mosquitoes daily for several weeks. In practice, in the field, a certain number of cases of malaria continue to occur in soldiers who stoutly assert that they have been taking their daily dose. One is at liberty to doubt their word; alternatively one may believe that the individuals have absorbed the atabrine less adequately or that they excrete or destroy it more rapidly than normal.

The effectiveness of atabrine as a suppressive may be examined by observing the incidence of malaria in the Army in 1943 and 1944. In the former year atabrine was relatively little used; in the latter year it was much more widely used. In 1943, in the five theaters where malaria was prevalent, there were 147,000 cases, an average incidence of 20.6 per cent. In 1944, in the same theaters, there were 118,000 cases, an incidence of 7.8 per cent. It is impossible to say what proportion of the cases occurring in 1944 were in soldiers who had not taken atabrine or had stopped their suppressive treatment. But even without the accent which such figures would furnish, the diminution in incidence is sufficiently striking. To be sure there were concomitant improvements in mosquito control during these years. There can be no possible shadow of doubt that the reduction in frequency of malaria was chiefly due to atabrine.

Atabrine thus emerged from the war as a much more effective instrument than there had been any reason to anticipate in 1941. The fears which had been entertained as to its toxicity proved to be grossly exaggerated. Relatively minor adjustments of dosage transformed it into an adequate agent in the treatment and suppression of malaria. These factors of low toxicity and high effectiveness, worked out by CMR investigators in the laboratory and in small groups of volunteers, had been translated to vast bodies of troops in the field with results which confirmed the accuracy of the original observations. The unexpected finding that atabrine truly cured and prevented *falciparum* malaria placed it head and shoulders above quinine. Had there been, in 1941, the same knowledge of atabrine which existed in 1944, the absence of adequate quinine supplies would have seemed a subject of no concern instead of one of calamitous importance. The chief defect of atabrine, aside from its occasional toxicity, which gave rise to a search for still better antimalarial drugs, was that it could neither truly cure nor prevent *vivax* malaria.

A major investigation on the synthesis and examination of new antimalarial drugs was started with the support of CMR in the spring of 1942. Proceeding rather slowly at first, the program was markedly accelerated following formation of the Board for Co-ordination of Malarial Studies in December 1943. The successful integration of this study, involving as it did the participation of chemists, physiologists, pharmacologists, and clinicians in a large number of institutions, made it an outstanding example of co-operative and organized research. The effects of over 14,000 compounds were examined in animals and more than 80 in man.

Since it was neither possible nor safe to examine the effectiveness of each compound in man, their antimalarial activity was first determined in animals, in the colonies of infected birds and monkeys which had been established for this purpose. There was of course no assurance that compounds which are active in birds would be active in man, or that compounds which are inactive in birds and are dismissed from the study on that account might not have proved active in man. The correlation is certainly not absolute, and several disappointments were suffered when a drug that definitely prevented malaria in the canary or chicken turned out to be totally inactive in man. Eventually each substance was studied in at least two types of avian malaria (canary, duck, or chicken) using different parasites, and under these circumstances good correlation was found between animal and human malaria in their responsiveness to the drugs. Since it was even more important to obtain a drug which would prevent or suppress malaria than to obtain one which would arrest acute attacks of the disease, the effect of each drug had to be examined on the early tissue forms of the Plasmodia as well as on those forms existing in the blood cells. The necessity of achieving and maintaining an effective plasma level of the drug, so that the infecting organisms might be constantly exposed to an adequate concentration, was recognized. Blood analyses were therefore performed and a routine of dosage established to produce the desired result. If, for example, it was desirable to administer the drug every three hours the birds were placed in a dark room and lights were turned on at appropriate intervals, so that they would eat a ration with which the chemical had been thoroughly mixed. When the techniques for examining a compound had been worked out on a sound scientific basis, they were applied uniformly in all of the OSRD testing laboratories and the antimalarial activity of each compound was expressed as a ratio of the activity of quinine.

To be acceptable for clinical trial the drugs must be relatively free from toxic effects. From the testing laboratories the drugs were therefore sent to toxicological laboratories. Preliminary tests were made on mice, since only small amounts of the drugs were initially synthesized, and the results of the tests were again expressed in relation to a known standard, quinine. If the compounds displayed high activity and low toxicity the chemists were then asked to synthesize larger amounts for administration to dogs and monkeys. It should be understood that, though these toxicity tests are useful and succeed in eliminating substances which would certainly be harmful, they yield no absolute assurance that the drug will be harmless in man, who alone constitutes the final criterion of success or failure. The production of skin lesions by atabrine is a case in point which could not possibly have been prophesied from animal experiments.

More than eighty compounds have been sufficiently promising in animal tests to deserve clinical trial. To make these trials it was necessary to find men who either had malaria or were willing to be infected with it. Patients who were receiving malaria as treatment for central nervous system syphilis were suitable subjects but were not available in sufficient numbers. The problem was solved when over 400 prisoners in penitentiaries at Joliet, Illinois, and Atlanta, Georgia, and inhabitants of the reformatory at Rahway, New Jersey, volunteered to serve as human guinea pigs. This was only one example, though perhaps the most important one, where the voluntary services of prisoners or conscientious objectors served to advance research projects sponsored by CMR in which exploration in man was essential before procedures could be recommended to the services, and in which the subjects underwent considerable discomfort and occasional hazard.

The first compound to show great promise in animal and clinical trials was chloroquine, a substance chemically related to both quinine and atabrine, originally referred to as 7618. It was sixteen times as effective as quinine against Plasmodia in the blood cells of birds and much less toxic at therapeutic concentrations. It prevented and cured *falciparum* malaria in man as atabrine does. Its activity so far exceeded atabrine that treatment of an acute attack of malaria could be completed within two days instead of seven and a single weekly dose would maintain protection against the disease. It did not produce the gastrointestinal symptoms which atabrine could produce. It did not produce any serious toxic effects in long and rigorous experiments carried out upon monkeys and man. These were important advantages. University and industrial chemists therefore devised new and cheaper methods for synthesis of the substance in large amounts, and supplies were available to the services early in 1945 for installations in this country and in the Pacific. Investigations in these hospitals confirmed the results obtained by CMR investigators. It was a valuable drug, a sort of "super-atabrine" which might well replace that substance. The question whether it would solve the malarial problem by truly preventing and curing *vivax* malaria as atabrine was able to prevent and cure the *falciparum* infection had to be answered in the negative. It had seemed eminently possible that a drug which, in low concentration, could kill Plasmodia in the blood stream would be able, in higher concentration, to kill the intracellular forms which are held responsible for *vivax* relapses. Atabrine was too toxic to permit an investigation of this sort, while 7618 was thoroughly suitable for it. But relapses continued to occur even when plasma concentrations of 7618 were maintained for periods up to two weeks at levels thirty to fifty times higher than those necessary to terminate the attack. Several other compounds of this series have shown ten to twenty times the activity of quinine against avian malaria. Some of these are still under clinical trial. One of them, oxychloroquine (SN 8137), is being used in service hospitals to determine whether it has any advantages over 7618

Several drugs of the quinine series have shown twice as high activity against avian malaria as those in the series which includes 7618, and are now undergoing clinical trial. Early experience with the sulfonamides had been disappointing, but a return to this series with the chemical knowledge won by experience accomplished the synthesis of a compound forty times as active as quinine and four hundred times as active as the compounds originally employed. This compound (SN 11437) is as effective as 7618 as a suppressive but, like the rest, has failed to cure or prevent *vivax* infections.

The demonstration that the high degree of antimalarial activity possessed by these several substances did not convert them into curative drugs was a great disappointment. It was accordingly decided to shift the direction of investigation from modifications of quinine, atabrine, and sulfonamides to those of plasmochin. Plasmochin itself was first examined and gave an unexpected and most promising lead. In nine cases of acute *vivax* malaria, given concurrently with quinine for two weeks, it cured the disease; no relapses occurred. Given alone, on the day of being bitten by an infected mosquito and for six days thereafter, it prevented the development of *vivax* malaria in eight men. The difficulty was that these curative and preventive effects were apparent only when the drug was given in toxic doses. Plasmochin itself could not be safely used but the problem was clearly defined: separate the curative from the toxic portion of the plasmochin molecule. On this problem practically all the chemists in the program are concentrating at the present time. Thus far one compound has been found which, on preliminary tests, shows as great curative properties as plasmochin and less toxic properties. It remains to be demonstrated that this decrease in toxicity is sufficiently great to permit clinical use of the drug.

At the moment it would seem that this new compound or some other modification of plasmochin may prove to be the perfect curative and preventive drug, the malariologists' ideal; that V-M Day is at hand. But even if this proves not to be the case the potent suppressive drugs already discovered, or others of their sort, may of themselves solve a problem which is of world-wide and permanent importance. The military and temporary problem of malaria in our troops was largely solved by the suppressive use of atabrine because its daily administration could be observed and supervised. No such daily dosing would be practicable for the inhabitants of India or South America on any useful scale. But one tablet a week of 7618 will provide protection. It is perfectly plausible to think that newer and more potent drugs will be discovered so that one tablet in two, or even four, weeks will provide similar protection. This puts the problem on an entirely different basis. It might still not be possible to treat villagers in the Burmese hills or tribes in the heart of Africa. It should be thoroughly possible to treat the inhabitants of cities, of organized villages, laborers on plantations. If this suppressive treatment be provided the entire population of such districts during the malarial season and for several years, malaria must disappear. There would no longer be a pool of infection in human blood from which mosquitoes could transmit the disease. Such a proposal, in the realm of fantasy before the war, has been transposed to the realm of possibility by the researches which have been described.

CHAPTER XXI

BLOOD AND BLOOD SUBSTITUTES

THE TYPES of wartime casualties for which the use of blood was particularly envisaged were those involving hemorrhage, burns, and a condition known as "shock." Their common immediate treatment lies in an attempt to restore blood volume to normal. This was known before the war, for automobiles and the normal homicidal tendencies of our population had made such cases no strangers to civilian hospitals.

In the case of hemorrhage, loss of blood is a loss of whole blood, cells as well as plasma. No wound can take place without some hemorrhage, though it may vary in amount from an ounce or so in the case of soft tissue wounds of the calf or buttock to complete and nearly instant exsanguination when a large artery is severed. In laboratory animals an acute hemorrhage amounting to 30 or 40 per cent of blood volume, corresponding to two quarts in man, will produce death within a matter of hours unless the blood be replaced. If this replacement be delayed, no amount of blood proves sufficient because the vital organs (such as heart, brain, kidneys, liver) undergo permanent and irreversible loss of function. The necessity of transfusing casualties with severe hemorrhage and of having transfusion material at least as far forward as the Battalion Aid Stations was clearly understood in 1941.

In the case of burns, the loss of blood is less obvious but nonetheless real. The effect of a burn, if it penetrates more deeply than the superficial layers of the skin, is to char the tissue cells, including those of the blood vessels. The integrity of the blood-vessel wall is not actually interrupted and corpuscles do not escape, but its permeability is so altered that the fluid component of the blood leaks out; the damaged tissues become swollen with fluid and large amounts escape onto the surface of the body. From a burn involving one third of the body surface, a third of the total plasma volume may be lost within twenty-four hours, and this drainage will continue day after day until tissue repair occurs. Burns involving more than half the body surface are usually fatal. The need for large and continued transfusions was therefore understood but it appeared that plasma rather than whole blood would be adequate for the purpose.

The term "shock" is not as self-explanatory as "wound" or "burn" and requires some description. Appearing as a form of collapse in soldiers who had been wounded some hours previously, shock was observed and studied during the First World War. In the intervening twenty-five years it formed the subject of vigorous investigation and debate that often generated more heat than light. Clinically it is characterized by a slowly developing circulatory failure with characteristic weakness, pallor, cold extremities, sweating, thirst, thready pulse, progressively falling blood pressure, and diminished consciousness. The chief difficulty in obtaining an understanding of its mechanism seems to have been that it is not a single entity but occurs in a variety of situations. In laboratory animals, too, a very similar picture could be produced by such diverse means as hemorrhage, a variety of injuries, the re-establishment of blood flow in a limb in which the circulation had been obstructed, the injection of certain drugs or hormones (for example, histamine, adrenalin). When attention was focused on the types of shock which would be encountered in wartime, those following hemorrhage or wounds or burns, there was general agreement that the underlying mechanism was diminished blood volume with consequent diminution in heart output and inadequate supply to the vital organs. Viewed in this light, shock became, not a separate entity from hemorrhage or burns, but simply an incident which might develop if the hemorrhage or burn were sufficiently severe, the loss of blood volume sufficiently large. It was therefore agreed that transfusions were necessary in the treatment of shock. There was no agreement as to whether the diminished blood volume was entirely caused by a loss of whole blood at the site of injury or whether, granting this direct loss to have occurred, there was not an additional and greater leakage of plasma through all the blood vessels of the body. This leakage, so said proponents of the idea, was caused by the absorption of some unidentified toxic substance from the site of injury which interfered with the ability of the blood vessels to retain plasma proteins. According to one school of thought the transfusion of whole blood was strongly indicated. According to the other, transfusions of plasma alone should prove adequate.

The transfusion problems presented by war were both qualitatively and quantitatively different from those which had existed in peace. In peace it had been possible to bring donor and patient together, in war they must be separated by thousands of miles. In peace it had been possible to inject the blood within minutes after it was drawn, in war days or months must intervene. In peace few hospitals had more than a dozen accident cases a day. In war 50 or 100 or 1000 wounded patients might pass through a single station in twenty-four hours, and in 1941 no one knew whether our troops were to have 100,000 casualties or 1,000,000 or 5,000,000. All that was clear was that the services were going to need enormous amounts of blood and that it must be furnished them in a condition that would permit transfer over great distances, at great extremes of temperature, and permit use in the very simple circumstances of the field. In the summer of 1940, when the services became definitely exercised over the problem and asked the National Research Council for advice as to how it should be met, four fields of investigation were being explored which, followed patiently, sensibly, sometimes brilliantly, provided answers to the problem.

Dried human-blood plasma was recommended to the services as transfusion material in the spring of 1941 and in direct response to their inquiry. The methods for producing it in small amounts had been developed. It fulfilled the necessary criteria of stability at all temperatures and over any periods of time, of ease of preparation for injection, and of freedom from toxicity. It had proved effective with the limited number of patients in whom it had been used since 1939. The chief problems facing the services in this field were the purely practical ones of obtaining a sufficient supply of blood and of establishing the industrial facilities for processing it.

Liquid plasma is more stable than whole blood, in which the cells gradually deteriorate, and it was liquid plasma rather than whole blood that was sent from New York to England during the "Blood for Britain" campaign of 1940. Its stability, however, is relative. Over a period of months certain changes occur in the plasma proteins and it forms such an excellent culture medium for bacteria that there is always likelihood of its becoming infected. On this account the dried product, first frozen and then dried from the frozen state to a yellowish-white caked powder, is superior and was the preparation chosen. Dried plasma remains sterile, utterly unchanging for years, and upon rehydration with water is again liquid plasma. It can be kept frozen with equal success but, for military use, the necessity of maintained refrigeration and of careful thawing prior to injection argues strongly for the dry preparation. With plasma there is no necessity for preliminary "grouping" of the donor and recipient as is the case with a whole-blood transfusion.

The methods for freezing and drying plasma had been developed before the war and were available. The blood was not. Vast amounts would be required and the only available source was the blood of the civilian population of the United States. Their co-operation in the program seems as clear an example of patriotism on a mass scale as our history affords. There was no question of being drafted or even inducted, no question of medals or rewards and very little chance that any particular blood would get to Johnny. The precise responsibilities of the various groups were fixed in the spring of 1941. The National Research Council was to prescribe the technique to be used in bleeding and in handling the drawn blood. The Red Cross agreed to collect the blood and transport it to the processors. The pharmaceutical houses undertook to process it subject to supervision and testing by the United States Public Health Service. The Army contracted to pay the cost of processing and to make a fair proportion of the product available to the Navy. A field director was appointed by the Red Cross in the summer of 1941 to supervise its part of the program. Blood donor centers were established, at first in three, eventually in thirty-five, of the larger cities throughout the United States. The area of activity of each center was extended by creating mobile units which cruised through the country within a 100-mile radius. The unit of bleeding was one pint, sufficient for the preparation of one-half pint of plasma. When the Army and Navy were first asked how many units they might need they estimated 100,000 units each. Before the program terminated on V-J Day, 13,300,000 units had been obtained in a crescendo which started with 50,000 pints in 1941, passed 1,000,000 in 1942, reached 4,280,000 in 1943, and exceeded 5,000,000 in 1944. One and a half million gallons of blood is a lot of blood.

From the hands of the Red Cross the blood, still liquid and refrigerated, went to the nine pharmaceutical houses who were under contract with the Army to process it. These firms faced mechanical difficulties no less great than the psychological difficulties faced by the Red Cross.

Administering blood plasma while evacuating wounded marine from
Tinian island

Giving a wounded Yank blood plasma at the height of the fight for Saipan

Equipment had to be obtained and installed, techniques had to be learned. The War Production Board provided priorities permitting purchase of the refrigerators and centrifuges and vacuum pumps which were necessary. This part of the program advanced more slowly than the blood collection; so, for a time, there were large accumulations of plasma in the frozen state waiting to be dried. Nine million bleeding units were processed into dried plasma; the first 3,000,000 in half-pint bottles; a second 3,000,000 in pint bottles when, after 1943, the necessity of larger transfusions was appreciated. As packaged in cartons for distribution, a transfusion unit consisted of two bottles, one containing powdered plasma, one containing sterile distilled water, each in a tin can with the sling, tubing, and needles necessary for rehydration and injection. The powder dissolved readily in the water and the preparations for injection required less than five minutes. This was one program which was planned with forethought and executed with skill. The method of preparation never had to be changed. The packaging never had to be changed. Dried plasma was available in Pearl Harbor within a few days after December 7, 1941. It was being used in the Philippines by the end of that month. And afterwards, it was one item of medical supply that was always there. Everyone took care of the blood and pushed it forward. It came in by boat to the beaches, dropped from the air into the jungles, climbed the trails on mules, or just came up the road on trucks.

Prior to the war there had been very little clinical experience with dried plasma for the simple reason that very little material had been available. It was sure to be safe. It was sure to be useful. And it was recommended to the services on that basis. But the exact limitations of its usefulness could not be defined till it was available in quantity. Since 1942 over 2,000,000 quarts of reconstituted plasma have been injected into man. The great bulk of this was given overseas, in first-aid stations and hospitals, under circumstances in which its safety and value were readily enough proved but which did not permit collection of precise data about its effectiveness. There was too much hurry, too little equipment, no other form of treatment with which to compare it. One necessarily emerged with impressions rather than demonstrated facts: "This chap looks better; guess he'll get back all right now" or "That chap with the belly wound looks as if he would stand operation." That sort of thing.

A small percentage of the plasma has been used in Stateside hospitals and laboratories by investigators working under contract with OSRD, and from their studies precise and valuable data have emerged. These investigators had the equipment and skills and leisure to perform measurements of blood volume or cell count or whatever other chemical and physiological procedures might be germane. Groups of surgeons and technicians were organized at nine large hospitals throughout the country in the fall of 1941 and, in the ensuing two years, studied 2200 cases of wounds and burns. Twenty-two additional investigations were conducted in the field of burns and forty concerned themselves with experimental and clinical shock. The primary concern of many of these studies was with the effect of drugs or with physiological mechanisms, but they all had an opportunity to evaluate the usefulness of dried plasma. It was in this direction of evaluation that CMR investigators played their role in the dried-plasma campaign.

In the field of hemorrhage the general experience of these groups was, as might have been anticipated, that patients or animals did better if they received whole blood transfusions than if they received plasma alone. Given in adequate amounts, plasma satisfied the emergency requirements. It stayed inside the blood vessels, increased the blood volume, restored the circulation. But since the lost cells were not restored, the patients were left with an anemia from which convalescence was slower than if they had received whole blood.

In the management of burns[1] also, plasma, given in large amounts and repeatedly, proved adequate as immediate treatment. If whole blood were not given, however, the investigators found that an anemia developed several days after the burn. The cause of this anemia is still not clear but its existence indicated that whole blood must be included in the course of treatment.

Shock caused by injury has been investigated in some admirable clinical studies by inserting catheters (hollow rubber tubes) through an arm vein for such distances that their tips rested in a chamber of the

---

[1]The local treatment of burned areas was completely revised as a result of these studies. As originally recommended to the services in 1942, the burned areas were to be sprayed with tannic acid or a triple dye preparation with the design of precipitating tissue proteins and thereby forming a pellicle, a second skin, which would relieve pain and stop loss of fluid from the body surface. It developed that firm pressure dressings applied over the burned areas were more successful in limiting the escape of fluid and avoided the damage which absorbed tannic acid apparently did to the liver.

heart and near the veins draining the kidneys. The investigators were thus able to record, in patients with shock, the pressure of blood returning to the heart, the amount of heart output, and the blood flow through the kidneys in addition to blood volumes and blood pressures. Blood volume and heart output were found to be reduced by 35 to 40 per cent in these cases and kidney circulation was even further decreased. This confirmed existence of the circulatory failure which had been considered characteristic of shock and provided it with objective, quantitative expression. Examination of the relative losses of plasma and red blood cells usually indicated that they had been lost in equal amounts and therefore that the blood loss had occurred as whole blood and, presumably, at the site of injury. This finding made it clear that transfusion with whole blood is preferable to transfusion with plasma alone.

The general conclusion derived from these investigations with dried plasma, a conclusion shared by medical officers as a result of observations in the field, was that it satisfied the emergency requirements in treatment of hemorrhage, burns, and shock. In this capacity it saved many, a great many, lives. But in no one of these situations was it a complete substitute for whole blood for the very obvious reason that it contained no blood corpuscles. Ideally and whenever possible, the investigators concluded, it should be supplemented by whole blood transfusions.

The wartime work with dried plasma represents primarily a sociological and industrial success. The work which led to the isolation of individual plasma proteins from human blood represents a chemical triumph of great distinction. The Department of Physical Chemistry at Harvard had been conducting studies in the field of protein chemistry for many years. Attempts, initiated as a matter of academic interest, to separate the various proteins from each other and from the other constituents of plasma had progressed by 1940 to the point where small amounts of pure albumin had been produced in the form of a dry powder. The impetus which led to immediate expansion of this work derived from the Navy's keen desire, expressed to the National Research Council in the spring of 1941, for a smaller and lighter form of blood substitute than was provided by dried plasma. A pint unit of plasma weighs 5.3 pounds and occupies 300 cubic inches. This, they explained, was too much for the limitations of space imposed by many vessels, by small landing craft, lifeboats, airplanes. They wanted something much better and, of course, they wanted it promptly. It seemed possible that crystalline albumin would meet the requirements and, after the formation of CMR in the summer of 1941, the project was vigorously supported and large extensions were made in the staff and equipment of the laboratory. The program proved successful and had the consequence, not envisaged at the time, of supplying other pure human-plasma proteins which had a wide usefulness.

The chemical procedures involved are difficult and complicated and must be carried out with precision, but the underlying process is the simple one of precipitating proteins by alcohol at very low temperatures (−5° C.). When the procedure is carried out in successive steps, gradually increasing the alcohol concentration and the acidity of the mixture and gradually decreasing the salt concentration, five distinct protein fractions are obtained. The first fraction contains chiefly fibrinogen, one of the two proteins concerned in the clotting mechanism of blood. The second fraction contains certain globulins which are responsible for immunity to such diseases as measles, catarrhal jaundice, mumps, and scarlet fever. The third fraction contains, chiefly, two additional globulins: agglutinins which destroy certain red blood corpuscles and are therefore concerned with the groups into which human bloods may be divided; and prothrombin, which reacts with fibrinogen to produce fibrin, the basis of the blood clot. These two globulins can be largely separated from each other by further splitting fraction III into III-1 and III-2. The fourth fraction contains other globulins, including hormones and enzymes, which subserve a variety of functions and which may prove a source of important materials in the future but are not our immediate concern. The fifth fraction contains albumin, with only 2 per cent contamination by globulins.

It was this last fraction, albumin, which seemed of most immediate interest in 1941. Albumin constitutes 60 per cent of the plasma proteins but, because of its relatively small molecular size, is responsible for 80 per cent of the colloidal osmotic pressure of plasma. It might therefore be expected to draw fluid into the blood vessels from the tissue spaces, to increase blood volume and therefore to be an effective substance for transfusion. This proved to be the case when it was subjected to prolonged clinical tests by CMR investigators during the winter of 1941–1942. It was found to be completely stable and nontoxic at all temperatures, and measurements of plasma volume made before and after its injection demonstrated that, for each gram of albumin injected, 17 cubic centimeters of fluid were drawn into the blood vessels. Observe that to attain this effectiveness adequate supplies of tissue fluid must be available, so that, if the patient was not well hydrated, it was necessary to give him larger amounts of fluid either by mouth or intravenously. These investigations having turned out satisfactorily, human albumin was formally recommended to the services as transfusion material in February of 1942. The Navy made contracts with seven firms, four of them already engaged in the production of dried plasma, to produce the substance, and though the technical difficulties of transfer from pilot plant to large-scale production far exceeded those encountered with dried plasma, they were finally overcome and the first deliveries were made to the Navy in November 1942. It was distributed in concentrated liquid form, a single bottle of 100 cubic centimeters containing 25 grams of dissolved albumin, more than the amount present in five times that volume (1 pint) of plasma. By the time the contracts were terminated, 2,250,000 Red Cross bleeding units had been processed to produce 600,000 units of albumin. Physiologically speaking, it is a more precise tool than dried plasma. Plasma is administered with the purpose of increasing blood volume. Albumin is the chief element in plasma which, staying within the blood vessels, attracts and maintains there the fluid which is responsible for the increase. It has no theoretical advantage over plasma. It fulfills precisely the same emergency requirements and has precisely the same limitations. It has, however, certain practical advantages. Since it is dispensed in a single bottle, in solution and in small volume, it can be administered more rapidly than plasma, which has first to be rehydrated and requires longer for the injection of its greater volume. It has the advantage, originally stressed by the Navy, that a unit weighs only one-sixth the amount and occupies only one-sixth the space of a plasma unit of equivalent effectiveness.

As peacetime economy is restored, as civilians no longer supply free blood and as emergencies again occur in reasonable proximity to the emergency rooms of hospitals where whole blood is available, the use of plasma and albumin in the more populous parts of the country will be limited. They must for one thing be more expensive than whole blood. But in one particular situation, a type of kidney disease called nephrosis, albumin solutions will probably have a sustained usefulness. The primary consequence of this disease is a deficiency of plasma albumin with the resulting development of generalized edema. Here albumin is precisely the substance required.

In the preparation of both dried plasma and albumin, half of the blood, all of the corpuscles, have been literally poured down the drain; 5,720,000 pints of corpuscles, containing 2,500,000,000,000 corpuscles per pint, have been discarded. These corpuscles contain a protein, globin, which has nutritive and osmotic properties similar to albumin. The question therefore arose whether this protein, either as globin or as hemoglobin, could not be isolated from the red cells and provide a safe and effective substance for transfusion. The question has been under study in two laboratories under OSRD contract and sufficient progress has been made so that several hundred transfusions have been performed in man. A considerable percentage of undesirable reactions have, however, occurred, the products have not been sufficiently standardized for general use, and animal experiments suggest that they may not be altogether harmless. The desirability of using these substances in the clinic therefore remains *sub judice*.

Initial interest in plasma protein fractionation had been focused on the usefulness of albumin as a blood substitute. As a by-product of its production, other relatively pure plasma proteins became available for the first time. It seemed very wasteful to discard them, just as it had seemed wasteful to discard the red blood corpuscles. They were accordingly set aside until they could be further studied. Several of them have now found fields of usefulness which promise to extend, at least in peacetime, beyond those apparent for albumin. Certainly this appears true for fibrinogen and thrombin in controlling bleeding during surgical operations. At the time of the Napoleonic Wars the method still in common use was the heated iron cautery with which surgeons completed amputations and, often, the life of the patient. This represented an improvement on boiling tar but not a very marked one, Sutures made of silk and catgut were introduced into modern surgery to ligate blood vessels, as well as hemostatic forceps with which the vessel could be grasped. More recently electrocauteries were devised by which small bleeding vessels could be coagulated without too much damage to surrounding tissues. But in several situations none of these methods were completely satisfactory; notably when bleeding occurred in friable tissues like the brain, liver, or kidney, in vascular tumors, and in general oozing of blood from vessels too small to see or ligate. In such situations fibrinogen obtained from protein fraction I and thrombin, from fraction III-2, have been tried and proved successful. Fibrinogen was first distributed to the services in the summer of 1944 as a preparation called "fibrin foam." It is not as billowy as the name implies but resembles a brown, rather compact sponge in blocks an inch or two in length and half an inch in diameter. When it is dipped into a solution of thrombin and pressed onto a bleeding surface, fibrin is formed and the blood clots. The pledget may be left in place for it is digested and absorbed by the body. Other products than fibrin foam have been found equally effective in controlling bleeding; foamed gelatin, dipped into thrombin, has this effect, and so have gauze and sponges made of oxidized cellulose. Both preparations are gradually absorbed and may therefore be left in the body. Both should thoroughly confuse the operating-room nurse who has charge of the sponge counts.

Other uses for fibrinogen appeared when it was processed into sheets of varying thickness called "fibrin film," a glycerolized plastic rather like latex. In this form it provides, in operations on the nervous system, a satisfactory substitute for the membranes which normally cover the brain, or serves as a conduit for nerve or tendon repairs when it is made into tubes. An additional use for the fibrinogen fraction has been found in the treatment of hemophilia, that rare disease which, occurring in the House of Hapsburg, has played a disproportionately large role in European history. Two hundred milligrams of fibrinogen, injected intravenously into these patients, will return their bleeding time to normal and maintain it there for eight hours. The disease is not cured but the acute episodes of bleeding may be controlled to a degree never before possible.

The globulin fractions concerned with immunity (II) reached the services in March 1944 as 5-cc. vials containing a 20 per cent solution. They have already proved useful in the prevention of measles and catarrhal jaundice (infectious hepatitis) and may be similarly effective in the case of mumps and scarlet fever. The existence in adult blood of protective substances against measles had been known for many years and injection of pooled whole blood and serum had been practiced to prevent the disease in children or to make the attack a milder one. The new preparation is more potent, since it contains the immune bodies which are specifically required and excludes the hundred and one other constituents of blood which have no bearing on the subject. Catarrhal jaundice was a frequent and a serious disease in certain theaters, important because of the long period of hospitalization which it required and its very definite mortality rate. The effectiveness of the immune globulin fraction in prevention of this disease was demonstrated when it was used by the Army for troops in Italy. Only 0.6 per cent of the injected soldiers developed jaundice, whereas 3.0 per cent of those not injected became infected.

A final fraction (III-1) which has proved useful contains the blood agglutinins which permit determination of the blood group to which an individual belongs. This fraction became available to the services in June 1944 as a powder ready for rehydration. Its potency is thirty times that of the sera previously employed and the accuracy of the determinations has been increased in consequence.

Because it was realized that whole blood was the ideal transfusion material under most circumstances, studies concerned with its refrigeration, transport, and storage were initiated in 1941. The difficulties which surrounded its use, difficulties which had been responsible for the continued use of direct transfusions in civilian life, arise from the inherent instability of red blood cells. When these cells break down, and even before the point of actual dissolution, toxic substances pass from them into plasma. On this account the transfusion of stored whole blood had been highly suspect. The difficulties had been partially surmounted by 1941, as the establishment of blood banks abroad and in certain of our own hospitals bore witness. Refrigeration at $4°-10°$ C. and the addition of sugar to the citrate solution into which the blood was drawn had prolonged the life of the red cells from four days to ten days. This did not, in 1941, seem long enough to permit the use of whole blood by the services, nor was the effect of the rough handling which it must receive known. The objective of research in this field was the discovery of more effective preservatives and this search was pressed in several laboratories under OSRD contracts. The permutations and combinations of a number of solutions were examined and the one called ACD (that is, *a*cid, *c*itrate, *d*extrose), originally developed by the British, was finally selected. With this preservative added to whole blood in the proportion 1 : 4, red cells remained intact for thirty days and appeared to be normal when subjected to certain tests. They were flown 6000 miles by aeroplane and returned with no signs of deterioration. The critical question was whether they would survive in the blood vessels of the recipient. This question was cleanly answered by experiments in which "tagged" red cells were used. Several weeks prior to transfusion the donor was fed or injected with radioactive iron. When this iron had become incorporated into the hemoglobin of his red cells, he was bled and the blood stored for thirty days. At the expiration of this time the blood was injected into the recipient and the survival of the transfused cells determined by successive measurements of radioactivity. It developed that 80 per cent of the cells survived for at least forty-eight hours, a fate analogous to that of freshly transfused cells. As these measures for the improved preservation of whole blood met with success, and as evidence accumulated and strengthened favoring the advantages of whole blood over plasma, its use in foreign theaters was repeatedly urged upon the services during 1943 by the Blood Substitutes Committee of the National Research Council. The difficulty of refrigeration remained but was materially lessened by the Navy's development of an expendable plywood box with fiberglass insulation, in which 10 pounds of ice would keep 16 bottles of blood at temperatures below 50° F. for two days at external temperatures of 85° F.

Finally adopted, the method proved as practicable as it had been desirable. The period over which the blood could be used was conservatively stated at twenty-one days, but air transport had improved so enormously that this was sufficient time for it to reach remote places. Blood habitually reached Guam two days after it was drawn. There were nineteen days left for its distribution and use. Serious transfusion reactions were not anticipated because only the bloods of "universal donors" were used in the program, bloods from the other groups being diverted to processing for dried plasma and albumin. They did not occur after the vital importance of continued refrigeration was made clear. The weight of the refrigerated product was no greater than that of dried plasma. Its administration was even easier. And though the requirements of transportation and refrigeration imposed restrictions on its use, these restrictions were no longer severe. Any reasonably accessible medical installation which could get a little ice every two days could now have whole blood for nearly three weeks. The first flasks of whole blood were flown to Europe on August 15, 1944, and between that date and the end of the war, 500,000 Red Cross units were sent by air to the European and Pacific theaters; 1600 pints of whole blood went ashore with plasma and albumin at Iwo Jima for use on the beaches there.

In a sense the most exciting part of the whole program was the attempt to find substitutes for human-blood plasma; substances that could be had from fruits or fish or the bones of animals or their blood; substances that were available in unlimited quantity so that the co-operation and sacrifice of people would be unnecessary. There was no thought of obtaining a complete substitute for whole blood. The toxicity to man of the globulins and red cells of animal blood made that out of the question. But it did seem possible to obtain a pure substance of large molecular size, presumably a protein, which would stay inside the blood vessels of man and retain or draw to it sufficient fluid to increase plasma volume. This characteristic it must have. The second essential characteristic was that it must be nontoxic.

Simple solutions of water and salts are, by themselves, relatively useless. They can be injected readily enough and harmlessly enough, but they diffuse rapidly through the blood-vessel walls into the tissues so that within an hour less than 10 per cent of the injected solution remains in the circulation. During the First World War the only other infusion material which had been available was acacia (gum arabic), an exudate obtained from certain species of acacia which had considerable viscosity and stayed reasonably well inside the blood vessels. At that time there was no dried plasma, no albumin, no possibility of transfusion other than by direct methods at rear installations. The preparation of nontoxic acacia solutions proved very difficult and, in the interwar period, even the purest preparations were found to produce so much liver damage that their use was no longer considered.

By the summer of 1941, four possible substitutes were under consideration and tentative experiments with them had already been made. Two of these substances proved of too inconstant composition or too toxic for use: isinglass, a form of gelatin prepared from the swim bladder of sturgeon, explored chiefly by the Canadians; and pectin, a hemicellulose obtained from certain fruits and used as a jellying agent. But two other substances, bovine albumin and gelatin, proved more promising and experimentation has proceeded with them throughout the war.

Beef blood was available in enormous, fantastic quantities at slaughter-houses throughout the country and was wholly waste material. The fractionation processes which could isolate albumin from human plasma were equally able to isolate it from bovine plasma, and such preparations had already been made on a small scale. The sole question at issue was whether the product thus obtained was safe for injection into man. One of the commercial firms preparing human albumin was engaged to make adequate supplies of the bovine product and extensive clinical tests were begun under OSRD contracts in the fall of 1941. At first these tests seemed successful and the brightest hopes were entertained. Bovine albumin stayed within human blood vessels and maintained plasma volume there quite as well as the human product. No immediate toxic reactions were observed in several hundred cases in which it was injected in single or repeated doses. However, as the experiments were continued, several serious reactions occurred and mild reactions have continued to occur in about 8 per cent of the patients. These mild reactions are delayed, appearing several weeks after the injection, and consist chiefly of fever, but their frequency has made the recommendation of this preparation to the services or its general use inadvisable at the present time. It remains possible that a completely globulin-free preparation will be nontoxic or that chemical treatment of the existing preparation will abolish these reactions and make the substance as harmless as it is useful.

Gelatin was sufficiently promising so that its possibilities were a subject of investigation by nine groups of scientists under contract with OSRD. It can be obtained from various sources including bone and skin, and in a variety of physical states. The fundamental difficulty encountered here, in contrast to experience with bovine albumin, was not so much with the toxicity of the preparation, for harmless types were developed, but with its tendency to escape from blood vessels. The ability of a molecule to pass through the walls of blood vessels is a function in part of its size, in part of its shape. Gelatin is a long thin rodlike molecule with a diameter (18 Ångstrom units) only half that of albumin, the smallest of the blood proteins, and small enough to pass quite readily through vessel walls. The very length of the molecules in the crude preparations makes their escape more difficult, but these preparations are solid at room temperature, rather viscous after injection, and have the obvious disadvantage of having to be warmed prior to use. If the molecules are broken up by appropriate chemical treatment the preparations remain liquid, but the shorter "rods" escape even more readily. The harmlessness of these preparations and their effectiveness in increasing blood volume were demonstrated in large series of normal dogs and in dogs which had been subjected to shock and hemorrhage; but the injected gelatin disappeared rather rapidly from the blood stream, so that the duration of its effect was substantially less than that of albumin. It has now been injected into several hundred hospital cases, with effects which appear quite comparable to those obtained with albumin or plasma, though the latter substances, as more "natural" substitutes for blood, have a theoretical advantage over gelatin. A recently developed polymerized gelatin preparation with branched chains in its molecular configuration shows less tendency to escape from blood vessels. It remains liquid at room temperatures and may prove superior in some respects to plasma itself.

It is difficult to record the events comprising this chapter without concluding that a good job was well done; a job in which civilian population, industrial firms, scientists, and medical personnel in the field all played their apportioned part. If any regrets are to be entertained it would be, perhaps, that the whole-blood program was not pushed more vigorously in the earlier days and that its products did not reach the field till late 1944. But the accomplishments are large. Thirteen million pints of blood, collected, processed, and distributed to the uttermost parts of the earth is an accomplishment. Saving of lives is an accomplishment. The mortality amongst casualties reaching front-line medical installations was 8.1 per cent in the last war, approximately 4 per cent in this war. No one can say how many of these lives were saved by the availability of blood, how many by sulfonamides and penicillin — all new since 1918 — how many by the improved knowledge and surgical skill without which all three would have been useless. But it does not require figures to know that plasma and albumin and blood saved the lives of many soldiers.

CHAPTER XXII

PENICILLIN

BEFORE THE discovery of sulfonamiaes and penicillin, the medical profession had practically no accurate and effective tools for the *cure* of infectious disease. The doctor's little black bag and, for that matter, the shelves of the hospital pharmacy contained chiefly drugs which would relieve the symptoms of disease: salicylates and morphine to diminish pain, digitalis and strychnine to strengthen the failing heart and respiration, bismuth and paregoric to check diarrhea. Useful drugs all, but no one of them striking at the root of the matter, at the cause of the disease. The great advances which had occurred since 1910 in the fields of vitamins and hormones had provided substances which controlled, if they did not cure, pellagra and scurvy, diabetes and pernicious anemia, certain disorders of the adrenal and thyroid glands. No parallel advance had occurred in the field of infectious diseases, where the greatest advance might have been expected; where the cause of the diseases, the particular microorganism[1] responsible for each, had been known and had lain open for attack for fifty years.

[1]To avoid endless circumlocution in a chapter which deals, as this one must, with bacteriology, certain definitions are introduced at this point. The microorganisms causing infectious disease may be divided into three groups: (1) protozoa, such as the Plasmodia causing malaria or the amoeba causing dysentery, larger in size than members of the other groups but still single-celled microscopic organisms; (2) bacteria; (3) viruses, such as those causing influenza and encephalitis, too small to be seen by the ordinary microscope. Bacteria may be subdivided on the basis of their shape into globular bodies called cocci, rod-shaped bodies called bacilli, and (or) corkscrew-shaped bodies called spirilla. Cocci are further subdivided: occurring in pairs they are called diplococci, in small compact groups staphylococci, in chains streptococci. Those diplococci causing gonorrhea are gonococci, those causing pneumonia, pneumococci, those causing epidemic meningitis, an inflammation of the membranes covering the brain and spinal cord, meningococci. Streptococci are subdivided on the basis of characteristics which they show during growth into hemolytic (red blood cell destroying), *viridans* (green-producing), and anaerobic (growth without air).

Staphylococci and streptococci are so widely present in nature, such constant inhabitants of the human skin and throat, that they are almost invariably present in wounds and have a marked inclination to invade the body tissues. When this invasion is merely local it produces a boil or abscess or cellulitis. When it reaches the blood stream and is distributed throughout the body, it produces septicemia, "blood poisoning." When it becomes localized in deeper tissues of the body, the lungs, meninges, heart valves, it produces pneumonia, meningitis, endocarditis, respectively.

Both cocci and bacilli can be divided into groups called gram-positive and gram-negative, depending on whether or not they appear blue when treated with an alcohol and iodine stain devised by the Danish bacteriologist Hans Christian Gram.

There had been in the beginning the hope of a drug for every "bug," Ehrlich's "magic bullet," each capable of killing a specific organism while leaving the tissues of the host, the patient, unaffected. For this hope there was only to show atabrine added to quinine in the treatment of malaria, both incompletely effective, and arsenic and bismuth added to mercury in the treatment of syphilis. There had been the hope of preparing vaccines from the microorganisms or utilizing them to produce antitoxins and antisera which would be specifically effective in each disease. For this hope there was typhoid vaccine to add to that for smallpox in the prevention of these diseases; there was diphtheria antitoxin with which to treat diphtheria and tetanus antitoxin with which to prevent tetanus; there were antisera which had some effectiveness in the treatment of pneumonia and meningitis. No mean harvest for any other half century perhaps, but very short measure for this one. The commonest microorganisms of all were left relatively undisturbed. Staphylococci, streptococci, gonococci, even pneumococci and meningococci, were practically as gay as they had been in the nineties. The antiseptics, carbolic acid, iodine, alcohol, effective enough against bacteria on the skin, were much too destructive for injection or for use in wounds. "Good nursing care and general supportive treatment" were about all the textbooks had to offer. It was against these groups that the sulfonamides, and later penicillin, were to prove primarily effective. From the point of view of the medical profession the change was epochal; from that of the bacteria it was atomic.

Sulfanilamide, the first of the sulfonamides to be employed, was rediscovered in 1932 in the course of one of those patient studies conducted in connection with the German dye industry; studies which, directly or indirectly, had already contributed arsphenamine and atabrine, the two drugs of major importance introduced into medicine within the last fifty years. In 1932 Domagk found that prontosil, as the red dye was then known, cured mice of septicemia caused by hemolytic streptococci. In 1933 and 1935 he and Forster reported that human cases of streptococcic septicemia had been similarly cured. Since this disease had been uniformly fatal in mice and very nearly so in man this was startling news. A delay in the introduction of prontosil to the world ensued largely because it was held by the Germans as a patented substance of unknown composition. When French and English laboratories discovered that the active ingredient was sulfanilamide, a white powder which could be readily synthesized, it was quickly evaluated and became available for clinical trial in the United States in 1936. This trial substantiated Domagk's claim. The mortality from hemolytic streptococcic septicemia in man fell from 80 per cent to 20 per cent. Since the structure of the drug was known, it was possible to prepare a number of other sulfonamides differing somewhat in composition from the original substance. This was done with the hope that the drugs thus prepared might have a wider applicability and a lower toxicity than sulfanilamide. It proved to be a profitable occupation. Sulfapyridine, sulfathiazole, sulfadiazine, sulfaguanidine, and uncounted others were successively introduced in this fashion. Of them all, sulfathiazole and sulfadiazine have proved the most useful. With these drugs severe hemolytic streptococci infections could be controlled. The mortality of pneumococcic pneumonia and meningococcic meningitis was reduced from approximately 30 per cent to 10 per cent. The great majority of cases of gonorrhea, rarely a fatal but often a chronic and incapacitating disease, could be cured within a week. These are bald and perhaps unimpressive statements. But consider. Here is not one disease, but a whole group of diseases previously without effective treatment suddenly susceptible of cure by a few white tablets. Not the unusual diseases which form the subject of medical seminars, but common diseases. There are approximately 400,000 cases of lobar pneumonia in the United States each year. A reduction in mortality from 30 per cent to 10 per cent means 80,000 lives saved.

The sulfonamides had been in widespread clinical use for five years before the outbreak of the war. Their effectiveness was understood and it was properly anticipated that they would be of great value not only in the medical diseases from which war offers no escape but also in the treatment of infected wounds and burns. With this latter thought in mind and on advice of the Committee on Chemotherapy of the National Research Council, a package of sulfadiazine tablets and of sulfanilamide powder was added to each soldier's first-aid packet and he was instructed, on becoming a casualty, to swallow the tablets and sprinkle the powder on his wound. The limitations of their usefulness were also understood and it was the knowledge of these limitations that made the introduction of penicillin so dramatic and so important. Sulfonamides were, in the first place, ineffective against a considerable number of bacteria. They were ineffective against a great majority of the gram-negative bacilli, the typhoid-colon group responsible for many intestinal infections. They were ineffective against staphylococci, which are quite as common as streptococci in wounds and quite as apt to invade the blood stream. They were ineffective against streptococci of the *viridans* group, which is the commonest cause of bacterial endocarditis, an infection of the heart valves which has always had a mortality approximating 100 per cent. They were ineffective against the spirochetes which produce syphilis. In the second place, sulfonamides were distinctly toxic drugs. Even sulfathiazole and sulfadiazine, which have much less harmful effect on the brain or intestinal tract than sulfanilamide and sulfapyridine, produced fevers with some frequency, occasionally destroyed red and white blood corpuscles, and could block the kidneys unless they were given with such large amounts of water that they were excreted in dilute solution in the urine. They had sufficient effects on co-ordination so that aviators were not permitted to fly while under treatment with them. In the third place, they were not uniformly successful even when used in the diseases in which their effectiveness was proved. Thus, certain cases of pneumonia or meningitis or gonorrhea failed to respond to sulfonamides. In these individuals the particular organisms present apparently had a natural or acquired resistance to the drug and were spoken of as being "sulfonamide-fast."

In June of 1929, Sir Alexander Fleming announced the discovery of penicillin. Some years previous to this, while working in the laboratories of St. Mary's Hospital, London, as Professor of Bacteriology, Fleming had found an enzyme in tears and sweat and egg-white which he called lysozyme and which proved capable of destroying bacteria. The effect was exerted only on harmless bacteria incapable of producing disease, so nothing useful came of the discovery, but partly as a result of his experience with it, partly no doubt as a result of his experiences as a surgeon during the First World War, Fleming's mind was prepared for the finding of a nontoxic substance which could destroy disease-bearing bacteria. In the fall of 1928 he was working with staphylococci and, as an incident of his labors, a number of the flat glass Petri dishes on which the organisms are grown lay about the room. As the staphylococci grow, they speckle and cover the surface of the nutrient agar which fills the

Sir Alexander Fleming, discoverer of penicillin, explains its properties

Preparing dried penicillin for use

dish with white and grayish colonies. Several of the dishes, exposed to the air for some time, had become contaminated with other organisms and, picking up one such dish preparatory to discarding it, Fleming noted a spot of greenish mold which had been blown in the laboratory window by some friendly breeze. "It was astonishing," he wrote, "that for some considerable distance around the mold the staphylococcal colonies were undergrowing lysis dissolution. What had formerly been a well-grown colony was now a faint shadow of itself. I was sufficiently interested to pursue the subject. The appearance of the plate was such that I thought it should not be neglected." The mold proved to be *Penicillium notatum.* The area of lysis around the mold proved due to the diffusion of a substance formed by the mold as it grew upon the agar. Fleming called the substance penicillin.

This may seem a very casual way to make a great discovery, and so it is. There were two large elements of luck. One was the appearance of this particular mold, for of the hundreds that have since been examined, few have had any effect upon staphylococci. The other was that the observation was made by Fleming. No series of experiments was ever conducted without some unexpected observation being made, some aberrant result being secured. The sins of the experimenter are threefold: not to make the observation; to observe, but to ignore the observation because it interferes with his conclusion; to neglect pursuing the observation if due consideration attaches importance to it. Fleming made the observation and "thought it should not be neglected."

He did not neglect it but proved his fundamental point up to the hilt. He transplanted the mold to culture media and, growing it there, found that his penicillin appeared in the medium. He tested its effectiveness against all the bacteria at his disposal, proving that it was even more effective against cultures of streptococci, gonococci, and meningococci than had been the case against staphylococci, that it was effective against gram-positive bacilli such as the diphtheria organisms but ineffective against gram-negative bacilli such as the influenza bacillus and the typhoid-colon group. He proved it was nontoxic to rabbits and mice by injecting it into their ear veins and abdominal cavities. He used it as a surface dressing in several cases of infected wounds and reported that they seemed to clean up rapidly. He made, in 1929, the specific prediction that penicillin may prove to be an efficient antiseptic when

injected into areas infected with penicillin-sensitive organisms. And at
this point he stopped. He had demonstrated an apparently nontoxic
substance which was effective against certain dangerous bacteria when
grown in laboratory media. The problems which remained were the
chemical one of producing penicillin in quantity and the clinical one
of determining its effectiveness. These problems remained unsolved
for ten years and even unattacked, save that, at the London School
of Hygiene in 1932, Raistrick grew the mold and attempted to ex-
tract penicillin from the culture media. He was dissuaded from continuing his experiments, as so many were very nearly dissuaded later,
by the chemical difficulties involved in isolating such an unstable
substance.

As Fleming had been the chief character in the first act of the penicillin drama so Sir Howard Florey, an Australian-born Professor of Pathol-
ogy at Oxford, and his colleague, Ernest Chain, became chief characters
in the second act — a sort of revival staged in 1939. The philosophical
implication of Fleming's work was clear. The war between the species
which we see going on all about us in the world, too closely about us,
extended beyond our vision into the microscopic world. A mold dropped
from the air onto a bacterial village, a colony, and its inhabitants were
promptly liquidated. A very neat parallel. The demonstration was not
entirely a new one. In Pasteur's laboratory the destructive effect of certain airborne bacteria upon the bacillus of anthrax had been observed.
And, just at the turn of the century, German bacteriologists isolated a
substance they called pyocyanase from certain pus-forming bacilli and
reported that it killed organisms that produced cholera and diphtheria.
Neither this attempt, nor indeed that of Fleming, had proceeded much
beyond the test-tube stage before 1939 and the first demonstration that
"good" bacteria could be enlisted effectively in the fight against diseases
of animals and man was made by Dubos at the Rockefeller Institute in
New York. In 1939 he reported the isolation of a substance, tyrothricin,
from certain bacilli found in soil. The active moiety of the substance,
called gramicidin because it destroyed gram-positive organisms, proved
to be too toxic for internal use in man but had a certain usefulness in the
treatment of surface infections. This was the situation when Florey focused the work of his group on the problem. Successively they had tried,
and abandoned, lysozyme and pyocyanase until, recalling Fleming's

studies, they obtained a culture of *P. notatum* from him and revived the work on penicillin.

They started where Fleming had stopped. He had proved penicillin effective against certain dangerous microorganisms growing in glass dishes. They must ascertain whether it was similarly effective against these organisms growing in animals or man. To determine this point it was necessary to produce penicillin in considerable amounts and they at once encountered difficulties which delayed the program for years in both England and this country, and were barely surmounted. It is an easy matter to mix a few stable, readily available chemicals and emerge, say, with a new sulfonamide. But penicillin is the product of a very fastidious organism. It grows readily enough from the spores which form its resting state to the long tangled green threads (mycelia) which can produce penicillin, but the production is irregular, the product exceedingly unstable; destroyed for example by boiling, by an excess of acid or alkali, by the presence of contaminating bacteria and by other molds. A prerequisite for the study was the development of an assay method by which the potency of any preparation they might secure could be measured. Florey's group used the same Petri dish cultures of staphylococci on which Fleming had made his original observations. They defined one Oxford unit as the amount which, placed inside an open-ended glass cylinder on the dish, would produce a clear zone, a zone free of bacteria, 25 millimeters in diameter. They grew the mold in liter glass flasks or flat earthenware pans, the bottoms of which were covered by an inch of liquid media. The vessels were sowed with spores and, after five days, the whole surface of the media became covered with dry white mycelia. Within a week this growth became a continuous greenish-blue felt and the media beneath became yellow with an accumulation of penicillin. They were producing penicillin; their assays proved it. But vary their media or their mold or the duration of its growth as they would, the filtrate from their flasks contained only about two units per cubic centimeter. Since, at any such concentration, impossible volumes of fluid would be required and since penicillin was relatively unstable in the liquid form, it became essential to concentrate this filtrate. They devised a laborious and complicated chemical process by which penicillin was extracted into relatively small volumes of organic solvents, re-extracted from the solvent into still smaller volumes of water, purified by adsorption onto alumina from which it was removed by ether and, finally, extracted into the watery solution from which it was dried. They emerged with a dry stable penicillin salt with a potency of about 50,000 units per gram. Since, in the course of their extraction, they lost nearly two thirds of the penicillin, this single gram of powder represented 62 liters of filtrate or the contents of about 300 flasks. It contained, as we now know, 97 per cent impurities and was only sufficient to treat a single man for half a day. They did have a dry stable preparation a thousand times as strong as the crude preparation used by Fleming in 1929. They obtained it only with enormous effort and in relatively small amounts.

Nevertheless it was sufficient to permit experiments on animals and with these they proceeded. Fifty mice were injected with fatal doses of staphylococci, fifty more with streptococci, fifty more with the organism producing gas gangrene. Half of each group were given penicillin, the other half served as untreated controls. All seventy-five of the untreated mice died. Seventy of the treated mice survived. The groups were large enough and the results decisive enough to make this a most important experiment. It was even more important because none of the treated mice, and none of the cats and rabbits in which this point was specifically investigated, showed any toxic effects. Not only did penicillin appear more potent than the sulfonamides or any other bacterial agent, but it affected some organisms which were immune to the sulfonamides and appeared much less toxic than they. The final criterion of success must be trial of the drug in man. Men, not mice, are the ultimate concern. Penicillin might still be ineffective in man or toxic reactions might appear which could not be observed in animals.

And to this question, the effectiveness of penicillin in man, Florey and his group were unable to give a decisive answer for the simple reason that they could not produce enough penicillin. After nearly two years of work, by the spring of 1941, they had been able to treat only five cases with intravenous penicillin. All of the five patients had severe infections with staphylococci or streptococci, three had proven septicemia, four had failed to respond to sulfonamides. They might all have been reasonably expected to die. As it developed, three recovered and two died. There were reasons for the two deaths: one had recovered only to relapse and die when the available penicillin was exhausted; the other died from an accident of his disease unconnected with the infection; both had been grossly undertreated by present standards. Taken in conjunction with the animal experiments the results were encouraging and supplied additional evidence of the nontoxicity of the drug. Taken by themselves they were indecisive.

In the course of the laboratory observations and the experiments upon animals and man, some valuable data were gathered which had importance in the subsequent use of penicillin. (1) Penicillin proved to be much more effective when injected intramuscularly or intravenously than when given by mouth — a consequence, they believed, of its being destroyed by the acid present in the stomach. This was a disadvantage for it implied that the drug, like insulin, would have to be given by injection. (2) After injection, it was demonstrable in the blood for only two or three hours. This finding was related to the large and prompt excretion of penicillin in the urine which, as Florey said, made it "like trying to fill a bathtub with the plug out." In this respect it was similar to the sulfonamides and it appeared that penicillin would share with them the disadvantage of frequent and repeated dosage. (3) The presence of pus grossly interferes with the effectiveness of sulfonamides. This proved not to be true with penicillin, which continued to affect a culture of staphylococci to which large amounts of pus had been added. This observation suggested that penicillin would be more effective than sulfonamides in the local treatment of infected wounds and in empyemas (collections of pus in the chest cavity). (4) By growing staphylococci for some weeks in the presence of concentrations of penicillin insufficient of themselves to affect the organisms, the staphylococci developed an increasing resistance to the drug so that, eventually, they were able to multiply exceedingly in concentrations a thousand times greater than would originally have destroyed them. This development of resistance supplies the theoretical basis for commencing treatment with large and decisive doses of penicillin rather than with small and increasing doses. (5) The mechanism by which sulfonamides affect bacteria had been demonstrated. The drug does not actually destroy them but prevents their multiplication by interfering with their use of an essential food, para-amino-benzoic acid (PABA). This was proved by showing that streptococci, for example, continue to grow in the presence of sulfonamides if an excess of PABA is added to the culture medium. Penicillin can also interfere with the reproduction of bacteria, though whether the mechanism of this action is similar to that of the sulfonamides is not yet known. In addition to this "bacteriostatic" action, penicillin is actually able to destroy bacteria when it is present in certain concentrations and when the bacteria are at certain stages of their development. The point is admittedly of theoretical rather than practical interest since a bacterium which is unable to multiply dies rather rapidly of old age.

The third and final act in the drama of penicillin opened in the summer of 1941 when Florey and one of his collaborators, Heatley, came to the United States. The first two acts had been played entirely in England. A new drug had been discovered. In laboratory experiments it had been proved to have great potency, wide effectiveness, low toxicity, all the great desiderata. Fundamental information about its fate in the body and its mode of action had been acquired. If its promise of clinical usefulness should prove true it could save an incalculable number of lives in the war and forever and ever. But large amounts of penicillin were required to prove this point and Florey could not provide them. The chemical methods for penicillin production would have to be improved. Factories would have to be built and equipped. England had neither the personnel nor the facilities to devote to this program in 1941 and, accordingly, Florey came to this country to enlist the assistance of its scientists and its industry. It was at the point of production, and only at this point, that the United States started to play its part. A very difficult part it proved to be.

Florey was traveling on a grant from the Rockefeller Foundation which had been, in part, supporting his researches. Going first to New Haven, he was referred to the National Academy of Sciences and then, through the Department of Agriculture, to its Northern Regional Research Laboratory at Peoria, Illinois, where extensive fermentation studies had been carried on for years under Dr. Robert D. Coghill, and where it seemed reasonable to think the chemical problems involved in penicillin production might be advanced. From Peoria, in September, he went to several pharmaceutical houses with the design of interesting them in the problem and, coming to Washington, consulted with the Chairman of the CMR. Dr. Florey's evidence was sufficiently convincing to make CMR an ardent and steadfast exponent of the program, chimerical as it was regarded in certain quarters. With the design of initiating and developing penicillin production, meetings were arranged by CMR in October and December between representatives of the National Research Council Division of Chemistry, the Department of Agriculture, and the pharmaceutical firms of Merck & Company, Chas. Pfizer & Company, E. R. Squibb and Sons, and the Lederle Laboratories. The Peoria Laboratory, which had started work immediately after Florey's visit, and the pharmaceutical houses agreed to conduct research aimed at increasing the production of penicillin. The firms agreed that the findings of any one group would be conveyed to the others through the medium of CMR. The Peoria Laboratory agreed to report its findings directly to the other groups and to make periodic visits to their laboratories for the purpose of giving such advice and assistance as seemed indicated. It was a fruitful collaboration and, on the whole, successfully maintained. It should be made clear that, apart from the transfer of some funds to the Peoria Laboratory, the research and the subsequent construction of pilot plants were conducted at the expense of the participants. The function of CMR was to encourage their initial interest, to co-ordinate the results of their work, to arrange with the War Production Board so that they might receive priorities for the equipment of their laboratories and pilot plants.

One way of estimating the difficulty of a problem, granting it to have been intelligently attacked, is to examine the results. It was six months from the time of Florey's visit to Peoria before there was sufficient penicillin available to treat one case, eighteen months before there was sufficient to treat 200 cases, thirty months before any could be allocated to nonresearch civilian use. It is impossible to exaggerate the difficulties and strains of those first eighteen months. The same difficulties encountered by Fleming and Raistrick and Florey were now encountered on a larger scale and with more at stake. It was scientists against time in a very real meaning of the phrase. Put mold and medium in a flask and, ten days later, assays would show a good yield of penicillin. Put larger amounts of the same mold, the same medium, in larger vessels and assays would show no penicillin; or penicillin would be there on the fourth day and, suddenly, on the fifth day it would be gone; or it would be present in the final filtrate and vanish during one of the stages of extraction. There were a great many lights burning for a great many nights in these laboratories and a great many headaches which no drug but penicillin would relieve. In retrospect it seems that, of all the minutiae to be observed and chemical processes to be perfected, the greatest losses were due to contamination of the media by other microorganisms. The same accident of contamination which led to the discovery of penicillin very nearly prevented its use.

It will be recalled that Florey's filtrate had assayed at two units per cubic centimeter. The chief direction which the research took was the development of improved media and the discovery of new strains of mold; the criterion of success in each instance was of course the production of more penicillin. The first advance came from the Peoria Laboratory. It was found that the addition of corn steep liquor[2] to the culture medium increased penicillin production tenfold. Strains of mold were brought to the laboratory in handfuls of soil gathered by Air Force personnel all over the world. One of these new strains doubled the production again. It was now 40 units per cubic centimeter. Step by step, taken in many laboratories and over many months, the yield increased. As further alterations of the media and molds, controls of sterilization and oxygen and acidity were introduced. Finally it reached 200 units per cubic centimeter. It is still in that range, with variations from 100 to 300 units with different procedures and even, for unknown reasons, in different batches prepared by the same process.

One difficulty that clearly had to be solved before large-scale production of penicillin was possible was that the mold must be grown in great vats rather than in liter flasks. The difficulties, the expense of handling thousands, hundreds of thousands, of glass flasks would have been enormous. To make this change it was necessary to find a strain of mold which would grow submerged and throughout a vat rather than only on the surface as Florey's strain had done; such a strain was found. It was necessary to develop methods for oxygenating, mixing, and cooling the media in these vats while growth was proceeding and this without allowing contamination by any other microorganism; such methods were developed.

In a typical plant the procedure in present use has the following pattern. Spores are grown in tanks for three or four days until they develop into mycelia. A small amount of this culture is then transferred into an 8000-gallon vat, previously sterilized by boiling water, containing cul-

[2]The water in which corn has been soaked as an incident in the production of starch.

ture media the acidity of which has been carefully regulated. There the mycelia grow for forty-eight hours, constantly stirred by a huge "egg beater," constantly oxygenated by streams of sterile air, their temperature regulated by refrigerating coils in the walls of the vat. At the end of this period the yellow fluid, assaying say 200 units per cubic centimeter, is filtered off and the concentration process started. The penicillin is first adsorbed onto charcoal, then dissolved in an organic solvent, finally extracted into watery solution by high-speed centrifugation. The potency of this solution is of the order of 50,000 units per cubic centimeter, 250 times that of the original solution. It is then passed through an asbestos filter to remove fever-producing substances and specimens are taken for assay of potency and for injection into rabbits and mice to determine the presence or absence of toxicity. It is now ready to be bottled, frozen, and dried. These processes are carried on in rooms specially equipped with ultraviolet light to sterilize the air, and by operatives who are masked and gowned in the best operating-room tradition. As the product emerges from the factory for distribution to the services, it is a yellow powder, 100,000 or 200,000 units to each rubber-stoppered bottle, ready for immediate use upon the addition of water. The product is not crystalline penicillin but is about 60 per cent pure, assaying approximately 1000 units per milligram or 20 times as much as did Florey's product made in 1941.

By the spring of 1943 the chemical procedures were fairly well standardized and production in the small pilot plants had increased from the 10,000,000 units which they averaged a month during 1942 to 40,000,000 units a month. It was time to build factories and the assistance of the Chemical Division of the War Production Board was invoked. At a meeting in May 1943, the WPB undertook to arrange for the priorities necessary to construct and equip the factories. The CMR was to continue its clinical evaluation of the drug and the experiments on structure and synthesis which were in progress. The Office of Production Research of the WPB agreed to support work in various universities in connection with technical improvements in production. The Defense Plant Corporation was to finance the small percentage of construction costs which some of the firms were unable to provide. The Food and Drug Administration of the Public Health Service assumed the testing of the firms' products which had previously been performed at Peoria.

With this organization the program burgeoned. Twenty-one firms were selected whose interests and abilities seemed likely to make them effective producers and they were provided with the necessary instructions. They were given AA-1 priorities on equipment and special "directives" when bottlenecks in construction developed. With this assistance, many new plants were completed and in operation within six months; all of them, at an expenditure of some $20,000,000, were completed within a year. Satisfactory exchange of information was obtained by monthly meetings between representatives of each firm and WPB, and the Department of Justice granted the firms freedom from prosecution under provisions of the antitrust laws.

Since the aim of the program was to produce penicillin, its success is best indicated by the figures of production. In evaluating these figures one million units may be taken as the average amount required to treat a single patient. In June 1943, 425 million units were produced; in December 1943, 9195 million units, a 22-fold increase; in June 1944, 117,527 million units, a further 13-fold increase; in December 1944, 293,376 million units; in June 1945, 646,818 million units. As production increased, the cost of the product fell. A package of 100,000 units which originally sold, at wholesale, for $20 now sells for considerably less than one dollar, of which 20 per cent is the cost of packaging.

A WPB allocation order issued in July 1943 assigned all production to the Army, Navy, Public Health Service, and, for research purposes, to CMR. By the spring of 1944 production had reached a point where the needs of the services could be satisfied and a surplus was left for civilian needs. Since this surplus was not sufficient to satisfy the anticipated requirements, the WPB established, on May 1, 1944, a Civilian Penicillin Distribution Unit in Chicago. An advisory board from governmental agencies and the American Medical Association selected a group of 1000 hospitals, strategically located throughout the country, which were appointed as depots for the storage, distribution, and use of penicillin in their communities. Each hospital was given a monthly quota of the drug, and instructions, prepared by CMR, for guidance in its use. As production figures rose, the quota of each hospital was increased and the number of depots increased to 2700, until finally, on March 15, 1945, all restrictions were removed. There was enough penicillin for everyone. It took from September 1941 until March 1945 to conquer the difficulties of penicillin production. But the first eighteen months were the hardest. In April 1943 shipments started to our troops overseas. In April 1944 Lend-Lease shipments were under way and the serious requirements of the civilian population began to be met.

The desirability of synthesizing penicillin was obvious from the beginning and became increasingly so as the difficulties of inducing the mold to manufacture the drug became more and more apparent. Synthesis would permit the production of infinite amounts at a fraction of the original cost of the biological product and would make it possible to prepare modifications of penicillin much as the whole series of sulfonamides had been prepared. To synthesize a substance, its precise chemical structure must be known; the position of each atom and its relation to the other atoms must be demonstrated. During 1942 and 1943 several pharmaceutical laboratories were working independently on the structure and synthesis of penicillin. By the fall of 1943 the work had progressed sufficiently so that synthesis within a relatively short period seemed possible. On the basis of a report to this effect, submitted by a special committee appointed by OSRD for the purpose, it was decided to launch a vigorous and co-ordinated attack. Five universities and ten industrial firms were selected to take part in the program, the latter without financial support by OSRD. Each unit, university and commercial, sent periodic reports of their results to all other units and to the English laboratories which were similarly engaged. It was agreed that the advised decision of the Director of OSRD would be accepted on the assignment of patents and licenses in the event that a discovery was made. An enormous amount of effort and some millions of dollars were expended on the program without achieving final success, and when the contracts were terminated on November 1, 1945, penicillin had not been synthesized. It had been obtained in pure crystalline form. Its empirical formula, the number of atoms of oxygen and hydrogen and nitrogen, had been determined. The side-chains, the limbs of the molecule so to speak, had been established. But the arrangement of atoms within the body of the molecule had not been ascertained and the arrangement which seems most probable at the present time poses entirely new chemical problems for synthesis. As the biological program succeeded, some of the advantages inherent in chemical synthesis disappeared. The penicillin requirements of this country can be readily met by the mold method of preparation and the cost, already very moderate, will presumably diminish further. The desirability of preparing variations of the penicillin molecule, however, persists, for it is always possible that one of the modifications might be effective against bacteria which are immune to the drug itself. On this account alone it must be hoped that penicillin synthesis will be accomplished.

The production of penicillin was started not perhaps on faith alone, but on what was certainly very slight clinical evidence. Florey had been able to treat only five cases, of whom two had died. The effort being expended on penicillin production in this country was justified only if the drug could cure disease in man. It was essential to determine, at the earliest possible moment, whether it had any effectiveness and, if so, against which diseases this was exerted. The manufacturers accordingly agreed to turn over their product to CMR for clinical evaluation and this they did, gratis, till January 1943; in the two succeeding years CMR expended $2,000,000 in purchasing penicillin to continue the evaluation. On March 14, 1942, there was sufficient penicillin available to treat the first patient, a case of streptococcic septicemia in New Haven, Connecticut, which had not responded to sulfonamides. The result was a brilliant success and constituted as compelling evidence as a single case could provide. A year later 200 civilian cases had received penicillin; by May 1944 the series had increased to 2000, and it totaled 10,500 in March 1945 when unrestricted civilian distribution became possible.

From March 1942 to May 1944 the evaluation program was directed for CMR by the Chairman of the Committee on Chemotherapy of the National Research Council, Dr. Perrin Long, and by his successor in that position, Dr. Chester S. Keefer, who later became Medical Administrative Officer of the CMR. The task was an exceedingly difficult and delicate one for, as soon as news of the success of penicillin became bruited about, the Washington and Boston offices were besieged by telephone and telegraph, by civilians and doctors, by day and especially by night, with requests for a supply of the drug. Only one procedure was possible in view of the minuscule supplies of the substance and the necessity of rapidly determining its effectiveness. This procedure was adopted and adhered to, rigidly and impartially. Penicillin was, at first, to be given only to patients with diseases that had a high mortality rate and were unresponsive to other forms of treatment. In this category were strepto-coccic and, particularly, staphylococcic septicemia. A relatively small series of cases of staphylococcic septicemia would, if the drug proved effective, establish the importance of penicillin at once, for four out of five people with this disease had always died. Later the drug would be used in other diseases; the administrator in each instance acquiring enough evidence to prove that it was or was not useful, then stopping its distribution to cases of this category and extending it to another. The drug was given only to doctors of known ability from whom accurate observations could be expected. It was given free with the written stipu-lation that a full account of results obtained be submitted to CMR.

By August 28, 1943, the range of common diseases had been fairly well covered and sufficient data had been collected to permit a report on the results in 500 cases. This report bore out to an extraordinary degree the observations which had been made by Fleming in 1929. The same or-ganisms which had perished in Petri dishes responded to penicillin in man. Diseases caused by staphylococci, streptococci, pneumococci, meningococci, gonococci, could be cured. These conclusions have not had to be modified, though, subsequent to this date, the effectiveness of penicillin in subacute bacterial endocarditis and, more surprising still, in syphilis has been demonstrated. An important study, proceeding simul-taneously with this, was initiated in April 1943 when CMR sent a sur-gical consultant, Dr. Champ Lyons, to the Bushnell General Hospital in Brigham City, Utah. This was done after arrangement with the Sur-geon General's Office and with the design of ascertaining the usefulness of penicillin in the wounded soldiers who had been so prominently in the minds of everyone connected with the program. The soldiers, chiefly from Guadalcanal, had been hospitalized for a year or more with frac-tured bones and burns become infected, with infected soft-tissue wounds, and with blood-stream infections. They had received sulfonamides and had not been cured. Although the barrel of supply was scraped to the bottom for this venture there was only enough penicillin to treat a hand-ful of the soldiers at Bushnell, but the Army was impressed by the re-sults obtained and Dr. Lyons, now commissioned in the Medical Corps, extended the study to similar cases at Halloran General Hospital, Staten Island, New York, where medical officers were sent to him for a course of instruction before returning to their installations. Larger supplies of penicillin became available during the summer of 1943, and by December a report could be made on 209 cases treated in eleven Army hospitals. The mortality rate in these severely infected cases was only 6.2 per cent, scarcely more than the average in all wounded soldiers, and their period of hospitalization was shortened by many months. From both these studies, on civilian and Army patients alike, there emerged the astounding fact that penicillin was a nontoxic drug. It was quite as harmless to man as it was to Fleming's mice and rabbits. This was unprecedented. A potent drug which destroys bacteria and yet, in the highest doses thus far used, is completely without toxic effects in man. It produces an unpleasant burning sensation at the site of injection but this effect became less as purer preparations were available. An occasional case of hives is the only recognized toxic effect of crystalline penicillin. Ehrlich's "magic bullet" in very truth.

The particular diseases in which penicillin has proved effective deserve some separate mention. In septicemias due to the hemolytic streptococcus, the sulfonamides had reduced the mortality from 80 per cent to 20 per cent. This was their shining success. Penicillin is equally effective without the toxic effects that attend the use of sulfonamides; effective, too, in many cases that are "sulfonamide-fast," as had been the first patient to receive penicillin in the CMR series. The sulfonamides have less effect upon the *Streptococcus viridans* and were practically ineffective when this organism involved the valves of the heart in a disease called subacute bacterial endocarditis. The mortality of this disease has always approximated 100 per cent. Every new drug introduced into medicine is tried here as it is in tuberculosis and cancer. All of them have failed. Dawson, who made some penicillin in his own laboratory and was the first to use the drug in this country, tried it against subacute bacterial endocarditis in 1941. He failed because, as is now clear, he was unable to use sufficiently large doses. There is a considerable difference in the sensitivity of various strains of *Streptococcus viridans* to penicillin, but with doses of 200,000 units a day sufficiently long continued, at least four out of five of these cases will now survive.

Staphylococci also produce septicemia and against them the sulfonamides had been relatively useless. Pencillin has effected precisely the reversal of mortality in this instance that it did with subacute bacterial endocarditis and with more importance, since the disease is a commoner one. Instead of four out of five of the patients dying, four out of five will now live. Penicillin is also effective against staphylococci localized in the soft tissues, the meninges, the heart valves, the lungs, the bones. But in the treatment of wounds infected with staphylococci, it is not usually enough to inject penicillin and wait for the patient to recover. Penicillin is no substitute for good surgery. On that point all are agreed. All dead and damaged tissue must be removed and full opportunity must be given for free drainage. In the case of chronically infected bones and infections within the chest cavity surgery must usually still be performed. The chief contribution of penicillin in these instances is to control the generalized infection and to make surgical interference possible at an earlier moment. Nor is penicillin any substitute for food and blood. The rapid destruction of proteins and red blood cells in wounded men and the consequent necessity of high-protein diets and whole-blood transfusions was one of the major surgical discoveries of the war. But in effective and wise combination with surgery and transfusions, penicillin has made a definite contribution to the treatment of war casualties.

The bacilli which cause gas gangrene are a most serious contaminant of wounds though a much rarer one than streptococci or staphylococci. Since they cannot grow in the presence of an adequate oxygen supply, they infect wounds where the blood supply has been decreased by a tourniquet too long applied or by a plaster cast too tightly in place. Once established, they cause rapid destruction of tissue, a peculiar-smelling wound with palpable evolution of gas, and quickly invade adjacent tissues and the blood stream. Amputation, immediate amputation, is the only course open to the surgeon. Penicillin cannot be expected to disinfect a gangrenous area; the blood supply of the infected tissue is so inadequate that the drug could not reach it in effective amounts. Its role is to prevent a spread of the infection and perhaps to make amputation possible at a lower level than could otherwise have been considered — amputation of a leg at the knee rather than the thigh, for example. This role it seems to have fulfilled successfully and, in combination with gas-gangrene antitoxin, it is thought to have decreased the mortality which accompanies the infection from 50 per cent to approximately 25 per cent.

Pneumococci and meningococci do not invade wounds but cause diseases, lobar pneumonia and epidemic meningitis, which are as common in peace as in war. The introduction of sulfonamides had decreased the mortality of these diseases from the order of 30 per cent to the order of 10 per cent. Fleming's observations in 1929 had indicated that penicillin would be useful against both organisms and this has proved to be the case. When supplies of penicillin were still inadequate, it was reserved for cases of pneumonia that did not respond to sulfonamides. Now that this difficulty has been overcome, it is recommended as routine treatment for all cases of pneumonia; with it, the toxic effects of sulfonamides are avoided; with it, the mortality should drop to 5 per cent or even less. One difficulty that has dogged the use of penicillin has been the necessity of giving it frequently and by injection. It has been used locally in the treatment of wounds, has been blown into the sinuses or throat by an atomizer, has been directly injected into the chest cavity in cases of empyema, but the usual methods of administration have been by injection into the veins or muscles. Continuous intravenous injections, during which a needle must be maintained in an arm vein for days, are difficult for both attendant and patient. Injections made, every three or four hours, deep into the muscles of the buttock or arm are an uncomfortable and even painful experience. Numerous efforts have therefore been made to improve the absorption of penicillin from the intestine and therefore permit its administration by mouth: by making less soluble preparations of penicillin, or by administering it in oil or surrounded by a capsule which will not dissolve until it has passed through the stomach into the small intestine. Attempts have been made to prolong the effects of a single injection by delaying its excretion through the kidney or by incorporating it in a mixture of beeswax and oil. None of these attempts have been completely successful but, if sufficiently large doses are given by mouth, enough absorption can be obtained to affect organisms which, like the pneumococci, are highly susceptible to penicillin. Now that supplies of penicillin are adequate to permit this practice, it would appear that pneumonia can be satisfactorily treated by giving the drug in tablet form. Meningitis offers peculiar difficulties to penicillin treatment because the drug, unlike the sulfonamides, does not reach the infected membranes of the brain and spinal cord satisfactorily from the blood stream. In consequence it is necessary to inject penicillin directly into the tissues of the central nervous system, and on this account is not advised for the routine treatment

of the disease but is reserved for cases that do not respond to the sulfonamides.

It is an odd thing to reflect upon that the two situations in which
penicillin proved of greatest quantitative importance to the services were
in the treatment of gonorrhea and syphilis. Its effectiveness against
gonorrhea could have been anticipated from Fleming's experiments for,
even with his impure preparations, a concentration of 1 : 2,000,000 was
effective against gonococci, whereas 1 : 1,000,000 was required to affect
staphylococci. The introduction of sulfonamides had vastly improved the
treatment of gonorrhea, commonest of venereal diseases. For acute gonorrhea there had, previously, been no drug available; for the chronic
form, only courses of injections and massage which were often worse
than no treatment at all. A single course of sulfonamide therapy cured
up to 90 per cent of acute cases of gonorrhea within a week. But the
frequency of the disease amongst troops made even this week of hospitalization a serious drain on manpower in the services. Orders were
issued that the men were to stay on active duty during treatment rather
than be hospitalized, but their efficiency was impaired and aircrews,
for example, were not permitted to fly. The fact that penicillin is largely
excreted in the urine, constituting a disadvantage in most diseases where
it is desirable to maintain an effective concentration of the drug in the
blood, is an actual advantage in the treatment of gonorrhea, for it thus
comes into intimate contact with the site of infection. It developed
that 100,000 units, given in less than twenty-four hours, cured 96 per
cent of cases which had failed to respond to sulfonamides. Properly and
at once penicillin replaced sulfonamides in the treatment of gonorrhea.
Whole wards which had gradually filled wih cases that refused to respond
to sulfonamides or other forms of therapy were promptly emptied.

Syphilis was a disease of primary importance to the services not alone
because of its frequency but also because of the prolonged and repeated
periods of hospitalization which its proper treatment required. There
were 127,345 new cases of syphilis in the Army alone between January
1942 and August 1945. When the diagnosis was first made each soldier
had to be hospitalized for several weeks and the standard course of
treatment required that he return to the hospital thereafter at weekly
intervals, over periods of many months, for injections of arsenic and
bismuth. The duration of this treatment and the great importance of

executing it with precision had made it particularly cumbersome for the services. A new and briefer form of treatment was therefore greatly to be desired. In the fall of 1943 Dr. John F. Mahoney of the United States Public Health Service injected penicillin into some syphilitic rabbits in his laboratory on Staten Island, New York. Within twenty-four hours all microorganisms disappeared from the ulcers, which promptly proceeded to heal. The experiment was transferred to man with equally successful results in four cases. This was a matter of great moment, the most important finding in the field of syphilis since Ehrlich's discovery of arsphenamine in 1909. An extensive investigation was indicated and was undertaken. Three laboratories and twenty-five civilian clinics undertook to study the effectiveness of penicillin under sponsorship of CMR. Thirty-five clinics maintained by the United States Public Health Service agreed to join the study. A carefully planned, integrated program was put into effect and a central office was established for statistical analysis of its results. This represented the first organized investigative effort in a field where both laboratory and clinical studies had always proceeded on an unorganized individualistic basis. The effects of penicillin as a single method of treatment for various stages of the disease were first studied. The results of varying the dosage, the duration of treatment, and the method of administration were all examined in large groups of cases. Subsequently the investigators explored the effect of combining penicillin with short courses of arsenic and bismuth and with fever therapy. The study is still incomplete, indeed the chronic nature of the disease requires that it be carried on for many years before final conclusions can be reached. But on the basis of preliminary results obtained from this study and from investigations of their own, the Army and Navy adopted penicillin as the routine treatment for early syphilis in June 1944, directing the injection of 2,400,000 units over a period of eight days. This was to conclude the treatment unless signs of activity persisted or redeveloped. There is no question about the saving of hospitalization that resulted or the immediately favorable response. The organisms promptly disappear from the chancre, and within a week or two it heals. The patient becomes noninfectious within a few days. At a more leisurely rate the blood reaction which is characteristic of the disease usually disappears. The permanence of this "cure" is not yet certain however and the tendency to relapse is distinctly higher than had been the case with arsenic and bismuth therapy. There can be little doubt that penicillin will be included in the future treatment of syphilis; that a new weapon of great importance has been found. But it seems probable that the recommendations emerging from the CMR study will modify the routine of administration and include, along with penicillin, some other treatment.

The success of the penicillin program has brought under control a whole group of infectious diseases, previously not susceptible to specific treatment or ineffectively treated. All of the diseases in which the laboratory experiments of Fleming and Florey suggested that penicillin would prove useful have responded to it. And other fields of usefulness, notably that of syphilis, have been added. This does not mean that penicillin is a panacea. It is not like the magic oil of the traveling medicine man which would "cure consumption, constipation, rheumatism, keep the hair from falling out and be good to eat on bread." There are certain diseases, cancer and leukemias for example, which are not due to microorganisms and could not conceivably be affected. It does not affect protozoa like the Plasmodia of malaria. It is without effect upon the most important viruses and the rickettsia which are responsible for influenza and encephalitis, the common cold and typhus. It has no effect on the organisms producing tuberculosis or on gram-negative bacilli like those causing typhoid fever. Now that it is to be available in unlimited amounts for popular distribution, it will probably be grossly misused in all these inappropriate fields as have other drugs in the past. That is too bad. But it does not alter the fact that a great discovery has been made. The part of our country in that discovery has been confined to development, to production and evaluation. But it was a difficult part and has been wisely and generously played. The event of fundamental importance has been the discovery, or rediscovery if you wish, of this chemical warfare amongst the microorganisms of our world. It would be odd if the blue mold which blew in through Fleming's window on that happy breeze should prove the only example of this warfare which could be put to use in curing the diseases of man. There may be other molds or bacteria, indeed a number are already under study, which will affect other dangerous bacteria so that some observer will again record that "what had formerly been a well-grown colony was now a faint shadow of its former self."

CHAPTER XXIII

INSECTICIDES AND RODENTICIDES

D URING HIS third year at school, the medical student is exposed to a course of lectures on the subject of tropical medicine.[1] In the majority of schools within the United States, this exposure is on a rather theoretical plane and the lectures admirably satisfy the old definition of transferring information from the notes of the professor to the notes of the student without passing it through the brain of either. The student obtains a list of diseases with strange outlandish names, of the insects which carry these diseases, of the involved life cycles which the microorganisms undergo. Being young and abnormally absorptive by training, he retains enough of this information to pass the examination which follows. Certain odd fragments of learning may even lie in the back of his mind for years. Thus, he will remember a good deal about malaria because the disease may occur in his practice. He will remember that hookworms invade man through the skin and only reach their eventual home in the intestines after being carried to the lungs by the blood stream, after climbing up the windpipe to the throat, after being swallowed. He will probably remember, because of its picturesqueness, the life cycle of the organisms causing filariasis which settle, male and female embraced, in the lymphatic tissues of the groin and send hosts of young into the circulating blood stream at night. He may even remember that the organisms causing schistosomiasis require a certain species of snail to complete their life cycle and that the commonest form of this disease therefore occurs chiefly in the Yangtze River Valley of China and in the Philippines. But these are esoteric recollections. He regards the course as providing theoretical background rather than practical information. He never seriously expects to encounter tropical

[1]Few diseases can be called tropical by strict definition. The practice adopted by textbooks on tropical medicine has been followed and the term is used to cover diseases which are more commonly encountered in hot moist climates than elsewhere and a few diseases which, like epidemic typhus, are present in the tropics but occur with even greater frequency in temperate climates. Malaria has been discussed in a previous chapter and therefore receives but casual mention as one of the group of mosquito-borne diseases.

diseases or to see the Yangtze River, or to wonder whether the soldier, lying there on a *tchung,* has schistosomiasis. It followed that, in 1941, not one out of a thousand doctors could have said offhand whether kala azar was caused by a leishmania or a schistosome, whether relapsing fever was carried by a louse or a mosquito. After war was declared, quite suddenly, this sort of information became very practical and desirable. Large armies must go and live in Africa and the Near East, in India and the South Pacific. First and foremost this meant exposure to malaria. But it also meant exposure to a host of other diseases about which American doctors knew even less: African sleeping sickness, yellow fever, sandfly fever, dengue, typhus fevers, cholera, perhaps plague, to name but a few. What help was to be expected from vaccines and drugs? Vaccines had been prepared for the prevention of epidemic typhus, cholera, and yellow fever. It was decided to give these vaccines to all troops being sent to areas where the diseases were prevalent; but it was far from clear that they would be effective. Of the drugs, it was known that atabrine, arsenic, and antimony would be useful in the treatment of five out of fourteen insect-borne diseases; but for the other nine no treatment was known. The prospect was profoundly disturbing.

Some advances were made during the war both in the prevention of tropical diseases by vaccines and in their treatment by drugs. The value of the vaccine against epidemic typhus was established to the satisfaction of the Typhus Commission appointed by Executive Order of the President in February 1943. It proved impracticable to conduct adequately the critical experiment of vaccinating one large section of a population exposed to epidemic typhus, leaving another section unvaccinated, and observing the incidence of disease in the two groups. But the fact that only 61 cases of typhus, and no deaths, occurred in vaccinated troops living in close contact with the infected civilian populations of North Africa, Italy, and later, Europe, is strong evidence for the effectiveness of the vaccine. So is the fact that laboratory workers, occasionally exposed to massive infections by errors in technique or the breakage of apparatus, developed mild cases, sometimes recognizable only by special diagnostic tests. It was the conclusion of the Commission that the vaccine usually prevented epidemic typhus and always diminished its severity. A vaccine for the prevention of another form of typhus, the mite-borne variety, was developed by the Commission but its value cannot be adjudged because it did not receive trial on troops in the field. A second new vaccine, for use against Japanese encephalitis, was developed under direction of the Army Epidemiology Board. This disease was first encountered by United States troops in Okinawa and some 60,000 soldiers were vaccinated against it there. The epidemic was not sufficiently severe to permit any conclusion as to the vaccine's usefulness. Research in the treatment of tropical diseases by drugs was carried on with OSRD support in a number of universities. The majority of these researches were undertaken rather late and have not yielded immediately useful results, but in two instances important progress has been made. The contributions to malaria control made by the extensive studies in this field have been described in a previous chapter. Laboratory studies at the University of California demonstrated that sulfonamides were useful in the treatment of plague in infected animals and outbreaks of the disease amongst the civilian population in the Dakar and Suez areas have established their effectiveness in human cases. These are important advances. In any other four-year span they would have been regarded as sensational. But the larger proportion of tropical diseases remain insusceptible of proven prevention by vaccines or of cure by drugs.

These diseases are open to attack by another method because the great majority of them are insect-borne. The spread of infection can be prevented in each instance by destroying the insect in which the organism causing the disease spends a portion of its life cycle. And in this direction, by the development of new insecticides, great advances have been made. Mosquitoes carry five important tropical diseases, lice carry two, sandflies two, rat fleas two, chiggers (mites) one, tsetse flies one, and — if the "insect" adjective be forgotten for the moment — snails one. Our animal friends indeed! It is not generally believed that house flies "carry" diseases in the sense in which the word is used here, but if it be admitted that they can contaminate food from feces by direct contact, the group of intestinal diseases could be added to the list: cholera, dysenteries, typhoid. Cockroaches and bedbugs deserve death on well-established principles of law and order.

It was therefore clear that the usefulness of effective insecticides would extend through the whole field of tropical medicine and far beyond malaria, from which interest in the subject originally stemmed.

Within a month after the outbreak of war, contracts were entered into between OSRD, the Gorgas Memorial Institute of Panama, and the Orlando, Florida, laboratories of the Bureau of Entomology and Plant Quarantine of the Department of Agriculture. The function of the Institute was primarily to be the conduct of field studies with substances which appeared effective against mosquitoes in laboratory tests. The broader function of the Orlando laboratories was to examine the actions of compounds against the whole range of biting and sucking insects. In the course of the three and one-half years of its continuance, this latter program involved the transfer of over $1,000,000 of OSRD funds. It was pushed with great vigor, had as many as 195 individuals on its staff, and was the source of important discoveries. The Food and Drug Administration contracted to make preliminary toxicity tests of compounds which were to be investigated and more extensive studies of substances which might appear suitable for clinical trial. These several projects were co-ordinated by CMR and, after its establishment in the late summer of 1944, by the Insect Control Committee appointed by the Director of OSRD. At the recommendation of the latter Committee, eight university laboratories were enlisted to study the fundamental mechanism of action and the toxicity of the more important insecticides which had been developed by that time. Chemical methods were developed for analysis of these newer compounds so that the purity of the products could be determined, and a great deal of attention was given to finding nontoxic substances in which they could be dissolved or emulsified.

In the development of insecticides, as in much other research, sustained and patient study with a dash of ingenuity and a backlog of common sense is the essential requirement. There is infrequent need for imagination or creative intellectual powers. To examine methods for killing insects, it was first necessary to have some insects. Accordingly colonies of mosquitoes and flies, chiggers and lice, bedbugs and roaches, had to be established and maintained in the laboratories. This is not easy. Take mosquitoes for example. It is not sufficient to maintain only the *Anopheles* species for, though they carry malaria, it is the *Aedes aegypti* which carries yellow fever and dengue. The two species may react quite differently to the same insecticide and colonies of both must be raised. The Orlando laboratories maintained 12,000 adults of a single species of mosquito. The eggs, 10,000 per day, were used to produce larvae for larvicidal studies and to renew the adult colonies. Larvae could be fed rather simply on powdered dog biscuit and yeast. Adults had to be fed on blood. This required the employment of men who were willing to be bitten repeatedly and on an unprecedented scale until it developed that egg production was adequate when rabbits were used as a source of blood. In similar fashion colonies of other insects, each with their peculiar housing and feeding problems, had to be reared and maintained.

An insect repellent, as distinct from an insecticide, is a substance which will prevent the insect from biting without necessarily killing it. They are useful against mosquitoes in areas where adults are present and where, in consequence, the only way of avoiding mosquito-borne infections is to prevent them from biting. The basis of the attraction exerted by human skin for the mosquito is not fully known. It is not understood why mosquitoes prefer certain individuals to others, why their egg production is higher when fed from one individual than another. Certainly they are attracted by the moisture and warmth of skin, by sweat present upon it, possibly by some product of its metabolism such as carbon dioxide. But ignorance of the distastes of the mosquito made it impossible to construct an ideal repellent on theoretical grounds and there was no alternative to the method of trial and error. Over 7000 substances have been examined for repellent qualities since the initiation of these studies. At their commencement, oil of citronella was the repellent in most common use, though, since 1920, certain other substances of the general type of Flit or Sta-way had been introduced by commercial firms. The more irritating substances submitted to OSRD laboratories for examination were eliminated from further study by applying them to the skin of animals. The less promising materials were eliminated by experiments in which the shaved belly of a guinea pig, anointed with the substance under investigation, was pressed against a cage containing twenty hungry female mosquitoes. The time before the first mosquito bit the animal and the frequency of subsequent bites were taken as a measure of probable repellent effectiveness. The more promising compounds were then subjected to similar human experiments in which an arm of the subject, protected by a coating of repellent, was thrust into a specially designed cage containing 400 mosquitoes. The observations were authenticated by recording biting rates when unprotected arms were offered the mosquitoes. The attraction exerted by sweat for mosquitoes made it necessary to re-examine the effectiveness of the substances after the subject had exercised. Finally field experiments were performed in which the subjects were taken to mosquito-infested areas after dark and record was made of the frequency with which their exposed hands and face were bitten. Any substance which prevented biting for more than three hours was regarded as promising. It could not be recommended for use until the effect of prolonged application to the human skin had been determined and until the acute and chronic effects of large doses upon animals had been examined. A majority of the substances thus observed for their repellent actions were subsequently studied for their effectiveness against larval and adult mosquitoes, against flies and lice and mites and fleas and roaches. A long and painstaking routine.

The ideal way of controlling mosquitoes is by killing the larvae, the immature forms. Prior to the war this had been attempted by covering the water in which mosquitoes breed with a film of kerosene or fuel oil or by sprinkling upon it powdered arsenic, Paris green. Arsenic lost its effectiveness after heavy rains because it became submerged and attempts to preserve its flotation by "coating" it proved ineffective. When new substances were introduced, they were examined in the laboratory by adding them in measured amounts to pans of water containing known numbers of larvae and, at intervals thereafter, counting the larvae that died or survived. These experiments were then transferred to field conditions, the larval content of water in a given pool or swamp being determined by examining specimens ("dips") from typical areas. Following application of the insecticide, larval counts were made on specimens from the same locales after varying periods of time to determine the completeness and duration of the effect.

Killing larvae is the best method of controlling mosquito-borne infections in permanent installations. It is inadequate in areas where troops are but briefly stationed since men are bitten by the adult mosquitoes already present and move on to other pastures before the younger generation could become a matter of importance. Pyrethrum, the powdered flower of a species of chrysanthemum, and rotenone, obtained from the root of derris, were the only effective adulticides known in 1941. The supply of both substances was limited and that of pyrethrum irrevocably so for wartime purposes, since Japan and the Dalmatian coast, its chief sources of supply, were in Axis hands. Only Kenya was left. When new substances became available they were investigated in the laboratory by spraying them into specially designed chambers containing adult mosquitoes or by carrying cages of mosquitoes through sprayed rooms, recording the promptness ("knockdown rate") and completeness of their effect. They were investigated in the field by making mosquito counts within dwellings and outdoors before, and for weeks and months after, the walls and vegetation had been sprayed.

The human body louse is the carrier of epidemic typhus fever and relapsing fever. In the last war it was familiarly, though without affection, known as the "cootie" and "reading your shirt" was the popular way of exterminating it. The prevention of epidemics of typhus, insofar as this is not accomplished by vaccination, involves killing enormous numbers of lice since the disease occurs when huge masses of people are crowded closely together. The fumigation or sterilization of clothes is an impracticable method of killing lice under these circumstances. Early in the war the British devised a garment, worn next the abdomen, called the Sherlice belt. The folds of this belt proved attractive to lice and it contained a thiocyanate preparation which was toxic to them. When more potent substances were discovered, they were studied by making daily louse counts on infested individuals before and after treatment. It was decided to impregnate underwear by dipping it into a solution of these substances. The underwear was then worn by subjects and the effectiveness of impregnation observed by placing 200 healthy lice on their skin, counting the survivors after forty-eight hours' contact. The duration of the effect was examined by applying additional lice at intervals over a period of ten weeks and after the underwear had been repeatedly laundered.

The mite (chigger) transmits a form of typhus called mite-borne or scrub typhus. It lives in low-lying grassy areas of Burma and the Southwest Pacific. As one walks through these areas or lies down in the grass, the mite attaches itself to one's outer clothing, crawls beneath it to bite and, if it be infected, produces the disease. When bivouac areas are cleared of long grass and underbrush the mites disappear, but since this is not always possible and since troops are not confined to bivouac areas, efforts were made to impregnate uniforms with miticides which would kill the insect before it could bite. The effectiveness of impregnation was gauged by placing mites on treated clothing and observing mortality rates before and after the garments were subjected to repeated washing.

Rats do not themselves carry any tropical disease but they harbor fleas which propagate both endemic typhus and plague. Since the obvious way to kill the fleas is to kill their hosts, rodenticides may be considered insecticides for purposes of the present exposition. The rats are a major cause of destruction of food and clothing supplies in their own right, and the subject of rodenticides was thus of practical interest to the Quartermaster General as well as the Surgeons General. The need for investigation was more acute since the supply of red squill, a rat poison, in 1941 was largely derived from the Mediterranean shores which were in Axis hands. Attempts were made by the Foreign Economic Administration to recruit the supply of squill by plantings in Mexico and Southern California. Despite several efforts by OSRD investigators to increase the yield of these plantings the shortage was not overcome until recovery of the Mediterranean permitted importations to be resumed. In the fall of 1943 the Research Laboratory at Denver, Colorado, of the Fish and Wildlife Service, undertook to enlarge their interest in rodenticides under OSRD contract, and eventually examined over 1500 substances. Their procedure was to investigate the toxicity of each compound by administering it to laboratory animals and then subject the more promising substances to field tests. Another important investigation in this field was carried on for CMR at Johns Hopkins University, where the feeding habits of rats had been under study for some years. It had developed that, presented with a variety of substances in separate containers (for example, sugar, fat, amino acids, vitamins), the rats would always select a beautifully balanced diet. Not only this, but when they were subjected to unusual needs by pregnancy or by the removal of certain endocrine glands, they would supplement their diet as wisely as if it were prescribed by the doctor in charge of some similar case in the clinic. The basis of this self-selection was found to lie in the taste of the various substances, for rats lost their discriminatory ability when their taste nerves were severed. The problem of selecting a rodenticide was therefore simplified by the probability that an effective poison would have to be tasteless.

Within the first months of study at the Orlando laboratories, three substances were selected and recommended to the services for adoption.

The selectees were DMP (*di methyl phthalate*), indalone, and Rutgers-612 (ethyl hexanediol). No one of the substances was new and all of them had been previously used as repellents. But the Orlando studies definitely established their value and ruled out, on the basis of lower potency or higher toxicity, a large number of other substances which had been suggested or had been in actual use. Continued investigation did not disclose any new compound sufficiently superior to these three to warrant recommendation, but a combination of the three proved more effective against a wider variety of insects than any one of them separately, and such a formula was adopted by the services in September 1943. The repellent was issued to troops in two-ounce bottles for application to exposed skin surfaces when insects were abroad. Supply and distribution were satisfactory from the beginning. It was nonirritant and easy to apply. But it did not provide complete protection. In certain conditions of heat and humidity, with certain individuals, its period of effectiveness was distinctly less than the three hours established for it in the laboratory. It was far from ideal and the disadvantage attached to it that must attach to all repellents: it required the co-operation of the individual soldier. A failure to co-operate cannot always be blamed upon the soldier. There are circumstances in which a two-ounce bottle is just two ounces more than one can carry. The trails of North Burma and, presumably, those of the Pacific islands are littered with bottles of mosquito repellent.

Discovery of the potency and broad effectiveness of DDT was the most important advance of the war in the field of insecticides. This compound (*dichlor diphenyl trichloroethane*) was first synthesized in 1874 but its activity against certain insects, moths and potato bugs, was only reported in 1939 by the Swiss firm, J. R. Geigy, which manufactured and distributed it under the patented name of Gesarol. Its usefulness was recognized by the Germans and modifications of it were employed by them throughout the war. Samples of the compound were sent to the Orlando laboratories October 23, 1942, by New York agents of the Swiss firm and its superiority over other insecticides was soon recognized. Laboratory and field studies were pressed with increasing enthusiasm throughout 1943 as the potential value of the substance became more and more apparent, and within a year of the initial observation it was being distributed in quantity to the services. The War

Going after mosquito larvae with an oil sprayer

"Dusting" with DDT to kill body lice

Production Board inaugurated a program to increase the supplies of DDT in December 1943, selecting four companies and providing them with AA-1 priorities to permit expansion of their manufacturing facilities. No chemical difficulties were involved and production, which had totaled only 153,000 pounds in 1943, increased to 10,000,000 pounds in 1944. In August 1945 it was being produced at the rate of 36,000,000 pounds a year.

It was first examined as a larvicide for anopheline mosquitoes. In this capacity it proved effective when sprayed on the surface of water at the rate of only two quarts of a 5 per cent solution per acre. Twenty-five gallons of crude oil had previously been required to produce similar coverage and had controlled larvae with less certainty. This represented an enormous improvement, and an enormous economy of the material, equipment, and labor involved in hand or power spraying. The small volumes of DDT solution required gave rise to the suggestion that it could be sprayed from airplanes and automobiles and thus further enhance the ease and extent of its application. Powdered arsenic had been used in this fashion as far back as 1923 but DDT promised to be far superior. This project, initiated at the Orlando laboratories, was pursued with co-operation of the Army and Navy Air Forces, the National Defense Research Committee, and other governmental agencies. Several methods of broadcasting the DDT as a mist from aircraft were finally developed, having a common reliance on the airstream from the propeller to effect distribution: in one the fluid was fed by gravity to a single nozzle hanging below the plane; in another a pump, activated by a wind-driven propeller, delivered fluid to a series of nozzles in long pipes constructed beneath the plane's wings; in still others the spray was generated by the motor's own exhaust or by a thermogenerator. To obtain adequate coverage from the air required the development of special techniques — the flight must be made at a certain height, runs over the target must be properly spaced, and some co-operation must be obtained from the winds of heaven. This constituted a difficulty as did the finding that the particle size of the spray was of great importance in securing an adequate kill. One difficulty was overcome by training, the other by research. The exhaust-generated sprays were adapted to use in jeeps. In small and accessible areas this method was much simpler than hand or power spraying and greatly extended its field of applicability.

Pyrethrum had been recognized as an effective agent with which to kill adult mosquitoes. In 1942 it was used in small enclosed areas such as rooms or to fumigate airplanes arriving from foreign ports which might be expected to introduce new and dangerous species of mosquitoes into the country. Its usefulness was increased by development of the small one-pound "mosquito bomb" which began to be distributed to personnel overseas in 1943. This bomb utilizes the expanding force of freon gas to drive a fine spray of pyrethrum in sesame oil into the air, where it stays suspended for some time. The spray effectively and promptly destroys mosquitoes and other flying insects in rooms or tents and even, for shorter periods of time, in such partially enclosed areas as caves or fox-holes. DDT is relatively ineffective by itself in the immediate destruction of insects because of the slowness with which it acts, but it has been added to pyrethrum in the more recent bombs in order to prolong the period of activity.

A most important characteristic of DDT now became apparent: not only is it a potent insecticide but, applied in large amounts, its effect is extremely persistent. If four times as much DDT is sprayed on stagnant water as is necessary to kill all larvae present at the time, a residual action persists which prevents their growth in the sprayed area for several weeks. Similarly, if DDT be sprayed on the walls and screens of a room at the rate of one gallon of 5 per cent solution per 1000 square feet, all adult mosquitoes coming into contact with the sprayed surfaces for from two to four months thereafter are killed. To a lesser but still definite extent the same principle obtains outdoors, where vegetation can be made poisonous to adult mosquitoes for considerable periods of time. This potent and persistent action by a substance which is available in unlimited quantities, which is effective upon both larval and adult mosquitoes, and which can be applied from aircraft and automobiles, has placed the attack against mosquitoes upon an entirely different plane. Previously it had been possible effectively to control mosquitoes in relatively small areas and with great expenditure of energy in draining and oiling surface water. Now it seemed possible to abolish mosquitoes over relatively large areas and with little difficulty, by infrequent spraying of larval breeding places and of the houses where adult mosquitoes swarm. The potentialities introduced by persistent effectiveness and airborne attack are still incompletely developed and were scarcely appreciated until well into 1944. Before that time mosquitoes had been eliminated from some of the smaller Pacific islands where occupation was prolonged and labor abundant. After that time the efforts to control larvae and adults were more ambitious and were applied in areas where they could not previously have been attempted. There remained, and still remain, certain situations where insect control can scarcely be contemplated: with mobile troops in jungle and paddy country, for example. There is no way of saying with any mathematical precision how much was accomplished during the war by insect-control measures in general and by DDT in particular. If one points to a decrease in malaria incidence from 1943 to 1944 as an example of their effectiveness, one could be answered by a rise in dengue incidence in the same years. Either figure is meaningless by itself. It is safe enough to say, in general terms, that there were a few places in which mosquito control was perfect and mosquito-borne diseases abolished; that there were many places in which, particularly after the introduction of DDT, there were fewer mosquitoes and less disease than if control had not been attempted.

DDT is as effective against lice as it is against mosquitoes; against the head and crab lice which are unesthetic though harmless, against the body louse which carries epidemic typhus and relapsing fevers. Experiments at the Orlando laboratories demonstrated that a powder containing 10 per cent DDT, though slower in action, was superior to one containing pyrethrins which they had previously recommended to the services. The issue of DDT as a lousicide was therefore started in the fall of 1943. Approximately one ounce of the powder, dusted over the inside of underwear and seams of the clothing, is effective for about one month. It must of course be reapplied if the clothing is changed or washed. It was found that duration of the control is doubled, and persists despite weekly laundering, if underwear is impregnated by dipping it into a solution of DDT. For purposes of mass treatment of civilian populations in North Africa and Italy, the Army introduced a simplified method by which powdered DDT was blown inside clothing and underwear when the individuals merely loosened their trousers and shirts. This procedure was held largely responsible for controlling the typhus epidemic in the Naples area which, smoldering throughout the summer, had reached an incidence of sixty new cases a day by December of 1943. Between December 21, 1943, and January 31, 1944, 1,300,000 persons were "dusted." By the latter date the incidence of new cases had decreased to ten a day. The method was later employed with similar success in concentration camps and in the *cordon sanitaire* which was established along the Rhine to prevent the spread of disease by displaced persons.

There is a considerable list of other and less dangerous insects against which DDT has proved to be effective. Adult flies, indoors, are as susceptible to the residual effects of DDT solutions as are mosquitoes. The spraying of mess halls, kitchens, and latrines controlled the fly population and removed the threat that they might transport intestinal diseases. Bedbugs and cockroaches are destroyed by spraying the bed and walls of barracks with 5 per cent DDT solutions or by blowing 10 per cent DDT powder into the crevices where they lurk. Animal fleas are a domestic rather than a military problem but they can be abolished from dogs and cats by application of a 5 per cent DDT powder or from rooms by a 5 per cent DDT solution, sprayed at the rate of one gallon per 2000 square feet. The one conspicuous failure to be recorded against DDT is in the case of fly larvae, maggots, which infest pit latrines and battlefield corpses and were a subject of real concern to the Army. Medical officers in the Southwest Pacific found that PDB (*p*ara *d*ichlor *b*enzene) was very effective in these situations and the British introduced 666 (benzene hexachloride) for a similar purpose.

The mechanism of the action of DDT and its toxicity were studied in numerous investigations initiated by the Insect Control Committee. In cockroaches, for example, it was observed that death is preceded by muscular twitchings and convulsions which indicate the action of DDT to be upon the nervous system, though the site has not been more precisely localized. Despite the enormous quantities of DDT which have been used there have been no reports of toxic effects in man which could be ascribed to the substance itself. This does not mean that it is nontoxic or can be used with complete impunity. It can be absorbed from oily solutions applied to the skin. It should certainly not be taken by mouth and, on that account, food must not be exposed when a room is being sprayed. It will kill laboratory animals with clear indications of liver and nervous system damage if it be fed or injected into them in large dosage.

DMP (*d*i *m*ethyl *p*hthalate) has been mentioned as an effective repellent against mosquitoes. When its action upon mites (chiggers) was first explored in 1942 at the Orlando laboratories, it was found to be distinctly toxic to them. This was an important observation, for in the summer of 1943 troops in the Southwest Pacific and Burmese theaters began to encounter scrub typhus, a mite-borne disease. The infection is at best a long and debilitating one with a mortality, under certain circumstances, as high as 30 per cent. DMP was available, it was used, and troops entering mite-infested areas were instructed to rub the substance over the surface of their clothing with particular attention to the openings of the garments, or to prepare a solution of DMP in a GI can and impregnate their clothes by dipping them into it. The procedure was awkward, difficult to enforce, and the effects of impregnation were only temporary, so that it had to be repeated each time the clothes were washed. Certainly, as the method was employed, it did not completely control scrub typhus. It was a sensible precaution to adopt and may have diminished the incidence of infection. The Australians had made similar observations on the effectiveness of phthalates and found another compound, dibutyl phthalate, superior to DMP in persistence. When the subject was reopened at the Orlando laboratories in 1944 a large number of compounds were examined and a third compound, benzyl benzoate, was found to be preferable to the other two. It was not, however, available in sufficient amounts for general use before the end of the war. Work is now in progress on substances which can be incorporated in clothing and, acting as "binders," make impregnations of this sort relatively permanent.

The one thousand and eightieth rodenticide compound examined by the Wildlife Laboratory at Denver proved to be extremely potent. As little as 0.1 milligram of this substance, #1080 (sodium fluoroacetate), produced death in rats. It was sent to the laboratory from a chemical warfare investigation carried on under the National Defense Research Committee and CMR during which its toxicity and the mechanism of its action had been extensively explored though its effect upon rodents had not been examined. It has the advantage of being practically tasteless in the concentrations required and of being readily incorporated into water or a variety of food baits. Studied at length in the laboratory and in large-scale field tests, it proved effective against all the common varieties of rats as well as against prairie dogs and ground squirrels, more effective than squill or any rodenticide which had been used up to that time. It was recommended to the services and has been used with considerable success by them and by the Public Health Service. It is not equipped with a moral sense and cannot, in consequence, distinguish between beneficent and malevolent wildlife. It will have to be used with due precaution on that account.

The discovery of a second effective rodenticide was a fortuitous result of the experiments on rats' taste perception which have been mentioned. A few crystals of a bitter substance (phenyl thiourea), supposed to be nontoxic, was placed on the tongue of six rats. Next morning all the animals were dead. Search was then made for a tasteless compound of the same series. Of more than one hundred substances prepared by the du Pont Chemical Company for this purpose, ANTU (*a*lpha *n*aphthyl *t*hio *u*rea) was found to be most satisfactory. It proved fatal for brown Norway rats, killing them by a specific action upon the blood vessels of their lungs. The damaged blood vessels leak fluid so profusely that the animals literally drown in their own blood. It is less effective against other species of rats and has the additional disadvantage of being toxic to dogs, though they are apt to escape death by vomiting as rats are unable to do. An extensive field study was carried on in Baltimore with ANTU and, properly and persistently executed, produced a marked decrease in the city's rat population.

When one recalls the profound misgivings with which this tropical adventure was faced in 1941, the results, viewed four years later, are nothing short of amazing. On the whole, and with the single exception of malaria, our troops maintained a prolonged and intimate contact with the tropics with a far lower incidence of tropical disease and a far lower mortality than had been feared. There were no considerable forces in areas where yellow fever and African sleeping sickness are endemic, so these diseases constituted no problem. But in 1943 the Army had nearly 1,000,000 troops in the North African, Near Eastern, CBI, and Pacific theaters, and in 1944 double that number. Up to August 1945, there were no cases of plague, 241 of relapsing fever, 13 of cholera, 60 of kala azar, and 61 of epidemic typhus. There were 344 cases of cutaneous leishmaniasis (oriental sore), 2110 of filariasis, 12,228 of sand-fly fever, and 82,392 of dengue. No one of this latter group of diseases is commonly serious or had any mortality in its own right. The single tropical disease with a significant mortality which the Army encountered in any quantity during this period was scrub typhus, of which there were nearly 7000 cases with some 300 deaths. When the Japanese islands were approached a few cases of Japanese encephalitis were reported and there were nearly 1000 cases of schistosomiasis amongst troops in the Philippines.

There was a widespread fear that certain tropical diseases might be brought back to the United States by returning soldiers and become established here. There is no proper basis for that fear. Even malaria is not expected to pose much of a problem because of the relative ease with which mosquito control can be imposed in this country. The only other soldiers who should return in any numbers with a transmissible disease are those with filariasis and schistosomiasis. In the former case, the transmissibility is a matter of theory rather than practice, for the disease has been so mild that the infecting organism is not present in the blood stream. In the latter case, no recognized carrier exists within the United States. On the whole, then, an extraordinarily successful escape from an extraordinarily dangerous experiment.

To what do we owe this escape? In part it must be ascribed to the vigilance of the Surgeons General's Offices, to their sensible directions for prevention and treatment of particular diseases, to their practice of sending commissions and specialists to areas where dangerous diseases made a first appearance. In larger part it must be ascribed to the alertness and training of the unit and hospital medical officers which enabled them to recognize diseases foreign to their experience and to treat them wisely.

It is more difficult to assess the role played by insecticides. The research program which has been described led to several definite and valuable accomplishments: (a) the development of a better repellent than had previously been known; (b) the discovery that DDT was a potent insecticide against a host of dangerous and annoying insects, that it could be applied by aircraft and automobile and could produce prolonged residual effects; (c) the discovery of three compounds which could kill mites; (d) the discovery of two compounds to destroy rats. These discoveries did not come all at once nor are they fully developed even now. There is room for a better repellent, more experience in the use of DDT, a more effective miticide. No one can say that because of this program the incidence of such a disease decreased by so many per cent; or that so many soldiers who would have died are now alive. No one can deny that the achievements of the program were useful and that, because of them, fewer soldiers were bitten, fewer diseases developed.

Nor is there any necessity for judging the success of the insecticide research solely by its effect upon the health of United States troops in the years 1942–1945. The results which flowed from it constitute a permanent advance in the prevention of insect-borne disease which will not cease with the end of any war. Improvements will of course be made, but even at the present level of knowledge it is clear that DDT, far more practicable than mass vaccination as a preventive against typhus, is an important weapon against the epidemics which have repeatedly ravaged Poland and the Balkans in the past and will return again. It is clear that a capable and determined authority could abolish mosquito-borne diseases from large areas of territory that are not dominated by jungle and paddy field.

It is interesting to observe that out of this rather frenzied search for means of killing lice in Italy and mosquitoes in Assam have come substances that will affect our own country, in which lice and mosquitoes have only a nuisance value. Nuisance values are not unimportant. In the tropics, really, it was the incessant heat, the repeating rains, the continuous rivulets of sweat, the long discomfort of sleeping on the ground, the necessity of eating K rations or even 10-in-1's, that played a greater part than tropical diseases themselves in reducing the eagerness and effectiveness of our troops. It is admitted that nuisance values cannot be accurately weighed and, even, that a certain number of fleas may be "good for a dog." It will still be important, in our own country, to be rid of flies and mosquitoes, lice and roaches. It is of course important to be rid of such infrequent insect-borne diseases as exist here.

There will be other and better "DDT's." There are other fields of usefulness for insecticides which have barely begun to be explored: veterinary medicine, the insect pests of agriculture, termites that destroy wood, barnacles that foul the bottoms of ships. They should be an important weapon, not to be used too indiscriminately until we know better which insects are immune and which susceptible to them, which insects play a useful role in our complicated economy and which may profitably perish.

CHAPTER XXIV

AVIATION MEDICINE

SCIENTIFIC progress usually brings new dangers with new powers, and reveals new human limitations as old ones are overcome. The history of aviation is replete with instances of this. Time and again physicists and engineers have developed machines which the human flier has been unable to use. Or the machines endangered the lives of those who used them. Then the progress of aviation again waited upon the aid of the biologist. Thus we have attained our present prowess in the air through the combined efforts of the physicist and the physiologist.

If this is not apparent to most people, it is because they have done their flying far behind the front lines of man's combat with the unknown forces involved in flight. Scientists and manufacturers and test pilots have faced the hazards and have overcome them before each new development has been given to the public. In military aviation this is not so. A strong concern for national security imposes on military forces the responsibility for quickly adapting each new scientific discovery to their needs. In order to gain the strategic advantage of time and surprise they have employed to the very limits of usability each new advance in aviation.

This was especially true during World War II. The elements of time and surprise were vital. The co-ordinated efforts of vast numbers of technicians gave us with bewildering rapidity new planes, instruments, and weapons that would have matured but slowly in peacetime. Machines that severely taxed the human organism had to be operated under difficult conditions in order to protect our armed forces and our nation against far greater dangers. To make our aerial operations possible under those difficult conditions, and to protect the lives and the efficiency of our airmen, was the mission of flight surgeons, aviation physiologists and psychologists, and the biologists in the laboratories.

The role of the civilian scientist in this undertaking was especially difficult in 1940. Few of them had any direct familiarity with the problems of military aviation; most of them had never flown in an army or naval aircraft; none had participated in military maneuvers. And yet the physiological dangers and stresses of aerial combat could only be recognized and comprehended by those who were intimately familiar with these problems. Nor were there more than a handful of regular officers in the Army and Navy who had both the practical knowledge of air force operations and the scientific training necessary to define and solve the difficulties that soon imperiled the success of our military campaigns.

Anticipating the potential dangers of this situation, Dr. Lewis H. Weed, Chairman of the Division of Medical Sciences of the National Research Council, organized a Committee on Aviation Medicine in the fall of 1940, with Dr. Eugene F. DuBois as chairman. This committee of physiologists, psychologists, and physicians immediately set about their own education in these matters. They toured airfields where our young men were receiving a belated training for the aerial war that soon came. They visited aircraft factories, and discussed with aircraft designers the characteristics of the new planes that would overstress the powers of the human body. They held frequent conferences with the leaders of our Air Forces who were planning the strategy and tactics of the campaigns that were to be fought far above the earth, by young men who were accustomed to life on the ground. Fortunately, they had as their guide Armstrong's recent report of his research at Wright Field.

And so it was that when the Committee on Medical Research was created some months later, there was a small group of scientists who had already formulated some of the more important physiological problems of human flight. Accordingly Dr. A. N Richards, Chairman of CMR, made them his advisers on the organization of a great co-ordinated program.

Throughout the war Colonel Loyd Griffis represented General David N. W. Grant, the Air Surgeon of the Army Air Forces, on the Committee on Aviation Medicine. Similarly Commodore Adams maintained day-by-day contact with the civilian scientists through Captain John Poppen, Commander Eric Liljencrantz, and their successors. The Committee, in turn, assigned Dr. E. Cowles Andrus and later Dr. Louis B. Flexner to keep them informed of the needs of the services. From time to time Dr. DuBois relinquished his position as Chairman of the Committee and assumed active duty as a captain for medical service in naval aviation. Dr. Detlev Bronk was continuously Co-ordinator of Research in the Office of the Air Surgeon of the Army Air Forces, a member of the Committee on Aviation Medicine, and Chief of the Division of Aviation Medicine in the Office of Scientific Research and Development. Through these strong links between the civilian and military organizations, practical problems were quickly analyzed and the results of research in university laboratories were soon translated into new equipment and operational procedures.

One of the most serious obstacles to modern aerial warfare that confronted these scientists was a human limitation that appeared early in the history of aviation. In 1862 Glaisher, the English meteorologist, and Coxwell, his balloon engineer, ascended to a reported altitude of 29,000 feet. Glaisher had lost consciousness, and both would have perished had not Coxwell, paralyzed though he was, seized the valve cord in his teeth and released the gas by vigorously nodding his head. Man had been freed from his earth-bound existence only to find that the full utilization of his new machine was restricted by his inability to live at high altitudes.

Paul Bert, the French physiologist, soon discovered that the danger of this new environment was the lack of adequate oxygen. Without a sufficient supply of this gas the nerve cells of the brain cannot carry on their normal activity, consciousness fails, and death ensues. It was then obvious to Bert that fliers who go to high altitudes must carry with them a reservoir of oxygen from which they can breathe enough to make up the deficiency in the surrounding air.

These were facts well known to physiologists and to the few adventurous aviators who dared flight into the substratosphere. But most of the commercial and military flying in aeroplanes before the war was at heights where the oxygen in the atmosphere is sufficient to maintain life. Accordingly, even in the late 1930's we were unprepared for keeping our fliers alive and alert at the altitudes to which they were later forced by enemy fighters and antiaircraft fire. In this war, young fliers had to be warned of the subtle prelude to loss of consciousness from lack of oxygen and schooled against the insidious feeling of well-being that quickly lapses into a complete loss of the mental faculties.

During the early years of the war many suggestions were made as to how the normal processes of the body might be altered by chemical substances, so as to reduce the need for oxygen. The chances of success were not great, but the importance of the problem required the exploration of every possibility. Adrenal cortical hormone, ammonium chloride, and methylene blue were among the many substances that were carefully tested by physiologists working under the Committee on Medical Research. By adding some of these chemical agents to the diet of fliers it was, indeed, possible for them to go three or four thousand feet higher without suffering from oxygen want. But the substances had other, less desirable effects, and they were never adequate to take a man to the heights at which many of our aerial operations were carried on. As is usually the case, it is more feasible to provide by physical means the proper environment for the human body than to alter the course of the normal mechanisms within the body.

Following the former method of attack, Dr. Walter M. Boothby and his associates of the Mayo Foundation, shortly before the war, developed a mask which covered the nose and mouth of a flier and thus delivered to him oxygen from a tank carried in the plane. Here was encountered a problem that frequently arises in technological warfare: the means for providing a reasonable degree of human protection limit the military usefulness of the instruments of combat. To furnish the crew of a large bomber with enough oxygen throughout a long mission requires hundreds of pounds of tanks and accessory equipment. Consequently, for a given design of aircraft the bomb load or the range of operations must be reduced. Accordingly, compromise between tactical requirements, physiological needs, and engineering design became necessary.

The Mayo scientists reduced this difficulty by conserving the oxygen and thus reducing the amount that had to be carried. This was done by placing a rubber bag in the oxygen supply line where it reached the mask. Part of the exhaled air, containing some residual oxygen from the lungs, escaped through a valve; part returned to the bag, where it was mixed with the incoming oxygen from the cylinder and thus conserved the precious supply.

This equipment proved admirable for moderate altitudes. At the higher altitudes to which we were ultimately forced by enemy action there was a danger that in the process of rebreathing the oxygen would be too much diluted, and too much expired carbon dioxide would accumulate.

Also, the exhaled water vapor froze at high altitudes and blocked the flow of oxygen.

The Navy employed a device designed to conserve oxygen by a similar process of rebreathing, but the exhaled air from the lungs passed through a chemical compound which absorbed carbon dioxide and in doing so produced some oxygen. Here, too, there was danger of freezing in the low temperatures of the higher atmosphere.

The Battle of Britain had given the American Air Forces a pretty clear idea of the specifications for an aerial war over Germany. High-altitude bombing was one of the essentials. The obvious need was a system that would supply just enough oxygen to satisfy the requirements of each flier under any condition of altitude or bodily activity, and do so with certainty. The natural indicators of what that need is at any moment are the nerve cells of the brain which regulate the rate and depth of respiration. A means was already available which controlled the flow of oxygen to the aviator's mask in response to the action of these nerve cells, through the respiratory movements the cells initiate. This was done by placing in the supply line a regulating valve which was activated by the suction created by each inspiration.

To conserve the supply of oxygen at low altitudes and to ensure an adequate supply at high altitudes, National Research Council scientists in 1940 designed an oxygen diluter valve which was controlled by an aneroid. It was thus possible automatically to furnish the lungs of fliers, at any altitude, a gaseous mixture corresponding to sea level or to some moderate, safe level. The feasibility of this device became apparent before it was put into operational use by our air forces, for a similar instrument was found on some captured German planes.

From these beginnings there was a continuing struggle to improve the oxygen supply systems so that they would, in a more compact and simple form and with less weight, give our airmen greater safety in their battles six or seven miles above the earth. To accomplish these ends scores of medical scientists worked in their laboratories or in partially evacuated steel "altitude chambers" to secure precise physiological data for the designers: the rate of oxygen supply required by the human body, the individual variations in that requirement, the additional oxygen needed at any altitude, the tolerable inspiratory and expiratory pressures, and the effects of varying degrees of work on the respiratory demands. Much of this important data was finally brought together in a *Handbook of Respiratory Data in Aviation.*

One of the most important requirements for the safe use of oxygen at altitudes above 25,000 or 30,000 feet was a suitable means for delivering the gas to the nose and mouth during inspiration. The mask devised by Boothby and his associates was a step in the right direction, but at the higher altitudes there was the threat of freezing and of the inward leakage of oxygen-deficient air. As early as 1940 Dr. Cecil Drinker, of Harvard University, anticipated these dangers and set about devising a suitable mask, under contract with OSRD.

This appeared to be a simple task; actually it was one of the most troublesome human design problems in aviation. Fliers are born and grow up without a rubber appendage on their faces, so they did not readily accept the new addition. The facial configuration of no two men is the same, and this caused poor fitting and excessive leakage. Freezing of water vapor in the air passages was a persistent problem; the mask and the goggles interfered with each other; it was difficult to integrate the communications microphone with the mask; and how was a man to move about a bomber when he was connected by a mask and a short rubber tube to a fixed oxygen tank, and how was he to survive during a slow parachute descent from a great height? To meet these difficulties there were many modifications of the first mask designed by the Harvard group. In their efforts to reduce the dangers from leakage, the Army Air Forces went so far as to employ a group of anthropologists to measure the facial dimensions of more than a thousand cadets. From these measurements five standard types of mask were constructed; then to each airman there was issued one of the appropriate size. Another group, working under the CMR, made a precise mathematical and experimental study of the effects of mask leakage on human performance under varying conditions of work and altitude. From this came a better basis for safe design and a better definition of the hazards.

It was such equipment that protected our fliers against the dangers of thin atmospheres in which they fought. But, successful as each improvement was in reducing the number of casualties from oxygen lack, the basic characteristics of the system were unsatisfactory. It was obvious from the start of the war that what was required was a sealed aircraft cabin, in which an adequate supply of oxygen would be maintained by compressing air from the outside with a mechanical compressor. Such a pressurized cabin finally appeared in operational use on the B-29's. Gone at last were the cumbersome oxygen mask, the restriction on free movement, and the bulky clothing for protection against the killing cold of high altitudes. The engineers had at last restored to fliers their natural environment, while taking them to altitudes unsuitable for life.

But it was only a thin metal shell that separated the friendly atmosphere within the cabin from the old dangers that lurked outside. And it was a wall readily pierced by enemy missiles. Suddenly the precious oxygen might be lost; in a brief second the crew might be exposed to a greatly reduced pressure.

Physiologists readily determined the length of time men could survive the loss of oxygen, and emergency masks and supply systems were provided. But there was little knowledge of the effects of quickly lowering the pressure on the human body. Normally there is an equalization of pressure inside and outside the body; the amount of gas in solution in the body fluids depends upon the external pressure. How a violent change of pressure from that of sea level, maintained within the cabin, to that of 40,000 feet, outside the cabin, would affect men was a problem the CMR requested physiologists to investigate.

To do this they evacuated one section of a steel "altitude chamber" with a suction pump to a pressure corresponding to a possible flying altitude. Another smaller section, containing the subjects of the experiment, was kept at sea-level pressure. Between the two was a thin wall. When this wall was suddenly ruptured, there was in the second section of the chamber a precipitate fall of pressure. Thus it was found that objects in the path of the air flow to the hole were violently disturbed, and subsequently there has been at least one instance of a flier being blown out of a ruptured port in a B-29. But the experiments showed that there are no harmful effects within the body resulting from the sudden change of pressure. Later, Army Air Force physiologists safely decompressed themselves at a rate of from 8000 to 30,000 feet in one hundredth of a second. From such evidence came the assurance that the physiological advantages of pressurized cabins are not offset by physiological dangers.

The height to which men can go in these cabins is limited only by the skill of the aircraft designer. This is not so for men flying with the aid of an oxygen supply system. Above 38,000 feet the barometric pressure is so low that insufficient oxygen goes into the blood passing through the lungs, even though pure oxygen be delivered to the mask. To satisfy the human requirements at these great heights, oxygen must be delivered under a pressure sufficiently high to load the blood adequately. Before the advent of pressurized cabins there was an uncomfortable possibility that this physiological limitation might determine the outcome of the three-cornered race for altitude between bombers, fighter interceptors, and antiaircraft fire.

The Germans sought to meet the difficulty by getting their interceptors up to 40,000, or 45,000 feet with jet propulsion, and down again, so quickly that the pilots would survive the oxygen lack. As a temporary expedient, physiologists of the Allied Air Forces modified the mask and regulating valves of the usual oxygen supply systems so that the pressure within the mask was greater than that of the ambient air. Thus, more oxygen entered the blood, and the top level of operations was increased some thousands of feet. The achievement of this posed a long series of physiological questions, such as the effects of the increased pressure on blood flow through the lungs, or what were the relative advantages of a constant high pressure and an intermittent pressure that varied with the respiratory cycle. These were problems admirably suited to CMR scientists in university laboratories.

Few fliers have experienced the explosive decompression of a pressurized cabin. But it is not unusual in modern fighter aircraft to climb at the rate of eighty feet a second, to reach an altitude of six miles in six minutes, where the barometric pressure is but one-third that at sea level. Even this change in the pressure acting on the body unbalances the equilibrium of gas pressures within its cavities and tissues. Indeed, the physiological consequences can be more harmful than those which result from the very rapid pressure changes of shorter duration, to which we have already referred. The painful inward pressure on the eardrum, when the eustachian tube cannot be opened, is a familiar experience of all who have flown. But only the military aviator who goes quickly to 30,000 or 40,000 feet knows the excruciating pain caused by the sudden liberation of gases from solution in the blood or other body fluids.

This was not an unknown problem before the days of fast fighter craft. Divers had experienced the painful consequences of coming out of the high pressure in a diving bell into the lower pressure of atmospheric air. To those symptoms physicians had given the names Caisson disease or bends or decompression sickness, and physicians concerned with diving operations had studied their cause. There was little question that the pain was in some way the result of gases coming out of solution in the fluids of the body. Beyond that our knowledge was scanty.

The prospect of pilots and aircrew writhing with the pain of bends at 35,000 feet did not augur well for the success of our aerial war. And yet there was the possibility that we should have to fight at those altitudes. Accordingly, the CMR supported many investigations under the supervision of a Subcommittee on Decompression Sickness of the Committee on Aviation Medicine. Dr. John F. Fulton, of Yale University, was chairman of this group; because of their research we know a good deal about the causes of bends in aviators, the frequency with which bends occur, and means for preventing them.

Several years were spent uncovering the sequence of events that takes place. It was found that during the sudden changes of pressure minute gas nuclei on the surface of cells or on the inner walls of blood vessels rapidly expand in size, growing with the nitrogen, carbon dioxide, and oxygen that are liberated from the surrounding fluid as it is decompressed. As bubbles of gas are thus formed and grow, some lodge in small terminal vessels where they obstruct the flow of blood. Nerve endings may thus be deprived of oxygen, and pain results. Or regions of the brain are likewise put out of action, with widespread and serious consequences.

These observations and the resulting theory of decompression sickness led to a practical and fairly reliable method of prevention. Assuming that the bubbles are largely composed of nitrogen — that being the most plentiful source of gas within the body fluids — it was suggested that the supply of nitrogen for bubble formation could be reduced by breathing pure oxygen for some time before a flight. Nitrogen in the tissues is thus replaced by oxygen. Because the oxygen is consumed by cellular metabolism, and because its tension in the blood falls rapidly when a little is removed, it is less potent as a source of bubbles. This was proved experimentally, and the practice of breathing oxygen before a flight, or on the climb to altitude, is now a proved, but not infallible means for preventing decompression pains.

Actually, the incidence of decompression sickness or bends among fliers was never very great. In large measure it was due to the fact that men were rarely at a "bends altitude" of 35,000 feet or more for long periods of time. But if operating conditions had been less favorable in this respect, we were prepared to meet the problem.

Radar and radio-controlled projectiles could take men out of the air in a future war. But World War II was fought by men with the aid of their senses; indeed, the instruments which have supplemented the senses have at the same time made greater demands upon them. Take the matter of night flying, for instance, which has been made possible by instrumental devices. The strategy and tactics of aerial war have thus been greatly extended, for the airman can now utilize nature's most effective form of camouflage. Unfortunately, this advantage is also available to the enemy, and this, then, requires a keen ability to see, through darkness, the dim form of an enemy aircraft or the contours of an unlit airfield.

To watch a night mission return to blacked-out Britain was to appreciate how unnatural such duties were, and how difficult, for the young airman who had grown up with a light switch at his finger tip and a flashlight in his pocket. Nor were there many physicians who knew enough about night vision to be helpful with advice. Few remembered the elementary facts that the cone cells of the retina, which are used in day vision, do not respond to dim lights; that the rod cells, which are used in night vision, are located in the peripheral regions of the retina, so that one sees a dim object best by looking a little away from it; that the sensitivity of the rods is destroyed for some time by a bright light, and is least affected by red of all the colors. And yet the translation of those principles into tactical practice by the scientists of the CMR was an important element in the success of our night operations. Advantageously for the United States, the world's leading authorities on night vision were available for this work: Dr. Selig Hecht of Columbia, Dr. Walter Miles of Yale, and others who formed a Subcommittee on Visual Problems of the National Research Council and thus advised the CMR. In a technological war, fortunate is the nation that has a corner on scientific talent in any field.

Because of the great military advantage of keen night vision there were many suggestions for improving the ability to see at night, by the use of chemicals and drugs. The most promising of these agents was vitamin A. The basis for that suggestion was the discovery by physiologists that a deficiency of this vitamin in the diet causes defective night vision. During the years before the war Dr. Hecht and Dr. George Wald of Harvard had thoroughly investigated its role in the visual process. As the pattern of our allies' war unfolded and revealed the importance of night combat, our scientists carefully tested the night vision of thousands of young airmen and sought to improve that vision by the administration of large quantities of vitamin A. As had been learned before, they found that inadequate diets caused partial night blindness, and this was an important fact for the flight surgeons who cared for the health and efficiency of our fliers. But the administration of extra quantities of the vitamin was without benefit. Enough of the vitamins is enough; there was sufficient in the normal diet of our airmen and more than that produced no effect. Nor was any other substance found that would improve night vision.

Although no means were found for improving the natural physiological endowments of our airmen for seeing at night, it soon became apparent that much could be done to protect vision and to use natural abilities more effectively.

One of the first steps toward this end was a revision of lighting practice on airfields and in aircraft. It was a problem first posed by Professor A. V. Hill of London when he was in this country in the spring of 1940, anticipating perhaps the conditions that would arise during the Battle of Britain. The considerations are these. Following prolonged exposure to bright light, the eyes require about half an hour in which to become dark-adapted; until then night vision is below normal. Accordingly, a pilot who turns his gaze from a lighted instrument panel out into the darkness, where enemy planes are hidden, can see but poorly for some time. To minimize this disadvantage, the CMR sponsored the design of a physiologically acceptable lighting system for aircraft enclosures which has as its principal feature the use of an appropriate wave length of red light. This practice, which was adopted by the Navy, makes possible cone vision for the precise observations within the aircraft, without affecting appreciably the subsequent sensitivity of rod vision for distant, dimly illuminated objects.

In line with this reasoning, red goggles were designed that could be worn by airmen prior to night flight. When they took advantage of this physiological aid they were able to go quickly into combat, without the handicap of meeting, relatively blind, a dark-adapted foe.

Typical of the new problems that were created by the unfamiliar environments of our world-wide war was the prolonged impairment of night vision discovered by one of the CMR visual experts among personnel on the glaring beaches of the tropics. There the visual purple of the retina was so much bleached by the sunlight that the ability to see in dim illumination was depressed throughout the night. To avoid this previously unrecognized handicap, the use of appropriate sun glasses and of care was recommended to our fliers.

The oxygen-deficient atmospheres of high altitudes were also environmental causes of poor night vision. Careful measurements show that night fighters at 5000 feet altitude could see less well than at ground level, and their vision deteriorated steadily as they went higher. After laboratory tests revealed the seriousness of this handicap, military regulations were established which required all airmen to use at night an auxiliary supply of oxygen, even at moderate altitudes. Only thus was it possible for them to take full advantage of their normal visual powers.

A second important activity of CMR visual scientists was the formulation of a campaign to teach our airmen how to see at night. Fortunately there were precedent and personnel for this undertaking. Both the Army and Navy Air Forces, from the beginning of the war, had found it necessary to teach their student fliers a good deal of physiology, so that they would understand the effects of high altitude and little oxygen on their bodies. Hundreds of physiologists were commissioned as instructors, and these young scientists taught the future fliers the rudiments of human biology, revealed to them the symptoms of oxygen want in partially evacuated "altitude chambers," and instructed them in the use of protective oxygen equipment. After convincing the military authorities that the ability to see at night could be improved by knowledge and training, our visual experts turned to these Aviation Physiologists for assistance in disseminating the information about night vision that had been learned through years of research.

Under the supervision of CMR a series of intensive training courses in visual physiology was organized for the Aviation Physiologists of the Army Air Forces. In groups of twenty-five, they spent a week learning or recalling the details of visual mechanisms, the principles of photometry, recent developments in optical instruments and visual aids, and the use of night visual training devices designed for them by the CMR, which had benefited much from the previous experience of Wing Commander Evelyn of the R.C.A.F. and of Captain Schilling of the U.S. Navy Submarine Service. Then the Aviation Physiologists returned to their training fields and to foreign theaters of operation, where they translated this knowledge into more elementary instruction that improved the effectiveness of night fighters and night bomber crews.

Military aircraft are designed to move men rapidly. But some of the movements men undergo in aircraft are not desired, and some are harmful to the human body.

Among these are the motions of a plane caused by air currents or "rough air." They are relatively harmless, but anyone who has experienced the nauseating symptoms of motion sickness will agree that they could seriously reduce the fighting efficiency of an airman. When large numbers of unseasoned fliers were recruited into our forces this condition became a threat to the effectiveness of our aerial operations. Accordingly the CMR fostered research, under the direction of Dr. D. Denny-Brown of Harvard and Dr. Philip Bard of the Johns Hopkins, Chairmen of the NRC Subcommittee on Motion Sickness, which was directed to the discovery of the conditions which are most likely to cause motion sickness and of drugs which will prevent it.

One group of investigators tried to determine the type of motion which is most objectionable. A "nauseator," not unlike an elevator, was constructed, and in this device men were moved through space — up and down at varying speeds, through various distances, with different accelerations. Ultimately the results of such tests should provide information that will enable aircraft designers to construct planes which will be freer of the movements which cause motion sickness. But that is a long-range undertaking. Begun under the emphasis of a war-accented need the work can best be carried forward in the more deliberate spirit of peacetime research.

In the course of such tests, information was also gathered concerning the type of individual who is most likely to experience motion sickness. Certain mental characteristics were found to be predisposing factors.

Also, habituation to the characteristic motion of an airplane was an excellent preventive of nausea. In accordance with these observations, the air forces found a remarkably low incidence of motion sickness among their flying personnel, due presumably, in part, to the type of men selected for flying duties; in part, to the fact that they were thoroughly accustomed to the movements of aircraft.

The situation was not so favorable among ground troops who were only occasionally carried by glider or aerial transport. There was a similar contrast between seasoned sailors and soldiers transported by landing barges or other vessels used in amphibious operations. In both cases the foot soldier was much more disposed to motion sickness. To protect these men, vigorous efforts were made to find drugs which would prevent the nausea. Many searching tests were made of the effectiveness of various drugs and of the efficacy of different bodily postures, especially in the course of amphibious training operations. No new drugs of value were discovered in the haste of the war effort, but improved combinations of previously known drugs were found to be effective in about 70 per cent of the individuals who would otherwise have suffered from motion sickness.

There is another type of harmful movement that is essential for good fighter planes. Their high speed and great maneuverability enable them to excel in plane-to-plane combat, to evade the heavier fire power of larger craft, and to give effective protection to our bomber missions. Engineers and metallurgists worked for years to develop these planes that will withstand the centrifugal forces of high-speed turns and "pull-outs," but during that time there were no corresponding improvements of the physiological characteristics of the men who were to utilize the new machines during such maneuvers.

A normal heart and circulation will deliver enough blood to the brain when the body is erect or recumbent, and will meet the needs during sudden changes in posture. Nerve messages, from pressure-sensitive nerve endings in the walls of certain blood vessels, promptly report to the nerve centers regulating the heart and blood vessels a drop in blood pressure within the vessels supplying the brain. The effect of this is an accelerated heart rate and a constriction of peripheral vessels. Thus the circulation of the brain is again increased. But the cardiovascular system and this reflex control were not evolved for pumping blood made five to ten times heavier by a suddenly applied centrifugal force. Yet such forces do act upon a fighter pilot as he makes a steeply banked turn at high speeds, or as he pulls out of a power-dive.

The most valuable instrument for this research was the human centrifuge. A long horizontal arm, rotating about a vertical axis, carried at the outer end a seat for the subject. A man, sitting in this, could be subjected to centrifugal forces of a desired magnitude, while various physiological reactions were measured. Following the example of the Royal Canadian Air Force, which had done important pioneer work in this field, two such devices were built in civilian laboratories within the United States. The first was at the Mayo Foundation, the second at the University of Southern California.

Under these controlled conditions, men were rotated so that they were under the influence of a centrifugal force that was five to ten times as great as the force of gravity. When this force was in the direction of the subject's feet, as is the case in most high-speed aerial maneuvers, "gray-out," then "blackout," of vision were the first effects. If the centrifugal force were sufficiently great, and prolonged for some seconds, loss of consciousness followed. Measurements of heart action and of blood pressure in various parts of the body during rotation showed that the heart was unable to pump enough blood to the brain. Accordingly, the brain was deprived of the oxygen it needs for carrying on its normal activity. With smaller centrifugal forces there were no obvious symptoms, but often-repeated reductions of the cerebral blood flow ultimately caused fatigue, irritability, and inefficiency.

Three methods were devised for aiding the heart to overcome this handicap imposed by swift combat planes. One was to place the pilot in such a position that the centrifugal force acted at right angles to the axis of his body. Under those circumstances, the heart is not required to pump the blood against the centrifugal force. In the centrifuge this was readily accomplished by holding the subject's body perpendicular to the rotating arm. In a plane, it would be necessary for the pilot to assume a prone position as a boy does upon a sled. This would have required a radical redesign of the aircraft and its controls as well as the techniques of operation. Accordingly, this procedure was not employed. Some steps were taken in this direction, however, by providing elevated footrests and provisions for crouching, so that as much of the pilots' body as possible was perpendicular to the path of the plane during the turn or pull-out. Greater accelerations were thus tolerated.

A second procedure derived from these physiological experiments was that of tensing the muscles of the abdominal wall and of the lower extremities with a closed glottis, so as to aid the return of blood to the heart and thus circulate more blood to the brain.

The physiological basis for the effectiveness of this procedure was also the basis for the "anti-g suit." This was the most useful aid to fighter pilots in overcoming blackout. At least three civilian groups working under the CMR in collaboration with service laboratories and those of our allies made important developments along these lines. In each case the basic concept was the same. By a constant force applied to the surfaces of the arms and legs and abdomen, or by pressures that increased as the centrifugal force increased, excess blood was prevented from accumulating in those regions. Thus the normal flow of blood to the brain was better maintained. With the aid of these suits, pilots retained their normal faculties under the action of centrifugal forces several times greater than a force which would otherwise have produced a temporary loss of consciousness.

The most severe forces of acceleration or deceleration to which an airman is subject are those which occur during aircraft accidents. A plane that crashes into the earth or another object may decelerate from a speed of hundreds of miles an hour to rest in a brief second, and thus exert tremendous forces upon objects which are free to move within the plane. Thus the bodies of the crew continue to move forward until they strike a fixed portion of the plane or the earth.

The avoidance of the human consequences of such forces has been the concern of engineers, training officers, and flight surgeons. But there had been little systematic and co-ordinated effort by human biologists and engineers to deal with the basic aspects of this problem. To meet that challenge the CMR supported a comprehensive program of research under the direction of Dr. Eugene DuBois of the Cornell Medical College, which had three objectives. They were: a determination of the causes of aircraft accidents and the nature of the resulting injuries; the analysis of the structural characteristics of the plane responsible for the injuries; the redesign of seats, safety harness, control panels, escape hatches, and other parts of the plane so as to reduce the likelihood of accidents and minimize the injuries that result from unavoidable accidents.

Through collaboration with the Office of the Air Surgeon of the Army Air Forces a detailed survey was made of the frequency of various injuries and their relation to the type of plane, the structural portion of the plane causing the injury, the training experience of the pilot, and the operating conditions at the time of the accident. This information suggested modifications in training practice and in operational practice which increased the safety of flight.

Of more far-reaching significance was the revelation of unnecessary structural characteristics that were frequently responsible for injury. Safety harness was improved, weak seat supports were strengthened, sharp projections were removed from in front of the pilot's head. To test the potential danger of these causes under controlled conditions and to assess the value of improvements, there was constructed at Cornell a crash car which could hurtle a dummy pilot and his protective equipment swiftly into an obstacle. From these and similar studies there began a movement for greater safety in aircraft which is continuing into the peacetime aerial age.

Part Five: Men and Machines

CHAPTER XXV

SELECTION AND TRAINING

WAR IS fought with machines. The machines are run by men, men who must be specialists in navigation, gunnery, electronics, signaling, or supply. Both the Army and the Navy labored to pick the right men for the right jobs. But the procedure sometimes broke down. The Army, which would never furnish 105-mm. ammunition for 88-mm. guns, occasionally assigned trained radar repairmen to duty as truck drivers; the Navy assigned a one-eyed man to learn to operate a stereoscopic range finder, just as it occasionally and accidentally assigned stutterers to duty on shipboard telephone circuits. Such misassignments were exceptions, but they happened often enough to make the services realize how serious is the problem of selection and classification.

What kind of equipment can men use most efficiently? How can they be trained most rapidly? These two questions pressed for attention from the moment the individual stepped out of civilian life. Here the psychologist was needed. Any ship captain knows that some of his lookouts can see farther than others; the psychologist wants to know how much farther. Two psychologists were assigned aboard a cruiser doing convoy duty in the North Atlantic. Each night they tested the ability of the lookouts on watch. After the records of each man were averaged, and corrections had been made to account for differences in the light and the sizes of the various ships observed, it was determined that the best man could spot a ship nearly four times as distant as that observed by the poorest lookout.

By the spring of 1942 the need of psychologists was increasingly apparent. The Navy wanted assistance in improving its traditional methods of classifying and assigning officers and men. Both Army and Navy wanted help on training problems. Engineers and physicists stressed that the complex new weapons they were developing could not be operated efficiently without a special training for the men who had to use them. This culminated in a formal request from both services to OSRD for the organization of a group of psychologists who could work with officers on problems of selection and training. OSRD's answer was to form a committee in the National Research Council, the Committee on Service Personnel, Selection and Training, which later, September 1943, became the Applied Psychology Panel of NDRC.

The Applied Psychology Panel was not of course the only group of psychologists working on military problems.[1] The Adjutant General's Office of the Army, the Air Surgeon's Office of the Army Air Forces, the Bureau of Medicine and Surgery, and the Bureau of Naval Personnel of the Navy each commissioned a number of psychologists for work on selection and training of military personnel or on special assignments. The Applied Psychology Panel, in contrast, was a research group available to all the military services for work on any psychological problem. It received requests for special studies from all three major branches of the Army — ground forces, air forces, and service forces — and from numerous bureaus and operational commands of the Navy. Some of these requests had to be rejected because the problem presented could not be answered at all with the facilities available.

The Panel immediately applied itself to selection and classification, a most urgent problem during the rapid expansion of the Army and Navy. Because the Navy was later than the Army in commissioning a group of psychologists of its own, most of the Panel's early efforts were designed to assist the Navy. Training was the next and never-ending responsibility. By 1943 operational difficulties had become apparent to many officers in both services, and the result was a series of requests for work on the psychological problems involved in designing and operating military equipment.

Judged by performance, the tests which the Navy and the Applied Psychology Panel constructed were good tests, for they allowed much better selection of Navy specialists — the gunner's mates, range finder

[1]Other NDRC divisions had earlier felt the need for psychological assistance. Division 6, working on problems of subsurface warfare, already had psychologists at work on the selection and training of underwater sound operators. Division 7 early in 1941 organized studies on selection and training of stereoscopic height-finder operators. Division 17 established the Psycho-Acoustic Laboratory at Harvard in 1940 to study communication equipment and problems for the Army Air Forces. Each of these groups, and occasional psychologists elsewhere in NDRC, continued their work until after the war ended.

operators, fighter director officers, and so on — than did the old tests. This meant that fewer men failed in their training. Fewer were misassigned. Fewer had to be transferred around by trial and error until something was found that they could do satisfactorily.

The Commander of Submarines, Atlantic Fleet, provides us with a case in point. Submariners have always been chosen carefully, but even so, many of those assigned to the Submarine Command for training had to be rejected. In one year after the new tests were used in classifying men, the percentage of rejects dropped from 18.3 to 7.8. In the same year, the percentage of rejects from the Fleet and other activities which were not using the new classification methods did not drop at all.

The Navy capitalized on these advantages by recording each man's test scores on a permanent record, which goes with him throughout his life in the Navy. The scores provide information on what he can and what he cannot do well. The Applied Psychology Panel, for instance, constructed a test of aptitude for learning radio code. The Army and Navy needed many more radio operators than were available. A few came directly from civilian life, but thousands more had to go through the slow and tedious training required of a radio operator. Failure to progress was frequent, particularly so when the men were not properly chosen; it was not unusual for as many as 40 per cent of the men starting a code class to fail before the class ended. The test was code school in miniature, consuming thirty-five minutes instead of three or four months. Only, in the test, there were three letters; in code school there are the whole alphabet, the numbers, punctuation marks, and message forms which one must learn to send as well as to receive.

The assumption, in making up this test, was that men who could learn quickly to recognize three letters at fairly high speeds would be better prospects for regular code training than men who had trouble with three easy letters. The results bore out this assumption. When the test was finished, and put on phonograph records, both the Army and the Navy adopted it as their official test for selecting radio code operators.

Shortly before the U.S.S. *New Jersey* was commissioned, its Executive Officer asked the Bureau of Naval Personnel and the Applied Psychology Panel to help in the task of finding the best assignment for each member of the crew. Here was a new battleship — the largest the Navy had ever built. Only some 750 of its 2600 crew members had ever been to sea before. Most of the other 1850 were raw recruits fresh from boot camp or shore-based schools. These crew members were assigned to the ship, but not yet to specific billets. Only a few could be rejected. The rest had, somehow, to become the trained and integrated crew of a fighting battleship. Getting each man into the job he could do best was the problem on which help was wanted.

This was not a carefully planned research study. There was no time for that. Men arrived, at first two or three at a time, and then around a thousand in one week end. It was necessary to do the best hurry-up job one could on the basis of past experience.

A co-operative program of testing, interviewing, and classifying was quickly organized. The Standards and Curriculum Section of the Bureau of Naval Personnel furnished a number of paper and pencil tests and supervised their administration and scoring. The Classification Section furnished interviewers and supervised the actual assignment of the men. The Medical Research Laboratory of the U.S. Submarine Base at New London tested the night vision of prospective lookouts. The Army lent a hand with tests of stereoscopic vision. NDRC tested the speaking and listening ability of men who might be used as telephone talkers, furnished several tests, and produced a shipboard card-record system to make the test scores and interview information readily available to the ship's officers after the *New Jeresy* joined the Fleet. The interviewers were first supplied with descriptions of each billet to be filled and with estimates of the characteristics necessary to fill that billet satisfactorily. The men were then given a battery of tests to determine their abilities. Some of the tests tried out on the *New Jeresy* proved to be quite ineffective. But the program as a whole, the Captain of the *New Jersey* reported, "definitely contributed to the apparent extraordinary rapid progress made during the shakedown period by the crew of this vessel." The new method worked faster. More men were properly assigned right from the beginning. Fewer had to be tried out, transferred, then tried out again somewhere else.

The satisfactory completion of the classification program on the *New Jersey* led to a request in February 1944 to perform a similar service for the Amphibious Training Command of the Atlantic Fleet. This command was classifying and training the crews of LCI's (Landing Craft Infantry), LCT's (Landing Craft Tank), LSM's (Landing Ship Medium), and LST's (Landing Ship Tank). Some of these amphibious boat crews participated in the landing on the beaches of Normandy. Others had their first combat duty in landing operations in the Pacific.

The Applied Psychology Panel immediately assigned men to the four Amphibious Training Bases to help in the preparation of billet specifications, to improve and standardize classification procedures, and to help with problems of training. Again there was close co-operation with the Bureau of Naval Personnel. Essentially, the job first done for one battleship, the *New Jersey*, was now done, with additions, for an entire training command. Upon completion of the program, the Commander in Chief, United States Fleet, directed the Chief of the Bureau of Naval Personnel to develop a similar classification program for Fleet-wide application.

Early in the war a major in the Signal Corps flew over New York Harbor in an Army bomber. Over the intercom the pilot called his attention to some object below. But the engines made so much noise the officer could not understand what the pilot was talking about. When he got back to Washington he wrote a request to NDRC for a project on the improvement of voice communication. The project was established, and became highly successful. Improved methods of using radio telephone and intercommunication equipment were worked out. So successful were the new methods that soon every aircrewman being trained in the U.S. was required to take the voice communications course. Two members of the project staff were sent to the Southwest Pacific area to install similar courses in the AAF bases there.

Training in voice communication was quite as necessary in the Navy. Navy officers and NDRC psychologists wrote a manual of instructions for telephone talkers which the Navy distributed throughout the Fleet. They also developed short training courses for telephone talkers. These courses were soon being taught to Navy personnel at training stations in this country and at some of our island bases.

The noise in a submarine engine room makes talking very difficult. This difficulty, plus the fact that terminology and procedures were quite unstandardized, led the Navy to request assistance in improving voice communications procedures in submarines. The Applied Psychology Panel co-operated with two other NDRC groups, the Division on Subsurface Warfare and the Section on Acoustics, in this venture. Training equipment and training literature were prepared. Phraseology and procedures were standardized. Training courses were developed, and Navy officers taught to teach them.

Both the Army and the Navy asked for assistance in the training of radar operators. This field was so new that standard methods had not been worked out. Nor had ideas on proper training had time to be tested. The Panel in one of its first reports demonstrated that training of radar operators sometimes actually made them worse instead of better. The training, obviously, was bad training. A psychologist studied the situation and made a number of recommendations. The result was a steady improvement of another group of men trained on the revised program at another Army base.

Success in improving the training of the operator of one kind of radar led to extended work on other radar devices. Perhaps the most interesting of these were the equipment for radar bombing which permitted bombing through clouds and overcast, the radar equipment on submarines, and the ground-controlled approach system which permits a plane to land safely through fog and low-lying overcast. For all of these, the Applied Psychology Panel wrote training manuals, outlined courses of instruction, and prepared training aids.

Part of the Applied Psychology Panel's work consisted of putting into practice the already-known principles of learning. Frequently it was possible to improve a training program greatly by training the instructors and supplying them with systematic lesson plans. Industrial psychologists and some verbally facile "apparatus men" wrote effective and detailed plans in which the material to be learned was organized in simple, logical form.

With the co-operation of experienced officers, lesson plans and work books were prepared for use with practically all Navy guns, from the .50-caliber machine gun to the big 16-inch main battery.

The third and final assignment of the Applied Psychology Panel was to study and modify equipment so as to adapt it to the capacities and limitations of the average soldier or sailor. When a new gunsight or director was being considered by the Navy, a pre-production model was submitted to an Applied Psychology Panel project for analysis and study. The project examined the pre-production model, sometimes suggested changes in the design to make its control and operation easier, and trained some men to use it. On the basis of their experience, the project members then wrote a pamphlet describing the equipment, outlined a standard procedure for operating it, and suggested methods for training operating personnel. Pamphlets of this kind, for example, were written for the Gun Director Mark 51, Mod. 3, the Gun Director Mark 52, the Gun Fire Control System Mark 57, and the Gun Fire Control System Mark 63. Special attention was given to the preparation of a sequence of pictures showing how a standard director team engages typical targets.

These "Operating Instructions" manuals being distributed at the same time that new equipment was sent to the Fleet were a welcome contrast with the situations which earlier prevailed. At best, all that the ship received was an ordnance pamphlet on maintenance, and it was not uncommon for a new director or sight to be installed on board a ship with no instructions for its use. Since no one aboard knew how to use it efficiently, the new equipment sometimes did not get used at all. To insure that there should be operating instructions for new equipment, and to continue the benefits of psychological analysis of that equipment, the Naval Research Laboratory established a new and permanent section on Psychological Factors in Fire Control Equipment. Members of the NDRC project were selected to direct and staff the new section.

The Field Artillery requested a project on psychological factors in the control of artillery fire. In controlling the fire of a battery of field artillery pieces the guns are first lined up on a visible target. During fire, the observer in an advanced post far enough ahead of the battery gives information on the correction of aim to a telephone operator who is with him in the observation post. The operator relays this information back to another telephonist who, in turn, gives it to the executive officer. The executive officer then yells correction orders to the guns.

There are many places in this system in which errors can be made, and errors are too frequent. But no one knew for sure who was most responsible. Because of the way in which the sight was built it predisposed gunners to make errors of 100 mils (6 degrees). Errors of that size are important. They mean wasted shells instead of hits. And sometimes they mean hitting your own troops instead of the enemy. A sight of better design, one which made 100-mil errors much less likely, was built and turned over to the Field Artillery.

In the final phase a request from the Army Air Forces for a study of B-29 gunners led to results which have important implications for the design of military equipment. Gunners on a B-29 have three jobs to do. They track an enemy fighter with the sight. At the same time they must continuously readjust the range reading of the attacking fighter plane by keeping its image accurately framed in an adjustable set of marks in the sight. The range information and the data on the enemy's course which comes from tracking are fed into an automatic computer which points the gun, not at the attacker, but at the point in space where he will be, provided he continues on the same course, when the bullet gets there. That is, the computer does this if the gunner tracks smoothly and on target, and frames accurately. In addition to these tasks, which are difficult, the gunner is supposed to squeeze the trigger.

For many gunners this last responsibility is just too much. They find it impossible to perform all three tasks (tracking, framing, and triggering) properly with only two hands and one brain. Consequently, as the project psychologists discovered, the gunners develop a regular rhythm of triggering which has nothing to do with the accuracy of tracking and framing. They squeeze the trigger, and let it go, squeeze it and let it go, in bursts of fire which are just as likely to come when they are off target as on; just as likely when they are framing poorly as when they are framing properly. The gunners are not to blame. The task is too difficult for them. It may not be too difficult for the engineers who designed the sights. But it was for the average GI who became a B-29 gunner.

In order to simplify the task to a level where the ordinary gunner could master it, the psychologists working on this problem did two things: they modified the controls, making them easier to operate, and they built an automatic triggering device which would allow the gunner to concentrate on tracking and framing. An experimental test demonstrated that men could track and frame better with the modified controls than they could with the standard ones. The men were "on target" about 25 per cent more of the time with the modified controls than with the standard ones.

The Army tried out the second suggestion — the automatic triggering device. Gunners used up twice as much ammunition since they fired steadily during an attack instead of in bursts. But, with twice as much ammunition, they got *three* times as many hits. Japan surrendered before the automatic triggering device could be tried in combat, but its value had been proved on aerial targets, and the new method will be available if it is needed. The Army Air Forces are continuing the type of work represented by this study of B-29 gunners. A laboratory has been established at Wright Field to study human factors in equipment design and equipment operation.

In all of the examples cited above, there has been one common element in the methods used: the requirements of the jobs men do, and the characteristics of the men who do them, have been carefully measured. In this respect research on personnel problems is exactly like research on matériel problems. In developing, for example, a new rocket projectile, it would never be assumed that one model was as good as another without trying both out. Before either was accepted, both would be given exacting tests to measure performance under operating conditions. In deciding upon selection tests, training methods, or operating procedures, it is just as necessary to try out alternative ideas, to measure the results, and to select those that work best. Matériel research is necessary to develop new weapons. Psychological research is necessary to ensure their most effective use.

CHAPTER XXVI

OPERATIONS RESEARCH AND FIELD SERVICE

> If, instead of sending the observations of seamen to able mathematicians at land, the land would send mathematicians to sea, it would signify much more to the improvement of navigation and safety of men's lives and estates upon that element.
>
> — ISAAC NEWTON

THE EXTENSION of scientific aid into the realm of operations is an innovation of World War II. When the Telecommunications Research Establishment set up aircraft-warning radar sets along the British coast in 1940, difficulty was found in co-ordinating them with the antiaircraft batteries and with the operations of the defending fighter aircraft. Professor P. S. M. Blackett, the father of operations research, was put in charge of a small group to study the effectiveness of the radar set in actual operation. It soon became clear that this work needed to be attached to the interested services rather than to a development laboratory, and Blackett set up Operational Research Sections for Fighter Command and Coastal Command before he became, in the spring of 1942, Chief Advisor on Operational Research to the First Sea Lord of the Admiralty. Similar organizations were created for the Army, Bomber Command, and Combined Operations.

Many war operations [Blackett pointed out] involve considerations with which scientists are specially trained to compete, and in which serving officers are in general not trained. This is especially the case with all those aspects of operations into which probability considerations and the theory of error enters . . . the scientist can encourage numerical thinking on operational matters, and so can help avoid running the war by gusts of emotion. . . .

The most important early development of operations research in NDRC came in the field of antisubmarine warfare. Studies by L. B. Slichter and S. S. Wilks in the fall of 1941 indicated that with the best underwater detection system possible, allowing for the refractive effect of temperature gradients in the water, only about one attack out of twenty would be likely to succeed if the usual depth charges were dropped. The request of Captain (later Rear Admiral) Wilder D. Baker, Commanding the Antisubmarine Warfare Unit, Atlantic Fleet, for the assistance of NDRC personnel in the study of antisubmarine tactics, led to the creation by Section C-4 in March 1942 of the Antisubmarine Warfare Operations Research Group (ASWORG).

Headquarters at first were with the Antisubmarine Warfare Unit, Atlantic Fleet, in Boston, and from May 1942 in Washington as part of the Headquarters of the Commander in Chief, United States Fleet. By midsummer of 1943 Dr. Philip M. Morse of M.I.T. with Dr. William Shockley of Bell Telephone Laboratories as Director of Research had recruited forty-four men: six mathematicians, fourteen actuaries, eighteen physicists, three chemists, two biologists, and an architect. So far as possible the members of Group M were afforded the opportunity of observing combat operations at first hand. Some were assigned to work with the antisubmarine operations officers at the headquarters of the Eastern, Gulf, Caribbean, and Moroccan Sea Frontiers; at Argentia, Newfoundland; the Navy Antisubmarine Tactical Development Unit at Quonset; and later with the Fourth Fleet in Brazil, and Seventh Fleet in Australia, and Fleet Air Wing 2 in Hawaii. Others took part in the antisubmarine activities of the Army Air Forces, at the headquarters either of the First Bomber Command or of the Antisubmarine Tactical Development Group at Langley Field.

A large part of the group's efforts was devoted to the search problem. Its many aspects included the best placement of escorts about a convoy, the devising of barrier patrols to keep U-boats from going through narrow passages like the Strait of Gibraltar or wider areas like the South Atlantic; the best course to be followed by a destroyer in trying to make sound contact with a submarine which has been forced down by aircraft; and the best combination of radar and non-radar flying against submarines equipped with radar search receivers. These studies involved the range of detection by eye, by radar, or by sonar gear, and, more important, the search rate, or number of square miles which a given craft can search over in an hour. It was soon realized that the situation must be described in terms of probability rather than a definite range of detection. From this probability of sighting could be computed the average range under certain conditions and the effective search rate. Operational data were punched on I B M cards and then analyzed by machine methods. On the basis of a sighting probability curve, obtained from operational data, different aircraft search plans could be compared in efficiency, and the best plan found. Plans resulting from this work were incorporated in the official antisubmarine doctrine. Similar studies were made as a basis for radar and sonar search plans, for air-sea rescue, and for the use of the magnetic airborne detector and the radio sonobuoy.

Assessments of antisubmarine action enabled ASWORG to devise a measure of efficiency for various types of attack and to compare the effectiveness of various attack tactics. Studies of the proper depth setting of airborne depth bombs, for example, led to a change of doctrine which doubled their effective lethal range. Similar analysis proved of great value in the field of countermeasures.

The success of these activities in the field and at the headquarters of Cominch led to an extension of operations to other fields, the renaming of Morse's force as the Operations Research Group, and the creation of specialized subgroups engaged on operations research for submarines (SORG), for aircraft (Air ORG), antiaircraft (AAORG), amphibious operations (Phib ORG), and countermeasures to kamikazes (Spec ORG). The remainder of the personnel, which constituted the Operations Research Center, took care of the administrative and general scientific activities of the group as a whole.

Like the Navy, the Army soon developed an interest in Operations research, especially keen in the Army Air Forces. As early as July, 1942, the Commanding General of the 8th Air Force asked for men to establish Operations Analysis Sections, and on October 24, 1942, a memorandum from the Commanding General, AAF, to all Air Force Commanders approved their establishment. By December 1942, officials of OSRD, supported by a letter from General Arnold's headquarters, were undertaking to select and train analysts at the Princeton University Station, and at the Radiation Laboratory at M.I.T.

The Princeton University Station offered a six-to-eight-weeks school with courses in probability, in mathematics, mechanics, and dynamics; in weapon analysis and ballistics; and in photographic interpretation and bomb damage analysis, to small groups of four to six scientists at a time.

Supplementary training was provided with the co-operation of the Applied Mathematics Panel and several divisions of NDRC, the Navy Bomb Disposal School, the Army Air Forces School of Applied Tactics, and the British operational analysts at Princes Risborough. After training these men OSRD turned them over to the Army Air Forces for service in every theater.[1]

The more active divisions of NDRC and their contractors became interested early in the war in getting people into theaters of operation. One motive was to seek information about combat conditions which was difficult or impossible to obtain at home. Another was the belief that if only the forces in the field could see or hear about the merits of some device they would apply pressure at home to break some of the jams which the divisions were encountering there. Some traveling scientists were too zealous, and ran foul of the accepted doctrine of the War and Navy Departments that weapons under development are not to be sold to commanding officers in the field.

The way in which these missions operated depended a great deal on where they were carried out. In Europe the visitors were introduced and guided by the highly efficient and well-connected London Mission of OSRD. In the early days in the Pacific, on the other hand, they had no guidance from a permanent OSRD group which knew the local ropes. Some missions left a trail of misunderstanding and antagonism; others were highly successful.

Properly speaking, the first "field service" consisted in the sending of individual OSRD people to assist in setting up experimental equipment for test at some Army or Navy establishment. At this stage when the services felt a need for such activity they commonly exerted pressure to take over OSRD personnel, preferably in uniform. In this way the Radiation Laboratory, for example, lost all told by transfer to the

[1]The story of their distinguished service will be told by the Historian of the Army Air Forces. The Operational Analysis Division, AAF, was ably directed by Major (later Colonel) W. Barton Leach, who was on leave of absence from the Faculty of the Harvard Law School, and the Operational Research Section of the 8th Air Force was headed by Colonel John Harlan, a well-known New York lawyer. These groups were not able to procure all the NDRC scientists they wished, because of the reluctance of the laboratories to part with key personnel, and in consequence procured from outside OSRD. They did, however, obtain a considerable number of NDRC personnel, including the mathematical physicist H. P. Robertson of Princeton, a mainstay of Division 2.

services something like 100 men in the first two years, and other units engaged in designing and developing equipment suffered in proportion. This was obviously a trend which could not continue indefinitely, and it became clear that what was needed was a method which would enable the laboratories to recover their men when the particular field job had been completed.

The Army and Navy helped in solving this problem by detailing to the larger laboratories as many officers as could be accommodated, to follow a project from research and development through production and then be ready as experts to go into the field with it. Meanwhile Divisions 6, 14, and 15 had all made notable experiments in providing field service by creating respectively the Field Engineering Division of the New London Laboratory, the British Branch of the Radiation Laboratory (BBRL), and American British Laboratory-15 (ABL-15) for radar countermeasures equipment.[2] They did a notable job in speeding operational intelligence back to the home laboratories, where, until one could learn about the operational performance of a new weapon one was likely to go off at tangents or to propose solutions which might be eminently sensible from the laboratory point of view but which were unrealistic in the light of human limitations in combat.

BBRL and ABL-15 were not fundamentally laboratories in the home sense of the word but rather pools of personnel, equipment, shop, and know-how, in direct communication by teletype with the home laboratories and charged with the responsibility of modification, "debugging," assistance in use of new devices, and all the myriad things which needed to be done to accelerate the efficient use of the many new techniques which were being thrust into the theater at such a rapid rate. The personnel of these groups, assisted heroically by a small group of advisory specialists from the office of Dr. Bowles—notably such men as Dr. David Griggs—played an extraordinary part in the D-Day landings, the campaign of Normandy, Patton's advance, and the Battle of the Bulge. They evacuated equipment at the last moment, they served as pinch-hit operators of gear in crucial spots, often under fire, and covered themselves with glory, noted in many official communications.

OSRD and other developmental agencies often found that the first

[2]Although ASWORG was placed under the Office of Field Service (OFS) for administrative purposes, these three activities were not.

reluctance about a new weapon was followed by an overenthusiastic acceptance. The time schedules of war frequently brought new gear into action before all the "bugs" in its operation had been cleared up, and especially before all concerned understood the real limitations which surround any piece of equipment. Under these circumstances, one of two things might occur. It was hard to say which was the more unfortunate. On the one hand a piece of gear, adequately tested at home, might reach the theater of operations with inadequate instructions and be improperly fitted or used on the first operational trial. Failure would ensue and a harassed command which needed results now and not six months hence might be prejudiced against a perfectly sound piece of equipment. On the other hand, the equipment might in the first instance score a signal success, as was the case in the Azon bombing of the Brenner Pass viaduct. Then the command might accept the new weapon as a universal miracle and ask it to do things it was quite unfit to do. This too resulted in failure, discouragement, and sometimes in ultimate rejection. The scientist in the field had, then, the responsibility to see in the first instance that the gear which he knew so well was properly tuned to its first appearance in combat and properly used there. If this were successful he had then the opposite responsibility of trying to reserve its use for the purpose for which it was intended, or to restrict proposed modification to what was technically sound and feasible.

A different but equally important type of aid was furnished the armed services by the Applied Mathematics Panel of NDRC. As the Panel became more and more involved in analyses of bombing accuracy, it increased its staff and assigned men as scientific consultants to the Army Air Forces Board, the AAF Statistical Control Division, the AAF Proving Ground, the Air Intelligence Group of the Navy, the Joint Army-Navy Experimental Testing Board, the Joint Army-Navy Target Group, the 20th Air Force, the Navy Operations Research Group, the Army Engineers Board, the Guided Missiles Committee, and the Optics Section of the Navy's Bureau of Ordnance. In some cases, problems involving a considerable amount of calculation were formulated by agencies overseas and worked on at the home office of one of the Panel's groups concerned with bombing studies.

This work of the Appfied Mathematics Panel was by no means confined to bombing, but included analysis of rocket accuracy and its application to rocket barrages and the hitting of point targets; and a multitude of problems concerning gunfire. This type of analysis provided a powerful scientific method of evaluating the effectiveness of weapons and improving it. Its application at all stages — original design, development, early testing, advanced testing, production, and combat — proved extremely effective in the development of new weapons and of the tactics for their employment.

By midsummer of 1943 the scientific consultants furnished by OSRD to the United States and British services were numbered in the hundreds, several of whom had already made notable contributions. In view of the shortage of scientific personnel, the increasing demands of the Army and Navy raised a serious problem. In Bush's opinion, as the war progressed the need for services of the scientist and engineer, to aid the Army and Navy in using effectively what they had, was probably greater than the need for these services in research on new weapons. This called for a shift of some personnel from laboratory research and development to activities in the theaters.

Some of the best men for this purpose were too old or were physically unfit for commissions in the Army or Navy. Others who might qualify for commissions preferred not to do so. The problem was to create a mechanism which would stimulate the flow from the laboratories to the theaters and would provide a means for centralized handling of these activities in OSRD.

Bush solved this problem by creating a new major subdivision of OSRD, the Office of Field Service, on October 15, 1943. The OFS could manage its own administrative work but would have to look to the older segments, CMR and NDRC, for scientific personnel and for detailed information on OSRD projects.[3]

"Experience has shown," Bush declared, "that successful use of such personnel . . . requires, (a) that the officer to whom they are detailed definitely wants them; (b) that they be allowed access to such informa-

[3]Dr. Karl T. Compton, President of the Massachusetts Institute of Technology and member, NDRC, was made chief of the new office and Dr. Alan T. Waterman, a Professor of Physics at Yale with a long experience in the affairs of old Division D of NDRC, was made Deputy Chief. Just before the end of the war, when Compton resigned to become Director of the Pacific Branch of OSRD, Waterman became Chief of OFS, and Professor John E. Burchard of M.I.T. succeeded him as deputy chief.

tion as they may need for their work; (c) that they be allowed reasonable freedom as to the way in which they do their work; and (d) that they be responsible to the Commanding Officer and make their reports and recommendations to him, distribution of such reports within and beyond the Command to be subject to his approval."[4]

It was necessary that scientific consultants retain civilian status in order that they might talk freely both to the Commanding General and to the lowliest GI, that they might not be assigned to routine administrative tasks, that they might retain a primary loyalty to the laboratories they were serving, and that they might be moved as occasion demanded.

Just as Bush had himself handled liaison at the top level to the great advantage of OSRD, Compton did much for the relations of OFS with the Army in the Pacific. Field service was already well covered in the European theater by the two radar laboratories and numerous representatives of the divisions and their contractors, operating with the help of the highly efficient London office under the able direction of Bennett Archambault. All that was needed here was the dispatch of some OFS teams on short-term missions or the assignment of projects to existing agencies. But in the Pacific, a great work remained to be done.

The Director of the New Developments Division, Major General Stephen G. Henry, was an ardent supporter of OFS, seeing in it a splendid group of assistants to provide the commands in the field with the most up-to-date and effective equipment and the best instructions for its use at the earliest possible date.[5] But written description of what OFS might accomplish for a theater command was cold tea and not likely to fire the imagination of an officer overseas to whom the idea was new. Compton's mission to the Pacific in December 1943 and January 1944 made the way smooth for those to follow.

From the commanding generals and their staffs he received a most cordial welcome. Generals MacArthur, Richardson, Harmon, and Kenney saw at once the great possibilities of the proffered collaboration and did their utmost to promote it. Compton's mission was followed up by others undertaken by three Assistant Chiefs of OFS, Paul Klopsteg, George Harrison, and John E. Burchard, and by a highly important

---

[4]Memorandum to members of the Advisory Council, August 14, 1943.
[5]His successor, Brigadier General William A. Borden, was equally interested and co-operative.

visit by the Deputy Chief, Alan Waterman, which paved the way for the establishment of a Pacific Branch of the OSRD at Manila.

Many of the OFS missions consisted of one or a few individuals sent out to assist in the supervision of highly specialized equipment. Typical was the dispatch of two experts on guided missiles to the European theater at the request of the Air Force to serve as consultants in the bombing of bridges; or the mission to the Mediterranean, at Navy request, of two experts on underwater sound-ranging gear for the location of mines. Twelve radar engineers were furnished to assist the 8th Air Force and the R.A.F. to adapt and install equipment built by American manufacturers. Although the Army had its own civilian technicians for this kind of work, a definite need appeared for broader-gauge engineers who could serve more in the capacity of consultants. The Navy in 1944 sent a top priority emergency request for sixteen radar countermeasures specialists to assist in the installation of equipment on a crash basis for use in covering the invasion of Normandy. These men were procured and their equipment assembled, and both were on their way within five days, thanks to the effective teamwork of the War and Navy Departments, NDRC, and the Office of Field Service.

A second class of projects undertaken by OFS included the dispatch of groups to active theaters for special study, report, and recommendation. The Commander in Chief of the Southwest Pacific Area requested a group to make a special study of radar and radio propagation with special reference to anomalous conditions which might be predicted in advance. Certain of the conditions would allow an enemy to approach unobserved, others to enable our own forces to count on abnormally distant radar coverage. Two groups were assigned to this work, one military and the other civilian. To this same theater was sent a group of eminent medical specialists in malaria. Another civilian team was sent to provide the Chief of Engineers, SWPA, assistance in the analysis of engineering operations. A similar group was dispatched to the European theater at the request of the Signal Corps to make a study of communications with special reference to systems planning and engineering. Very favorable reports were received from the Southwest Pacific Area concerning the work of two civilian experts in time-and-motion studies which helped to simplify the work in communications centers.

Four scientists were sent to follow the Allied forces into Italy and to discover any significant scientific information which might be obtained from captured personnel or establishments. More elaborate was the similar ALSOS mission to the European theater, a joint Army-Navy-OSRD enterprise conducted under the auspices of the Assistant Chief of Staff, G-2. The responsibility for the scientific side of the mission rested with OSRD, through the agency of the Office of Field Service. Its primary object was to secure an immediate and comprehensive picture of German scientific research in relation to the war effort and to find out with all possible speed what progress the Germans had made in the development of an atomic bomb. Under the able leadership of Dr. Samuel Goudsmit and Colonel Boris T. Pash, this mission proved to be one of the finest examples of the co-operation of the scientists and the armed forces. It involved the assembling of lists of personnel, the names and location of laboratories and industrial firms, the prompt securing of the target areas as the armies rolled forward, the intelligent investigation of files and laboratories, the questioning of German scientists and laboratory workers, and the final systematic reporting of the findings to the proper authorities in America.

A third class of activity, operational analysis, was carried out for the Navy with distinguished success by ASWORG. The Office of Field Service also co-operated from time to time by the detailing of men on temporary assignment with the Operational Analysis Division of the Army Air Forces and with the Air Technical Analysis Division under the Office of the Vice-Chief of Naval Operations.

The personnel of OFS came in the main from the Divisions and Panels of NDRC and CMR. It was not always easy to persuade a division chief that his research work was so near completion that he could spare some of his key men for field service, but the top officers of OSRD lent every support. The services were not looking in field service for some generally qualified and intelligent men with technical training, for they had those already in abundance in their officer cadres. They needed in general men who knew a great deal about some small but important subject, men who would know more about that subject than anyone else in the theater, or top men with broad familiarity.

The civilian in field service did not become a member of the armed services, though he wore an army uniform with a shoulder patch in-

scribed "Scientific Consultant." He was accorded assimilated rank which
entitled him to the privileges of an officer as to messing, housing, and
transportation. The way in which he bore this suddenly imposed glory
was one measure of his competence as a combat scientist. If he took it
in his stride, it was probable that he would be all right. Most men did.
A few became more military than the military.

The successful were of many types. One, a sixty-two-year-old derma-
tologist, spent eight months in the Southwest Pacific studying tropical
diseases of the skin. Tall and spare, slightly stooped but with unexpected
stamina, he moved from one field hospital to another over jungle roads
along the northern coast of New Guinea. In one front-line hospital he
slept through an artillery bombardment. After landing in the Philippines he hitch-hiked a ride in a dive bomber and took part in an air
strike against the Japanese still remaining in Manila. He received six
commendations for his scientific work in the field.

A burly civil engineer from New England built airports in Greenland
and the tropics before OFS sent him to New Guinea to act as the adviser to General Casey on general engineering matters. On Leyte the
Army needed building materials for roads and airfields and the only good
source was on the opposite bank of a small tropical river. When asked
his advice he suggested the river be diverted through an old channel
beyond the gravel deposit. In two days a steady stream of trucks was
hauling that gravel to the strip.

An English-born writer, yachtsman, and naval architect, in his thirties,
was caught in Shanghai by the Japanese and made his way homeward
via Siberia to work with Sparkman and Stephens on the development
of the Dukw. After assisting in training Dukw crews for the Normandy
landings, he took charge of the Dukw training school for the famed
10th Army. Landing on Okinawa shortly after the Japanese surrender, he
initiated the same sort of activity there preparatory to the invasion of the
Japanese homeland. While at Okinawa he participated in the capture of
Japanese troops on small near-by islands and eventually accompanied a detachment to Korea, where his war ended not far from where it had begun.

One tall young New England artist turned his talents to camouflage,
spending a year in the forests of Southeast Asia. He landed with the
British on the southwest coast of Burma, flew the Himalayas in a C-54,
trained native hill tribesmen to drive jeeps, and spent weeks in the

Burmese jungle behind the Japanese lines. He returned riddled with virulent malaria to tell of fierce tribesmen who, having killed all the Japanese in their area with modern arms furnished by us, were now reverting to type and hunting indiscriminately.

A professor of metallurgy from Pittsburgh arrived in a South German town to find chaos. A thousand released Russian prisoners were looting the town, and the population was terrified. He located a cache of weapons, armed fifty French prisoners of war as gendarmes, and ruled as major for three days until United States forces arrived to take control. Then he went on with his metallurgical investigations.

One OSRD civilian in the field was killed by enemy action; only one was wounded; none was ever ditched at sea from an airplane or court-martialed or given punitive discipline by a theater commander. On the other hand 42 different men (12 per cent of all in its service) were picked out for special mention in letters from officers who had a chance to observe their work and who felt the forces had gained thereby.

Following Compton's first visit, an OFS office was established at General MacArthur's headquarters in the Southwest Pacific; and another, at General Richardson's request, at Central Pacific headquarters. The conquest of the Philippines gave to General MacArthur for the first time a large base nearer to the heart of the enemy. There was talk in the theater of associating with the Research Section now at Manila a field electronics laboratory; and a duplication of the field radar and counter-measures laboratories established by Divisions 14 and 15 in England appeared profitable. On April 20, 1945, Dr. Waterman left for Manila to discuss these new developments, and try to gain general agreement on a definite program.

At home this idea, pushed actively by Burchard as Acting Deputy Chief, gained impetus from the high commendations accorded by the Air Forces to the work of the OSRD laboratories in the European theater. Waterman had already found that the High Command in the theater recognized the need of special assistance to cope with such problems as defense against suicide attacks, location of enemy mortar and artillery positions, and radar aids to tactical air offense. It soon appeared, therefore, that far more than the proposed laboratory was desirable and that the scientific needs of the theater could be fully met only by the presence of a fairly complete cross section of OSRD.

With the enthusiastic backing of General Kenney and the statesman-like co-operation of General MacArthur's Chief of Staff, Lieutenant General Sutherland, a plan for establishment of a Pacific Branch of OSRD (PBOSRD) was proposed and approved by the Commander in Chief. Its aim was to provide

a. A senior consulting scientific staff to which problems might be referred in the priorities demanded by the military situation.
b. A pool of scientific specialists to give assistance on temporary duty as needed in the field.
c. Laboratory facilities suitable for emergency work such as might be possible in the theater.

To accomplish these aims, the Pacific Branch was to be an operating unit, occupying a place in the command similar to General Krueger's 6th Army or General Kenney's Far East Air Force. In this way it would be available to serve directly any element of the command. Its director was to report to the Commander in Chief, Army Forces, Pacific, who would exercise operational control on policy, priority of theater needs, movement of personnel and equipment, and general behavior. It was to be staffed and financed by OSRD, though necessarily dependent upon the Army for accommodations, food, and other necessities. It was permitted to have direct communication with OSRD at home on technical and internal administrative matters by radio or by letter, just as Army Technical Services overseas have with their offices in the War Department.

The appropriate requests were transmitted from General MacArthur to Dr. Bush, and Dr. Bush agreed on behalf of OSRD that full support would be given.

There could be no temporizing with the effort that was to deliver the final blows. The Director of PBOSRD had to be a man of the highest caliber, both for what he could do himself and as a signal to the whole OSRD organization that OSRD meant business. Under these circumstances, Dr. Compton, Chief of OFS, was selected as Director of the PBOSRD. With Edward L. Moreland, Dean of Engineering at M.I.T. and Executive Officer of NDRC, who had received a War Department appointment as special staff officer to General MacArthur on scientific and technical matters, he departed from Hamilton Field on August 3.

When Dr. Compton and Dean Moreland arrived in Manila on August 5, there were about sixty scientists at work for the command and about 200 more had been lined up for duty there within the next few months. The Japanese surrender, eight days later, put an end to these plans. Compton and Moreland proceeded with General MacArthur to Tokyo, where Moreland headed a scientific unit to investigate Japan's wartime scientific development.

This is the history of OFS, an experiment in the organization and mobilization of scientists out of the laboratory and into the field in such a way that both could profit; an experiment in delicate balance between the needs of operators and of laboratories when personnel was inadequate to serve both according to their full behests; an experiment in the relations of civilians with officers when the civilians are walking on the terrain of the soldier; a successful experiment which yielded much experience through trial and error to profit the next OFS, which one hopes will never be needed; but an experiment from which much can also be learned for peacetime operation.

Part Six: The Atomic Bomb

CHAPTER XXVII

RESEARCH TO MAY 1, 1943

THE FASHION among historians in recent years has been to poke fun at attempts to divide history into sharply defined periods and to describe it as a seamless robe in which the pattern of individual lives is discerned with difficulty and the things that stand out are long-run trends and basic forces. The explosion in southeastern New Mexico on July 16, 1945, however, blasted the web of history and, like the discovery of fire, severed past from present. The atomic age, which was born in that blinding flash of energy, had its roots in the extraordinary development of modern physics in the past quarter-century. But the demonstration that man could tap the basic power of the universe changed the world from one in which wars could be permitted into one in which an effective organization to preserve peace was as much a condition of the survival of civilization as air or sunlight.

President Truman learned the news of the successful experiment at Alamogordo while in Potsdam. He was now master of power such as no man had held before, and on July 26 he gave the Japanese warning, in the name of the United Nations, that unless they surrendered on terms there laid down, ruin would rain on them from the skies. The war-weary Japanese Government had already asked the Russian Government to undertake mediation; but it was not yet ready to surrender. After the refusal of the Potsdam terms Truman and Churchill saw no other course than to put the new weapon to the test. The first atomic bomb fell on Hiroshima on August 6, the second on the seaport city Nagasaki three days later. The Russians, who had been preparing an attack for months, at once declared war on Japan. The Japanese Emperor sued for peace on August 10, attributing his surrender to the new weapon. Convinced that Japanese troops would have continued a defense as stubborn as that of Iwo or Okinawa, Churchill estimated that by shorten-

ing the war the atomic bomb had saved the lives of 1,000,000 Americans
and 250,000 British.

"The atomic bomb," said President Truman, "is too dangerous to be
loose in a lawless world. . . . We must constitute ourselves trustees of this
new force — to prevent its misuse, and to turn it into the channels of
service to mankind."

Six years earlier the achievement of two German scientists had rocked
the world of the physicists almost as dramatically, and pointed the way
to Alamogordo. Otto Hahn and Friedrich Strassmann, bombarding uranium with neutrons, had produced barium. Speculating on this result,
two Jewish exiles in Denmark, Lise Meitner and her nephew, Otto
Frisch, guessed what had happened — that the absorption of a neutron
by a uranium nucleus had caused that nucleus to split into two approximately equal parts. Their colleague at Copenhagen, Niels Bohr, reported
the news of this fission to American scientists who had gathered on January 26, 1939, for a conference on theoretical physics held in the building of the Carnegie Institution of Washington, which was later to become
the headquarters of the Office of Scientific Research and Development.
The news that German scientists had produced an atomic fission which
could lead to vast release of atomic energy caused the greatest excitement. Physicists who lived near by hurried back to their laboratories
to check the experiment. Others from a distance telephoned or tele-
graphed their colleagues at home to get busy. By the end of the year
nearly a hundred papers on the epoch-making experiment had appeared
in print.[1]

The reason for this excitement was that if one added the mass of the
two fission fragments, the total was less than the mass of the original
uranium nucleus. The matter which had disappeared must then have
been transformed into energy. Applying Einstein's famous formula
$E = mc^2$, it was clear that though the matter which had been transformed was small, the energy released must have been immense, for the
mass has to be multiplied by the square of the speed of light, which is
186,000 miles per second, to find the equivalent energy. The possibilities

[1] In this chapter no attempt will be made to give the lay reader more than the minimum
of background necessary for understanding the development of the atomic bomb. The
physicist or chemist who wishes further details will turn to the survey prepared by
Professor H. D. Smyth of Princeton which the Army released to the press on August
12, 1945.

of atomic fission, for the good or ill of mankind, were seen to be boundless. In comparison, the efforts of the alchemists to transmute base metal into gold seemed child's play.

The physicists who were recovering from the blast effect of the news brought by Bohr knew that each of the 92 elements consists of a small, heavy nucleus, containing very nearly the whole mass of the atom, and from one to 92 electrons, each carrying a negative charge of electricity. The nucleus of each atom is composed of protons, each carrying a positive charge, and neutrons, with no charge whatever. Most of the atom is empty space, containing a submicroscopic sort of solar system consisting of the nucleus, like the sun, and electrons, like the planets, all bound together by the basic force of the universe. It was known, moreover, that elements may have more than one species, chemically almost identical but different in weight. Such species of the same element are called isotopes.

In their attempts to break up some of these atoms to find out more about them, physicists had developed several kinds of projectiles and used them to bombard the nuclei. Most of these projectiles had a common defect: they carried an electrical charge which caused them to be repelled as they neared the target. The neutron, which carried no charge, seemed to be the best of the possible missiles, since it proceeded unchecked until it struck the nucleus. Neutrons had not been as easy to produce in quantity as some inferior projectiles, but the fission of uranium opened the way to larger supplies of them. For whenever a neutron produced the fission of a uranium nucleus, one or more other neutrons were released. There was thus the possibility that a multiplying chain reaction might occur with explosive force. If one neutron caused a fission that produced more than one new neutron, there would be a chain reaction. The number of fissions would then increase almost instantaneously, releasing enormous amounts of energy.

Uranium, the heaviest of the then known elements, constitutes about four parts in a million of the earth's crust. Ore deposits have been found in Colorado, near Great Bear Lake in northern Canada, in Czechoslovakia, Russia, Sweden and Norway, and in the Belgian Congo. Natural uranium contains three isotopes, U-234, U-235, and U-238, which occur to the extent of 0.006, 0.7, and 99.3 per cent respectively. The amount of U-234 was therefore negligible and U-235 was distributed through amounts of U-238 that were 140 times greater. Not more than a few grams of uranium metal had thus far been produced in the United States.

By midsummer of 1940 the insatiable curiosity of the physical scientist had provided the knowledge necessary for a full-scale attack on the problem of controlling atomic power and producing atomic bombs. Well-informed scientists on both sides of the Atlantic knew that it was the isotope U-235 in which fission had taken place and that both slow or fast neutrons could produce this result, though slow ones were more likely to do so. One approach was to place unseparated uranium in a "pile" with carbon or heavy water as a moderator or "slower down" of neutrons to increase the chances of a chain reaction. The other approach was to separate the isotopes and accumulate a stock of U-235.

The chemical properties of the isotopes of an element are so nearly identical that chemical methods could not be used to separate Uranium 235 from Uranium 238. Such separation could be made, if at all, only by processes depending on the nuclear mass. Several approaches seemed promising. Study of diffusion methods had started as early as 1896 when Lord Rayleigh had shown that if a mixture of two gases of different atomic weight is allowed to diffuse through a porous barrier, the molecules of the lighter gas will, because of their higher average speed, pass the barrier faster. Despite the great difficulties of this gaseous diffusion method, F. W. Aston had used it to effect a partial separation of the isotopes of neon. In the separation of heavy isotopes like uranium the centrifuge method was a natural favorite, because the separation factor depends on the difference between the masses of the two isotopes, and not on the square root of the ratio of the masses as in diffusion methods. Gaseous diffusion would certainly involve the erection of acres of barriers and an immense amount of recycling.

At the start of operations, a gaseous diffusion plant has to run for some time before any product can be drawn off. The start-up time and the amount of material involved, or hold up, constitute serious problems. The electromagnetic method of separation avoided both these difficulties, but the ordinary mass spectograph could handle only minute quantities of material. The overcoming of this obstacle was to be the work of the great California scientist, Ernest O. Lawrence.

It is interesting to speculate on what would have been the fate of the world had the experiment of Hahn and Strassmann taken place three to five years earlier. Germany, bent on world conquest, might conceivably have mobilized her scientific manpower while her neighbors toyed with appeasement. Working secretly, she might have crossed the bridge between pure and applied science, and developed weapons that would have ensured her world dominion.

American scientists were more interested in 1939 in exploiting the fission of uranium as a source of power than as a means of destruction. Professor Fermi, an Italian winner of the Nobel Prize who had recently joined the staff of Columbia University, pointed out to representatives of the Navy Department in March the possibility of achieving a controllable reaction with slow neutrons or an explosive reaction with fast ones. That summer three other foreign-born scientists, Leo Szilard, Eugene P. Wigner, and Albert Einstein, interested Alexander Sachs, an economic adviser to Lehman Brothers, in the problem. He in turn induced President Roosevelt to appoint an Advisory Committee on Uranium, with Dr. Lyman J. Briggs, Director of the National Bureau of Standards, as its chairman. This Committee held two meetings, in October 1939 and April 1940, and received $6000 from the Army and Navy for purchase of supplies. As a result of the Committee's work the two services approved an allotment of $102,300 for investigating the separation of the uranium isotopes.

Meanwhile public interest remained keen as a result of predictions, some of them from scientists of established reputations, that the enormous energy latent in uranium could be tapped for explosives and for controlled power. At its meeting on May 23, 1940, the Executive Committee of the Carnegie Institution voted an appropriation of $20,000 for studies of uranium. This was only a fortnight before Bush's memorable interview with President Roosevelt, who informed him on June 15 that Briggs's Uranium Committee would be placed under the National Defense Research Committee.

On July 1 Briggs submitted to Bush a request for $140,000 for further measurements of the fundamental constants. These funds would permit experiments with uranium and carbon but in amounts smaller than the "critical amount" at which it was estimated a chain reaction would maintain itself. These proposals were approved in principle by NDRC at its first meeting the next day, with the recommendation that due attention be paid to safety precautions. A contract with Columbia University for work along these lines was signed on November 8, and other contracts followed with Harvard, Minnesota, Chicago, Iowa State College, Princeton, and California. Funds were also transferred for work by scientists of the Department of Agriculture and the Bureau of Standards.

To at least two members of NDRC these appropriations seemed questionable. The order creating the agency defined its objective as research and development of instrumentalities of war, and did not seem broad enough to include the advancement of nuclear physics or the development of atomic energy for peacetime use. Eventually atomic power might be harnessed to propel battleships or submarines, but not for many years to come. In view of all the high-priority problems pressing for solution was it desirable to commit many of the limited group of first-rate physicists to the uranium job?

The exchange of scientific information with the British, which had begun at the time of the Tizard Mission, in the previous September, had included studies in uranium. Conant's mission to England in February produced further exchange and led to a suggestion that a member of the uranium group go to London for consultation. Bush realized that the British were doing as much in that field as the Americans, if not more; and that "if the problem were of really great importance, we ought to be carrying most of the burden in this country." It was hard to say, however, how large an expenditure would be justifiable, for uranium looked like a long gamble and he thought there was "certainly no clear-cut path to defense results of great importance lying open before us [in this field] at the present time [April 15, 1941]."

At Briggs's suggestion, Bush asked Jewett, as President of the National Academy of Sciences, to appoint a committee of physicists to review the uranium problem, "preferably composed of men who are not now deeply involved in the subject, but rather men who have sufficient knowledge to understand and sufficient detachment to cold-bloodedly evaluate." He pressed for early and vigorous action, and hoped the Committee's advice "on the possible military aspects of atomic fission" would be helpful whether it "called for a radical expansion of our efforts or whether it merely called for careful procedure in the way in which we are now heading." The committee included W. D. Coolidge,

E. O. Lawrence, J. C. Slater, and J. H. Van Vleck, with Arthur H. Compton as chairman.

This group of distinguished scientists met on April 30 and May 5, conferred with Dr. Briggs's committee and recommended "a strongly intensified effort," involving expenditures of $350,000 in the next six months. Although they deemed it "unlikely that the use of nuclear fission can become of military importance within less than two years," they favored experiments looking towards a chain reaction using unseparated uranium, recommended an enlargement and reorganization of the Uranium Committee with better dissemination of information among those working on the problem, and urged that more information be obtained as to progress in Great Britain.

Bush thought the Academy Committee report excellent and felt "sure that in a matter of this inherent importance necessary funds will be available if and as needed." He enlarged the Uranium Committee, and named Dean Pegram of Columbia its vice-chairman. On June 12 the NDRC had before it the report of the Academy Committee and a letter from Briggs proposing that special emphasis during the next six months be placed on the intermediate uranium-carbon experiment and on methods for the quantity production of heavy water for use as a slowing-down agent in a "pile." The experiments he proposed all dealt with unseparated isotopes, as the outlook for separation did not seem to him encouraging. The Committee voted to transfer $241,000 from funds expected to be allocated to NDRC for the next fiscal year to the Bureau of Standards for materials for the uranium project. The chairman, however, was to ask the National Academy to have the uranium program reviewed by a committee which should include persons qualified to pass on the engineering aspects of the program.

Reinforced by O. E. Buckley of the Bell Laboratories and L. W. Chubb of Westinghouse, the Academy Committee held a two-day meeting and concluded that the prospect of military application was such as to justify an intensive drive. They therefore recommended on July 11 the establishment of a central laboratory devoted to the chain reaction, with $250,000 for a year's operation plus $500,000 to $1,000,000 worth of material.

Backed by this report, Briggs argued his case so well before the NDRC on July 17 that approval was voted for fourteen contracts and three transfers amounting to $387,000. The work was to include studies of the possibility of a chain reaction and of full-scale equipment for the production of power, and continuation of "work on the difficult problem of separating the uranium isotopes in quantity since this appears to be the only way in which the chain reaction could be brought about in a mass small enough to be carried as a bomb." In the opinion of the NDRC the *development* program should be entrusted to the Army or the Navy.

In England as well as in the United States the spring and summer of 1941 were a period of re-examination of the uranium problem and reshuffling of committees. British interest had centered on heavy water instead of graphite as a moderator in the chain reaction; and much work had been done on the diffusion process as a means to separate the isotopes. Emphasis on the military aspect of the problem was naturally stronger than in America. Scientists who had just survived the blitz were acutely conscious of what it would mean if Germany had atomic bombs at her disposal. That she was active in this field seemed to be indicated by the production of several kilograms of heavy water a day in Norway and orders for considerable quantities of paraffin to be made using heavy hydrogen. Just how this would fit into an atomic bomb program no one knew but it looked suspicious. The MAUD Committee, which was in charge of uranium studies, centered its report of July 15 on the development of a bomb of U-235.

We entered the project [they declared] with more skepticism than belief. ... We have now reached the conclusion that it will be possible to make an effective uranium bomb which would be equivalent as regards destructive effect to 1,800 tons of TNT.

As the United States moved closer to war in the summer and autumn of 1941, American physicists who were "in the know" on the uranium problem became more confident of the possibility of separating the isotopes and impatient for more rapid progress. After talking with A. H. Compton, Lawrence, and Pegram, at the Fiftieth Anniversary of the University of Chicago in September, Conant proposed to Bush that the Academy Committee be enlarged and be asked to make a third report. He and Bush had learned of the increasing optimism in Great Britain though they did not receive the British report of July 15 until October 3, and then under terms which did not permit disclosure to the Academy Committee, to which W. K. Lewis, R. S. Mulliken, and G. B. Kistiakowsky were now added.

Bush had discussed the whole problem with Vice-President Wallace on July 23 preparatory to having policy determined at the highest level. On October 9 he had a long conversation with the President and Vice-President in which he reported the British view that a bomb could be constructed from U-235 produced by a diffusion plant. He made it clear that all such prognostications were based on calculations using laboratory data and that no one could state categorically that an attempt would be successful. President Roosevelt endorsed complete interchange with Britain and instructed Bush "to hold consideration of policy on this matter within a group" consisting of the President, the Vice-President, Secretary of War Stimson, General Marshall, Bush, and Conant, which will hereafter be referred to as the "top policy group." It was agreed that a broader program would require a different administrative setup, and funds from a special source.

The Academy Committee, which had been instructed by Bush to consider particularly "the possibilities of an explosive fission reaction with U-235," came out strongly on November 6 for an expanded program focused on the development of an atomic bomb.

The possibility must be seriously considered [they declared] that within a few years the use of bombs such as described here, or something similar using uranium fission, may determine military superiority. *A fission bomb of superlatively destructive power will result from bringing quickly together a sufficient mass of element U-235.* This seems to be as sure as any untried prediction based upon theory and experiment can be. . . .

In their opinion the mass of U-235 required to produce explosive fission would be somewhere between 2 and 100 kilograms (4.4 and 220 pounds). Military security does not permit it to be stated what in fact the "critical mass" turned out to be, but it can be said to fall within these wide limits. They estimated at that time the explosive energy actually liberated per kilogram of Uranium 235 to be equivalent to about 300 tons of TNT.

In view of the damage done by the then existing TNT bombs, the Committee pointed out that if their destructiveness were increased 10,000-fold "they should become of decisive importance." The amount of uranium required, however, would be large. "If the estimate is correct that 500,000 tons of TNT would be required to devastate Germany's military and industrial objectives, *from 1 to 10 tons of U-235 will be required to do the same job.*"

In the Committee's opinion the gaseous diffusion and centrifuge methods were so far advanced that isotope separation had reached the development stage, and should be placed in the hands of a competent engineer. Other methods which were less advanced might ultimately prove superior. They concluded that, with an all-out program, fission bombs might be produced in significant quantity in three or four years.

In his covering letter to President Roosevelt on November 27, transmitting this report, Bush pointed out that it was "somewhat more conservative than the British report. . . . This may be due to the fact that the Committee included some hardheaded engineers in addition to very distinguished physicists. The present report estimates that the bombs will be somewhat less effective than the British computations showed, although still exceedingly powerful. It predicts a longer interval before production could be started. It also estimates total costs much higher than the British figures."

An administrative reorganization of the uranium program did much to facilitate more rapid progress. Conant, A. H. Compton, and E. O. Lawrence were added to Briggs's committee which was no longer to report to NDRC but direct to Bush. The physicists engaged on the atomic bomb problem were to be grouped under three program chiefs, Compton, Lawrence, and H. C. Urey, all Nobel Prize winners. Contracts relating to the diffusion and centrifuge processes were to be recommended to Bush by a group of eminent chemical engineers to be called the Planning Board, which included E. V. Murphree of the Standard Oil Development Company as chairman, W. K. Lewis, L. W. Chubb, G. O. Curme, Jr., and P. C. Keith. All other contracts were to be recommended to the Director of OSRD by Conant, Briggs, and a program chief.

The attack on Pearl Harbor reinforced the decision to make an all-out attack on the uranium problem and to proceed with only one end in view — the production of an atomic bomb within the shortest possible time. At a meeting of the top policy group on December 16 all felt "that OSRD should press as fast as possible on the fundamental physics and on the engineering planning, and particularly on the construction of pilot plants."[2] It was agreed that when the time came for full-scale construction the Army should take over.

By this time it was clear that the critical amount of fissionable material was somewhere between 2 and 100 kilograms, that is, within practical limits for the manufacture of a bomb, and that a highly destructive explosion could be obtained if sufficient quantities of U-235 could be separated from the more prevalent isotope U-238. As yet no appreciable amount had been so separated but hopes were high for both the gaseous diffusion and the centrifuge method. Columbia was the headquarters for the work on both of these approaches, though important work on a high-speed centrifuge was done by J. B. Beams and others at the University of Virginia, and the mass spectrographic methods developed by A. O. Nier of the University of Minnesota proved of great value to the diffusion project. By December 1941, the theory of diffusion for separating U-235 had been well worked out at Columbia, and several different small barriers had been made and tested. The difficulties were great, for the only gaseous form of uranium then known was the hexafluoride, UF_6, which is highly corrosive, decomposed by moisture, and altogether one of the most disagreeable substances man could find to work with.

The difficulties in the way of the electromagnetic method of separating the isotopes were overcome by E. O. Lawrence. He brilliantly developed this method by using the magnet of his famous 37-inch cyclotron at Berkeley. The cyclotron was disassembled on November 24, 1941, and its magnet used in a new device, named the Calutron. At a meeting of the Uranium Committee held the day before Pearl Harbor, Lawrence could report that with this new setup he could deposit one microgram (one 500-millionth of a pound) per hour of U-235 from which a large proportion of the U-238 had been removed. At the first meeting of the reorganized Uranium Committee on December 18, Urey and Pegram had recently returned from a visit to England. Conant recorded that "enthusiasm and optimism reigned." Lawrence explained how the magnet taken from the cyclotron might be used not only for the separation of small amounts of material but perhaps to accomplish a large-scale separation. By December 24 he had prepared 50 micrograms of U-235 although they were only partially separated.

[2]Bush's notes. General Marshall and Conant were absent.

Fortunately for this development a huge cyclotron, with a pole diameter of 184 inches and a pole gap of 72, had been under construction at Berkeley. Though work on it had been suspended because of the war, it was now resumed with a supplementary appropriation from the Rockefeller Foundation and speeded by the grant of necessary priorities. By the end of May, 1942, this big magnet was ready for use in a giant Calutron.

Despite the great precautions taken to keep the work in this field secret, physicists knew that studies were being pushed and wondered what the future might hold. Pollard and Davidson, in their excellent volume, *Applied Nuclear Physics*, published in 1942, reflected this sentiment: —

> The separation of the uranium isotopes in quantity lots [they reported] is now being attempted in several places. If the reader wakes some morning to read in his newspaper that half the United States was blown into the sea overnight he can rest assured that someone, somewhere, succeeded.

Because of the small amount of U-235 in existence in comparison with U-238, which was 140 times as prevalent, and because of the difficulties of separating the isotopes, another approach to the problem seemed attractive. Would it not be possible to produce a chain reaction in unseparated uranium? It was a question of probabilities. The neutrons produced by fission might (1) escape entirely from the uranium; (2) be captured by impurities; (3) be captured by uranium in a process not resulting in fission, as in the case of the absorption of a neutron by the nucleus of the prevalent U-238, or (4) produce another fission. Obviously no chain reaction would take place unless the loss of neutrons by the first three processes was less than the surplus produced by the fourth. The critical size was therefore defined as "the size for which the production of free neutrons by fission is just equal to their loss by escape and non-fission capture."

Since slow neutrons have the higher probability of splitting U-235 and the neutrons produced by fission had high speeds, it seemed desirable to slow them down by a moderator. Heavy water had certain advantages for this purpose, but was very difficult to produce in sufficient quantity. Fermi and Szilard suggested that lumps of uranium be imbedded in a matrix or lattice of graphite. It was not easy to produce carbon of sufficient purity to serve as a moderator, but two American companies turned the trick.

The problem of how to produce a chain reaction by using unseparated uranium fell in the province assigned to A. H. Compton; and it was decided in January 1942 to concentrate this work at the University of Chicago, in what was cryptically described as the Metallurgical Project. The Columbia group under Fermi and a Princeton group which had been studying the absorption of neutrons soon moved there. The complete report of the scientific results of this project will run to thirty volumes.

The first pile designed to produce the chain reaction was erected in November 1942 on the floor of a squash court under the West Stands on Stagg Field. The difficulties overcome in getting materials beggar description. Adequate tonnages of uranium ore were available, but almost no metal could be had until late in 1942. By that time a method for removing impurities from uranium oxide by a single extraction had been devised at the National Bureau of Standards and developed by the Mallinckrodt Chemical Works at St. Louis to produce a brown dioxide of a high degree of purity at a rate of 30 tons a month. This is now used as a starting point for all metal production. Thanks to this and other developments for later stages of production, six tons of metal were available for incorporation in the Stagg Field pile.

It is important to grasp the relation between the Chicago project and some of the work done by Lawrence and his associates at Berkeley before secrecy descended. They had used the cyclotron to transmute uranium into two entirely new elements which they named neptunium and plutonium, of which only the latter concerns us here. Lawrence saw that the chain reaction, if it succeeded at Chicago, would produce the new element, plutonium, by a fast neutron reaction. The nucleus of U-238 would capture a neutron, transmutation to neptunium would take place by the emission of what is called a beta ray, and with the emission of a second beta ray the neptunium would be transmuted into plutonium. He guessed that this would have the same property of fission as did U-235; and he managed to produce a minute quantity of plutonium, $_{94}Pu$-239, and to prove it would give the fission reaction like U-235.

This much was known before money really started flowing in the reorganized work. Huge sums were committed on this portentous gamble before enough plutonium was produced to prove that more than two neutrons were emitted in this fission, an equally essential property if a fast chain reaction was to work.

Pile No. 1, a graphite spheroid, shaped like a doorknob, containing lattices of uranium metal and numerous measuring devices, was put to the test on Stagg Field, December 2, 1942, and proved completely successful. It was the first self-maintaining nuclear chain reaction on record. On the largest scale hitherto attempted by man, Einstein's theory of relativity had been proved in a very dramatic fashion. In this pile chemical elements were being transmuted into other chemical elements with a loss of matter and consequent release of energy. This energy was being released at a controlled rate which could be measured in kilowatts by reading a meter, an unheard-of procedure in previous nuclear physics.

Elaborate precautions were necessary to control within safe limits what was going on within the pile. The reaction was controlled by inserting in the pile some strips of cadmium or boron steel, materials which absorb neutrons. To operate the pile all but one of the control strips were taken out and the remaining one was slowly pulled out till the desired reaction took place. Reinsertion of the strips would check or stop the process.

This splendid success at Chicago has been described as the halfway mark on the road to the atomic bomb. It proved that a controllable chain reaction could be produced in unseparated uranium and that U-238, 140 times more prevalent than U-235, could be transmuted into a new element which was itself fissionable. Because plutonium was a new element, of different chemical properties than uranium, its separation was more feasible than the separation of the uranium isotopes.

It is hard to imagine, however, a more daring idea than the production of an atomic bomb by means of an element only just discovered, in time to be of use in the war then raging. The experimental pile at Chicago would have had to run at least 70,000 years to produce a single bomb. "The technological gap," says Smyth, "between producing a controlled chain reaction and using it as a large scale power source or an explosive is comparable to the gap between the discovery of fire and the manufacture of a steam locomotive." It was necessary to proceed with giant strides to large-scale production of the new element, of which only a few millionths of a gram were available for experimentation. It is hard to speak in measured terms of the superb achievement of the engineers and of the microchemists in the work which followed. Microchemistry itself was a branch of science less than twenty years old. Working with infinitesimal quantities these pioneers made such remarkable progress that by the end of 1942 they knew as much about the chemical properties of plutonium, a substance entirely unknown two years earlier, as those of several of the older elements. They had worked out the process of separation before enough plutonium was available to be seen by the naked eye.

In the discussions of the all-out program early in 1942 it was generally assumed that only one or two of the alternative methods under consideration would be carried through to the stage of large-scale production. Although predictions were made as to a continuing time schedule for all the rival methods, it was felt that some would be eliminated in the race, indeed they might all be. By February 10 contracts totaling over one million dollars had been authorized, distributed among twelve different institutions. Conant recommended to Bush that "work should be pushed vigorously on all the present competing methods, at least until July 1," by which time he hoped that many of the contracts could be eliminated or revised. If by that time the electromagnetic method of separating U-235 was "clearly capable of producing grams per day . . . work on the other methods might be abandoned, or at least given very low priority. . . ." Even if the decision had to be postponed until January 1, 1943, "and all the horses continue to be running at full speed down the course," he estimated that the OSRD research program could be completed for something between $10,000,000 and $17,000,000, an estimate which proved reasonably close to the mark.

The progress report sent by Bush to the President on March 9 reflected the optimism of those in close touch with the program, but pointed out the tentative nature of all the conclusions. "The possibilities of actual production appear more certain," but "the way to full accomplishment is still exceedingly difficult. . . . The best estimates indicate completion in 1944 if every effort is made to expedite. . . . A short cut, under intense examination, would if successful move the completion date ahead six months or possibly even a year." The short cut failed to develop, but Bush was not far wrong in his expectation "that next

summer will find the matter ready to turn over to Army control for
actual plant construction."

When called on in May to produce a budget for the next eighteen
months' operations, Conant found five horses running neck and neck.
There was still little to choose between the centrifuge, diffusion, and
electromagnetic methods of separating U-235 and the uranium-graphite
pile and uranium-heavy-water pile methods of producing plutonium.
The boldness of his proposed solution led General Groves to remark,
after the success of the first bomb: "Conant has the gambling spirit of
the New England pioneers — a calculated gambling spirit."

All five methods [Conant reported to Bush on May 14] will be entering
very expensive pilot plant development within the next six months; furthermore, if time is to be saved, the production plants should be under design
and construction before the pilot plant is finished. To embark on this
Napoleonic approach to the problem would require the commitment of
perhaps $500,000,000 and quite a mass of machinery. . . . Anything less than
this will mean either the abandonment or the slowing down of one of the
. . . methods. While all five methods now appear to be about equally
promising, clearly the time to production . . . by the five routes will certainly
not be the same but might vary by six months or a year because of unforeseen delays. Therefore, if one discards one or two or three of the methods
now, one may be betting on the slower horse unconsciously.

In his opinion the decision as to proper scale of effort turned on the
military appraisal of what would occur if either side had a dozen or two
bombs before the other. "If the new weapon is not in reality determining
but only supplemental, then the reasons for betting heavily are much
less." Analyzing the imperfect intelligence available as to what the Germans might be up to, he concluded that they might be a year but not
more ahead of us and argued that there was "desperate need for speed. . . .
Three months' delay might be fatal." If the Germans could drop a dozen
atomic bombs on England, they might be able to follow them up with
a landing.

The program was thrashed out at an important meeting on May 23,
1942, attended by Briggs, Murphree, and the three program chiefs,
Urey, Compton, and Lawrence. They recommended that $85,000,000
be made available for contracts to be placed before July 1, 1943. This
would permit the construction of a centrifuge plant, a diffusion plant,

an electromagnetic separation plant, a pile to produce plutonium, and a plant to yield half a ton a month of heavy water. They estimated the annual operating cost of these plants at $34,000,000, and recommended that as soon as pilot plant experience was available, the expenditure on what then seemed the best method should be doubled. They concluded that either U-235 or plutonium could be used to make a bomb which would explode at the desired instant and would release as much energy as several thousand tons of TNT. A small supply of these bombs, they believed, could be available by July 1, 1944, with an uncertainty either way of several months.

It is interesting to note that this estimate was in error by one year. The chief reason was that at that time (May 1942) the amount of fissionable material believed necessary for a bomb was very much smaller than turned out to be the case. In addition there was the usual tendency of scientists to underrate the time and money required for development and construction.

With the concurrence of Brigadier General W. D. Styer, whom General Marshall had instructed to follow the program, Bush and Conant forwarded this report to the other members of the top policy group on June 13. In a covering memorandum they proposed that $31,000,000 be transferred to OSRD for research and development and that the Army undertake the construction of the pilot plants, detailing a qualified officer designated by the Chief of Engineers and reporting to him.

It would be unsafe at this time [they argued] in view of the pioneering nature of the entire effort, to concentrate on only one means of obtaining the result. . . . When four separate methods all appear to a highly competent scientific group to be capable of successful application, it appears certain that the end result will be attained by any competent enemy, with sufficient time and adequate energetic efforts.

They proposed therefore to back all the horses, but to make a more careful study than had yet been possible of the ultimate demands of the uranium program in terms of scientific personnel and critical materials, on which the synthetic rubber, shipbuilding, and other large programs were making heavy competing demands.

Bush and Conant estimated that $54,000,000 would be required in all in the fiscal year 1943. The Vice-President and the Secretary of War and

General Marshall agreed to these proposals on June 17 and the President promptly affixed his O.K. At the same time Bush dissolved the old Uranium Committee and created what was called the S-1 Executive Committee which included Briggs, Compton, Lawrence, Murphree, and Urey, with Conant as chairman. The other members and consultants of the former committee were to serve as a panel of consultants for the Executive Committee. The program had entered a new phase, destined to last until May 1943, of joint OSRD-Army operation.

The decision to push ahead on all the rival methods involved more than expense. The difficulty of getting sufficient manpower and critical materials was a strong argument for concentrating on a single approach. Conant expressed the view, however, at the meeting on August 26, that it was "too soon by one or two months to make such a decision." And the committee wisely decided to continue to back all five horses.

If a choice had been made in August, Lawrence's electromagnetic method would have been the favorite. As time went on the difficulties and cost of this approach seemed to increase. The success of the Stagg Field experiment on December 2 brought plutonium production to the fore. In the spring of 1943 all the horses except the centrifuge were still running strongly, though heavy water was soon to be scratched, reducing the field from five to three.[3] The bets on these rivals, gaseous diffusion, electromagnetic separation, and plutonium production with uranium-graphite piles, reached staggering proportions, but all three finished the course strongly and shared the laurels.

By the end of April, 1943, OSRD had authorized research contracts totaling $19,205,413 for the atomic bomb project as compared with $28,180,000 for the Radiation Laboratory of Division 14. Immense commitments had already been made by the Army for pilot plants and large-scale production. The time had come, which Bush had long before envisaged, for the Army to undertake the whole operation, and on May 1, 1943, the outstanding OSRD contracts concerning the atomic bomb and its constituents were taken over by the Corps of Engineers.

---

[3]Heavy water had certain advantages as a moderator, as it was more effective than graphite in slowing down neutrons and was somewhat less likely to absorb them. A small pilot plant for plutonium production with uranium and heavy water was built near Chicago on what is known as the Argonne Forest site. It gave good results when tested in May 1944, but the idea of large-scale production by this method was dropped on account of the difficulty of producing adequate amounts of heavy water in sufficient time.

The S-1 Executive Committee, September 1942

Left to right: H. C. Urey, E. O. Lawrence, J. B. Conant, L. J. Briggs, E. O. Murphree, A. H. Compton

Harnessing atomic energy at Oak Ridge

The development of the atomic bomb is a classic example of the relation between pure and appplied science. Eternal curiosity had led physicists in Europe and America to cross the frontiers of knowledge, deep into unexplored territory, where they mapped out in extraordinary detail the submicroscopic universe of the atom. By 1940 they had placed at the disposal of every major government the necessary information on which an approach to the atomic bomb could be made.

There remained some of the most baffling problems that ever confronted engineers and statesmen. In a war in which new weapons might prove decisive, how much of the limited supply of scientific manpower and critical materials should be diverted from synthetic rubber, high-octane gasoline, shipbuilding, radar, and other new weapons, and hazarded on the atomic bomb? Within the bomb program itself, should funds be staked on every process that held hopes of success, or should the field be reduced from five to three, or five to one? What was the surest way of overtaking a relentless enemy, believed to have a head start of perhaps a year? Never perhaps have scientists and statesmen played for higher stakes, or has the sense of breathless urgency driven men to more extraordinary exertions. The men working with such feverish energy distrusted the fruits of their own success. Was civilization capable of controlling a weapon of such power? Everyone concerned with the project who understood its implications would have been relieved and delighted if something had developed to prove beyond a doubt the impossibility of an atomic explosive. The remark, "I hope the thing won't work, but we must be sure it won't," became a commonplace. Yet the spur of a possible German success roweled our scientists and engineers and drove them on to success. They gained it just in time, not only to save countless lives in the Pacific, but to demonstrate on the field of battle, beyond argument and hypothesis, that man had now a weapon at his disposal that confronted him with the choice between the enforcement of durable peace and the destruction of urban civilization.

CHAPTER XXVIII

THE TRIUMPH OF THE MANHATTAN DISTRICT

SOME OF the great advances of science have been made by a genius in his laboratory; some by the combined efforts of hundreds or thousands of men. The development of the atomic bomb is the finest example of the co-operative method. Secretary Stimson described it as "the greatest achievement of the combined efforts of science, industry, labor and the military in all history."

This amazing success was achieved not by the regimentation of science or industry but by the country where greatest pains had been taken to leave both free to make the most of their creative powers. Secrecy was maintained without a Gestapo. Labor volunteered for the work without asking to be told its purpose. Great corporations made available their managerial skill and vast scientific know-how without patent rights or profits. Scientists left their homes and their research associates and disappeared into the thin air of the New Mexico desert.

As an engineering project the development of the bomb was of the first order of magnitude. Expenditures climbed to nearly $2,000,000,000, roughly twice those involved in the huge synthetic rubber program. The two developments competed with each other for manpower and critical materials, at the same time they competed with high-octane gasoline production, radar, ordnance, and shipbuilding conducted on a scale which the world had never before seen. It was a triumph of the nation, in which others of the United Nations played their part.

Yet in a special sense it was a triumph of the Corps of Engineers. From the early days of the project under NDRC sponsorship the idea was to turn the development over to the Army as soon as the stage of development was reached. Only under service control were funds and priorities obtainable on so great a scale. From the summer of 1942 to the following May the Army was responsible for pilot plants and the planning of huge plants for the separation of U-235 and the production of plutonium. From May 1, 1943, it took charge of all aspects of the vast enterprise.

On June 18, 1942, Colonel James Marshall was ordered to form a new district in the Corps of Engineers to carry on special work which, for security reasons, was described as the "DSM Project" (Development of Substitute Materials). The new administrative district was established on August 13, and was named the Manhattan District. In September the Secretary of War placed Brigadier General L. R. Groves of the Corps of Engineers in complete charge of all Army activities relating to the project, reporting directly to the Secretary and to General Marshall. Groves conducted its complex activities in a manner beyond praise. Billion-dollar corporations that have found as skillful and successful administrators as he proved himself to be have been indeed fortunate.

On September 23, 1942, the top policy group which had been earlier designated by the President set up a Military Policy Committee, to plan policies relating to materials, research and development, production, strategy, and tactics, and to submit progress reports to the top policy group. Bush was named Chairman of the Committee with Conant as his alternate, and Major General Styer and Rear Admiral W. R. Purnell as the other members.

General Groves sat with this Military Policy Committee and had Conant and Richard C. Tolman, the Chairman and Vice-Chairman of NDRC, as his scientific advisers. Bush and Conant played an important part in the negotiations with Great Britain concerning the project. As the scientific manpower of Great Britain was too heavily committed to other projects to permit her an all-out attack on the uranium program, it was agreed by President Roosevelt and Prime Minister Churchill that the development should be concentrated in the United States. A Combined Policy Committee was set up in August 1943, consisting of Secretary Stimson, Bush, and Conant for the United States; the late Field Marshal Sir John Dill (now replaced by Field Marshal Sir Henry Maitland Wilson) and Colonel J. J. Lewellin (since replaced by Sir Donald Campbell) for the United Kingdom; and the Canadian Minister of Munitions, C. D. Howe. Dr. Richard C. Tolman for the United States, Sir James Chadwick for Great Britain, and Dean C. J. Mackenzie for Canada composed a technical committee.

In the normal transition from research to large-scale production, as soon as the work in the laboratory has reached a satisfactory conclusion a small pilot plant is constructed in which the crucial engineering problems of the process can be solved and the necessary information obtained to make possible the effective design of a full-scale production plant. The roads to the atomic bomb, whether via the separation of U-235 or via the production of plutonium, were strewn with engineering difficulties of a magnitude never before encountered. Although the pilot plant stage of this development was therefore of enormous importance, there was too little time to make the most of it. Fear that the Germans would be the first in the field with atomic bombs led to a telescoping of stages, in which pilot plant work often overlapped research in the laboratory, and the design and construction of some of the huge production plants were carried out before lessons could be learned and obstacles surmounted in the pilot plants.

This telescoping of the stages is illustrated by the fact that no pilot plant for the electromagnetic process was built, though six experimental separation units at Berkeley afforded information that was helpful in the design of the large-scale plant in Tennessee. No complete pilot plant was ever available for the gaseous diffusion process, though numerous so-called pilot plants tested various components or groups of components. Nowhere were the production problems as novel and fantastically complex as those concerning the new element, plutonium. Yet the semi-works constructed for this process was, for reasons that appear later, not a true pilot plant except for that part of the process which concerned chemical separation. The engineers who designed the huge plutonium plant had to lay out plans for an operation that would separate several grams a day of plutonium from several tons of uranium, on the basis of information obtained from studies involving only half a milligram of plutonium, a millionth of a pound. "In peacetime," says Smyth, "no engineer or scientist in his right mind would consider making such a magnification in a single stage, and even in wartime only the possibility of achieving tremendously important results could justify it."

The novel problems of design which confronted the engineers would have been difficult enough if they had had all the time in the world. They were greatly increased by telescoping the stages. That Americans could succeed with all three production methods in the face of such obstacles is due to the extraordinary skill and resourcefulness of our great engineering firms.

Colonel Marshall had selected the Stone and Webster Engineering

Corporation as his advisers and had recommended a site on the Clinch and Tennessee Rivers eighteen miles west of Knoxville, which General Groves approved after his appointment in September. Here, in what was known as the Clinton Engineer Works of the Manhattan District, the plutonium pilot plant was built in one of three adjoining valleys, the electromagnetic separation plant in a second, and the huge gaseous diffusion plant in a third. Steam from the great powerhouse of this last plant was used in a thermal diffusion plant built in 1944 for the partial separation of U-235, on lines which had been worked out by R. Gunn and P. H. Abelson at the Naval Research Laboratory and tested in pilot plants built by the Navy at Anacostia and Philadelphia. The product of this fourth plant was fed into the electromagnetic plant near by, increasing its production rate.

It had been originally assumed that the large-scale plutonium plant would be located near by, but fear that a large pile might scatter radioactive material over a wide area and endanger neighboring towns and cities led to the decision, in January 1943, to build the big plutonium plant on a large tract of about 670 square miles on the Columbia River at Hanford, Washington.

On the 59,000-acre site in Tennessee there grew up the modern city of Oak Ridge, whose population of 78,000 ranked it fifth in the state. The M. W. Kellogg Company created a special subsidiary, the Kellex Corporation, to design the immense gaseous diffusion plant, with its thousands of miles of barriers and recycling through thousands of stages. It was built by the J. A. Jones Construction Company of Charlotte, North Carolina, and successfully operated by the Carbide and Carbon Chemicals Corporation, which also took over in March 1945 the Columbia laboratory created for research on this process.

The construction of the large-scale electromagnetic plant at Clinton was authorized by General Groves on November 5, 1942. He allotted research and development to the University of California, the manufacture of the mechanical parts to Westinghouse, the electrical equipment and controls to General Electric, and the construction of the magnets to Allis-Chalmers. The Stone and Webster Engineering Corporation was responsible for the construction and assembly, and the Tennessee Eastman Company for operating the plant.

At this point the reader may well be asking, Why all this vast construction program? Surely the Policy Committee could not be thinking in terms of thousands of atomic bombs a month, as if they were engaged on the production of ordinary bombs filled with TNT. If the atomic bomb did what was expected of it, only a few would be needed. Then why these enormous plants?

The answer is best supplied by an analogy. Suppose you wanted to find a needle in many loads of hay (and getting U-235 from unseparated uranium is much more difficult). If you wanted your needles in short order you would have to have a big plant to handle the hay in the shortest possible time. The relative volume of the hay and the needle would determine the cost of your construction.

In the plutonium project a plant of intermediate size was needed for two reasons — as a pilot plant to throw light on the problems of large-scale operation and as a producer of a few grams of plutonium badly needed for experimental purposes. At the time the first chain reaction was achieved at Chicago, no cooling devices were incorporated in the pile. That built at Clinton was air-cooled, but the piles of the Hanford plant were cooled by water.

To engineer, design, and construct the intermediate plant at Clinton, and to engineer, design, construct, and operate the large-scale production plant at Hanford, General Groves turned to the E. I. du Pont de Nemours Company. This firm had already taken on all the war work which it could be expected to handle with its existing organization, but on assurance that the War Department considered the work of the utmost importance, the du Pont Company agreed to undertake it, provided it be conducted without profit and without patent rights of any kind accruing to them. This contract, which eventually involved hundreds of millions, was therefore concluded on the basis of cost plus a fixed fee of $1.00.

Because of its close connection with fundamental research, the Clinton semi-works was to be operated under the direction of the University of Chicago. The marriage of this group of scientists to the du Pont engineers was a successful one, and contributed greatly to the design and operation of the plants in Tennessee and Washington.

The Hanford Engineer Works on the Columbia consists of three large piles several miles apart and of a number of separation plants well removed from the piles and from each other. Ground was broken on April

6, 1943, for a construction camp which is now a ghost town but once housed 60,000 inhabitants. Richland, the home of the operating crew, became a thriving town of 17,000.

The difficulties surmounted in the development of these large-scale producers defy description. Two of the most stubborn problems, the development of suitable barriers for the gaseous diffusion process and of a means of "canning" the uranium slugs in metal jackets at Hanford, were not solved till the eleventh hour. The dangerous nature of the plutonium process requires that each pile be enclosed in thick walls of concrete, steel, or other absorbing material, and that these shields must be both air- and radiation-tight. Not only is plutonium itself a highly dangerous substance if it gets into the body, but the fission products which result from the splitting of uranium include some thirty radioactive elements. All the stages of the precipitation process in the separation plants must therefore be handled by remote control from behind shields.

Since nearly all work in the radioactive field is dangerous, extensive studies of the best means to protect the health of workers had been carried on from the early days of the project. As soon as large-scale production was attempted it became necessary to handle amounts of radioactive material far larger than had ever before been dealt with. What was needed was not only the installation of shields, remote controls, and high stacks to carry off gases, but research on the effects of radiation on persons and the development of instruments and clinical tests measuring exposure of personnel. Each worker entering a dangerous area was issued two pocket meters about the size and shape of a fountain pen which were electrostatically charged at the start of each day and read at the end of each day. Later small pieces of film were introduced in the identification badges which could be developed at regular intervals and examined for blackening by radiation. At certain exit gates concealed counters sounded an alarm at the approach of anyone whose clothing, skin, or hair was contaminated. Great success was achieved by the safety devices, and a high standard of health and morale was maintained.

It would have been much more convenient to centralize the pilot plants, large-scale plants, and laboratories of the atomic bomb project on the seventy square miles which the Army acquired in Tennessee in 1942. But just as a desire for greater safety led to the selection of the

Hanford site for the great plutonium plant, considerations of secrecy and safety led to the establishment of a separate laboratory for those working on the bomb itself. It was financed under an Army contract with the University of California. The site chosen in November 1942 was on a mesa about twenty miles from Santa Fe, New Mexico, where there was nothing but a few buildings which had belonged to a small ranch school. On this lonely spot, reached only by a winding mountain road, was constructed in the spring of 1943 the best-equipped physics research laboratory in the world. Here were assembled a cyclotron from Harvard, two Van de Graaff generators from Wisconsin, a Cockcroft-Walton high-voltage machine from Illinois, and three carloads of apparatus from the recently terminated Princeton project.

With them came an extraordinary group of scientists. From 1940 on a large and increasing proportion of the best scientific minds in the country had been engaged on the problem of the atomic bomb under one or more of the 102 NDRC and OSRD S-1 contracts. Most of these men were still at work when success was finally attained in July 1945, and by that time they had been joined by scores of others, who had "taken the veil" and vanished from the groups working on other problems. Their chief was J. R. Oppenheimer, a 41-year-old theoretical physicist on the staff of the University of California who had taken part earlier in the extraordinary advances made there and at Chicago. His insight, resourcefulness, and sound judgment led to his selection as the Director of the Los Alamos Laboratory, where he showed scientific and administrative abilities of the highest order. Kistiakowsky, Chief of the Explosives Division of OSRD, became Chief of the Explosives Division of the Los Alamos Laboratory. Captain (now Rear Admiral) W. S. Parsons, U.S.N., who had headed a top secret Navy-OSRD project with distinguished success, made a notable contribution as Chief of the Ordnance Division and later performed the task of arming the atomic bomb in the flight against Hiroshima. The Radiation Laboratory sent an outstanding group including the gifted Alvarez and, on a part-time basis, the Nobel Prize winner I. I. Rabi. Between December 1943 and June 1945, moreover, research work on various aspects of the bomb was entrusted by the Manhattan District to three divisions and one section of OSRD. The task, however, involved not merely a national but an international effort. Sir James Chadwick, the discoverer of the neutron, headed a

Official Photo U. S. Army Air Forces

Devastation wrought by the first atomic bomb — Hiroshima

Victim of the second atomic bomb — Nagasaki

British group, and Niels Bohr, who had escaped from Denmark in a small boat in 1943, contributed his services.

In the research on plutonium the assumption was that the pile must not blow up. The investigators in New Mexico, on the other hand, were seeking to produce an atomic explosion. The fact that a self-sustaining reaction could be produced by slow neutrons was an assurance that fast neutrons could produce a chain reaction of the kind needed for the bomb. Studies of this type of reaction had been undertaken in 1941 at the Carnegie Institution of Washington, the National Bureau of Standards, Cornell, Purdue, Chicago, Minnesota, Wisconsin, California, Stanford, Indiana, and Rice Institute, under the general direction of Gregory Breit of Wisconsin. In the summer of 1942 this work was centered at Chicago in a group headed by Oppenheimer.

Even with a good indication of adequate supplies of U-235 and plutonium the task of designing and assembling the bomb was of extraordinary difficulty. It was out of the question to proceed by the usual method of small-scale experiment because no explosion occurs unless the mass of fissionable material exceeds the critical mass necessary for the full-scale bomb. Progress thus depended on improvements in the theoretical approach, to take account if possible of all the complex phenomena involved. By developing new techniques of extraordinary ingenuity, such as the "time of flight" method, it became possible to measure the nuclear constants of U-235, U-238, and Pu-239 over a range of neutron energies from the thermal level of 0.025 up to 3,000,000 electron volts.

Although the size and the construction of the bomb are veiled in secrecy, it is known that its casing is made of a material of high density, which reflects many neutrons back into the mass and acts as a tamper, delaying the expansion of the reacting material. As Professor Smyth explains it, "until detonation is desired, the bomb must consist of a number of separate pieces each one of which is below the critical size (either by reason of small size or unfavorable shape). To produce detonation, the parts of the bomb must be brought together rapidly."

In addition to these intricate problems of bomb design, exhaustive calculations were made to estimate the amount of military damage that an atomic bomb might be expected to produce. The increase in destructiveness of a bomb is not proportional to the increase in energy released,

Here the earlier studies of shock waves in air, earth, and water that had been undertaken by Divisions 2 and 8 of NDRC proved helpful.

On the accuracy of all these calculations depended the lives of those who took part in the assembly of the first bomb and its detonation. The tension among those present derived less from that than from the sense of the significance of what they were doing, both for the war then raging and for the world's future. The final assembly of the bomb began on the night of July 12, 1945, in an old ranch house. Dr. R. F. Bacher of Cornell University had the ticklish job of assembling the vital core. Brigadier General Thomas F. Farrell, General Groves's deputy, has left an unforgettable record of this occasion: —

During final preliminary assembly, a bad few minutes developed when the assembly of an important section of the bomb was delayed. The entire unit was machine-tooled to the finest measurement. The insertion was partially completed when it apparently wedged tightly and would go no farther. Dr. Bacher, however, was undismayed, and reassured the group that time would solve the problem. In three minutes' time, Dr. Bacher's statement was verified and basic assembly was completed without further incident.

On Saturday, July 14, the bomb was placed on the top of a steel tower which had been erected in a remote part of the Alamogordo Air Base, 120 miles southeast of Albuquerque. The instruments needed to record the performance of the bomb had already been set in place. The weather was threatening, and high wind and rain increased the tension. Two billion dollars had been spent on this project. The war with Germany was over. Could success be achieved in time to give us victory in the Far East before the scheduled invasion of the Japanese homeland? If so, would mankind learn to solve its quarrels without war, or would the new weapon spell the doom of civilization?

The bad weather delayed the test from 4 to 5.30 A.M. on Monday morning, July 16. Dr. K. T. Bainbridge of Harvard directed the detonation from a timber and earth shelter 10,000 yards from the tower, filled with controls, measuring instruments, and radios. As Dr. S. K. Allison, who was broadcasting from this shelter to the observation points, announced "minus forty-five seconds," an automatic mechanism took over the controls.

We were reaching into the unknown [says General Farrell] and we did not know what might come of it. . . . Dr. Oppenheimer . . . scarcely breathed. He held on to a post to steady himself. For the last few seconds he stared directly ahead and then when the announcer shouted "Now!" and there came this tremendous burst of light followed shortly thereafter by the deep growling roar of the explosion, his face relaxed into an expression of tremendous relief.

Violent as was the shock wave, the flash was most impressive of all. "The whole country was lighted by a searing light with an intensity many times that of the midday sun." "A massive cloud," says General Groves, "surged and billowed upward, with tremendous power, reaching the substratosphere in about five minutes." The steel tower proved to have been entirely vaporized.

The feeling of the entire assembly, even the uninitiated, was one of profound awe. Drs. Conant and Bush and myself were struck by an even stronger feeling that the faith of those who had been responsible for the initiation and carrying on of this herculean project had been justified.

EPILOGUE

BEFORE the atomic bombs burst over Hiroshima and Nagasaki, the progress of technology had already made warfare between great powers so terrible that the choice lay between adequate world organization and ruin. The two bombs broke the deadlock in the Japanese cabinet and shortened the war.[1] More important — if we can learn the lesson — they proved beyond peradventure that life in an international society whose members were competing in the production of atomic weapons would be intolerably precarious.

We, therefore, need to muster in the field of international relations as much inventiveness and engineering skill as was required to produce the bombs themselves. We must avoid our penchant for New Year's resolutions like the Kellogg Pact, which tend to produce a false sense of security. Even a treaty between all the great powers to outlaw the military use of atomic power will be a trap, not a safeguard, unless it provides for international inspection and control. The great powers, except for the United States and Japan, renounced gas warfare by a formal international agreement, and later expended vast sums in preparing for it. If the use of gas promised as quick military results as atomic bombs do, is it likely that a power bent on aggression would be deterred from gas warfare simply by a pledge in a treaty? The atomic bomb is not merely devastating, it is the perfect surprise weapon.

At the close of earlier wars, sensible men and women have demanded that international anarchy be supplanted by international organization and that swords be turned into plowshares. But the good resolutions of the morning after have not yet become the basis of durable peace. The development of the modern state and the progress of technology, which have made wars so terrible and so costly, have strengthened in many ways the spirit of nationalism which balks at international controls. When technological change comes so rapidly there is danger that a power may overrate its own superiority and make its bid for hegemony, believing in a quick, relatively inexpensive victory like those Germany thought she had won in 1914 and 1940. Indeed it may be argued that the increasing tempo of technological advance has made it more likely that a nation may be seized by an insane desire to dominate the world, thinking it has a new weapon that will for a time make it irresistible. It is one thing for military ascendancy to rest in the hands of a de-

[1] U.S. Strategic Bombing Survey, *Japan's Struggle to End the War.*

mocracy like the British or the American, which hates war and has territory and resources enough to meet most of its needs. In a world of unrestrained power politics, on the other hand, it would be very dangerous if technological as well as numerical superiority lay in the hands of a dictatorship or an oligarchy bent on aggression.

Until the world creates an international organization strong enough to control the genie who escaped from his bottle at Alamogordo, we must keep our powder dry. Only a strong United States can give sufficient support to the peace structure of the United Nations during the difficult period of transition in which the statesmen of the world must build more securely the foundations of international order. A generation ago some of our pacifists preached unilateral disarmament, in the belief that by setting other nations an example we should encourage them to decrease their own armaments. Such a course was dangerous then. It would be suicidal now. It would place in jeopardy both our national security and the contribution we must make to the enforcement of peace. If war comes again, it probably will come quickly, leaving us no opportunity for the lengthy preparations we made in World Wars I and II while associates and allies held the fronts.

Our preparations must, therefore, provide for great offensive and defensive power from the outset of hostilities. Much of our strength will depend on the use we make of our scientists and engineers. It is not a question of scientific preparedness versus expenditures on ships, guns, and planes. We need big battalions, fleets, and air squadrons as well as factories, pilot plants, and laboratories. As Dr. Bush so eloquently argued in his report of July 1945, to the President, *Science the Endless Frontier*, the Federal Government should support generously research in pure science as well as the application of science to war.

It was our good fortune, in World War II, to have a better organization of science for war than our friends or foes had. There is no reason to believe, however, that OSRD is the pattern we should follow in organizing science for war purposes in the days to come. We are not likely to be allowed such a long time between the outbreak of another war and its decisive battles as was vouchsafed us in 1917–1918 and in 1941–1945.

What is needed is the reorganization of scientific work within the armed services in such a way as to draw in first-rate scientists and give them the freedom necessary to do their best work. To do this inside great military organizations requires administrative skill of the highest order, for reasons made plain in earlier portions of this volume. Already the steps taken to reorganize scientific efforts within the Army and the

Navy hold out high hope for the future. Early in July, 1946, the White House announced the establishment of an authoritative committee headed by Dr. Bush to co-ordinate research and development of joint interest to the Army and Navy. "The committee is, in a sense, a court for the arbitration and determination of a specific class of overlapping interests."[2] No conflict is involved with the National Advisory Committee for Aeronautics or with the National Science Foundation if one is formed.

In the reorganization under way in the services it is to be hoped that better methods than those hitherto adopted will be found to bring together the knowledge and experience of the scientist and the requirements of the military at the level of strategic planning. It is heartening that the program for the new National War College, established in 1946, stresses the importance of the scientific factor throughout its curriculum.

What we need is military strength without militarism and realistic advancement of the structure of world peace without the self-deception to which pacifists are liable.

[2]Bush to the Secretaries of War and of the Navy, May 21, 1946

APPENDIX A

ORDER ESTABLISHING THE NATIONAL DEFENSE RESEARCH COMMITTEE

Pursuant to authority vested in it by section 2 of the Act of August 29, 1916 (39 Stat. 649), the Council of National Defense, with the approval of the President, hereby establishes as a subordinate body of the Council a committee to be known as the National Defense Research Committee. The following persons shall be members of the Committee: Dr. Vannevar Bush, who shall be Chairman, Dr. James B. Conant, Dr. Richard C. Tolman, Dr. Karl T. Compton, Dr. Frank B. Jewett (as President of the National Academy of Sciences), Conway P. Coe (as Commissioner of Patents), one officer of the Army to be designated by the Secretary of War and one officer of the Navy to be designated by the Secretary of the Navy. Vacancies occurring in the membership of the Committee shall be filled by appointment by the Council with the approval of the President. The members of the Committee and of such subcommittees as may be formed by the Committee shall serve as such without compensation but shall be entitled to actual and necessary transportation subsistence, and other expenses incidental to the performance of their duties.

The Committee shall correlate and support scientific research on the mechanisms and devices of warfare, except those relating to problems of flight included in the field of activities of National Advisory Committee for Aeronautics. It shall aid and supplement the experimental and research activities of the War and Navy Departments; and may conduct research for the creation and improvement of instrumentalities, methods, and materials of warfare. In carrying out its functions, the Committee may (a) utilize, to the extent that such facilities are available for such purpose, the laboratories, equipment and services of the National Bureau of Standards and other Government institutions; and (b) within the limits of appropriations allocated to it, transfer funds to such institutions, and enter into contracts and agreements with individuals, educational or scientific institutions (including the National Academy of Sciences and the National Research Council) and industrial organizations for studies, experimental investigations, and reports.

The Committee shall promulgate rules and regulations for the conduct of its work, which rules and regulations shall be subject to the approval of the Council and the President.

Louis Johnson, ACTING SECRETARY OF WAR
Lewis Compton, ACTING SECRETARY OF NAVY
Harold L. Ickes, SECRETARY OF INTERIOR
Approved: *H. A. Wallace*, SECRETARY OF AGRICULTURE
        FRANKLIN D. ROOSEVELT   *Harry L. Hopkins*, SECRETARY OF COMMERCE
                                       Frances V. Perkins, SECRETARY OF LABOR
The White House
        June 27, 1940

APPENDIX B

EXECUTIVE ORDER NO. 8807, dated June 28, 1941 (as amended by Executive Order No. 9389, dated October 18, 1943)

ESTABLISHING THE OFFICE OF SCIENTIFIC RESEARCH AND DEVELOPMENT IN THE EXECUTIVE OFFICE OF THE PRESIDENT AND DEFINING ITS FUNCTIONS AND DUTIES

By virtue of the authority vested in me by the Constitution and the statutes of the United States, and in order to define further the functions and duties of the Office for Emergency Management with respect to the unlimited national emergency as declared by the President on May 27, 1941, for the purpose of assuring adequate provision for research on scientific and medical problems relating to the national defense, it is hereby ordered:

1. There shall be within the Office for Emergency Management of the Executive Office of the President the Office of Scientific Research and Development, at the head of which shall be a Director appointed by the President. The Director shall discharge and perform his responsibilities and duties under the direction and supervision of the President. The Director shall receive compensation at such rate as the President shall determine and, in addition, shall be entitled to actual and necessary transportation, subsistence, and other expenses incidental to the performance of his duties.

2. Subject to such policies, regulations, and directions as the President may from time to time prescribe, and with such advice and assistance as may be necessary from the other departments and agencies of the Federal Government, the Office of Scientific Research and Development shall:

    a. Advise the President with regard to the status of scientific and medical research relating to national defense and the measures necessary to assure continued and increasing progress in this field.

    b. Serve as the center for the mobilization of the scientific personnel and resources of the Nation in order to assure maximum utilization of such personnel and resources in developing and applying the results of scientific research to defense purposes.

    c. Co-ordinate, aid, and, where desirable, supplement the experimental and other scientific and medical research activities relating to national defense carried on by the Departments of War and Navy and other departments and agencies of the Federal Government.

    d. Develop broad and co-ordinated plans for the conduct of scientific research in the defense program, in collaboration with representatives of the War and Navy Departments; review existing scientific research programs formulated by the Departments of War and Navy and other agencies of the Government, and advise them with respect to the relationship of their proposed activities to the total research program.

e. Initiate and support scientific research on the mechanisms and devices of warfare with the objective of creating, developing, and improving instrumentalities, methods, and materials required for national defense.

f. Initiate and support scientific research on medical problems affecting the national defense.

g. Initiate and support such scientific and medical research as may be requested by the government of any country whose defense the President deems vital to the defense of the United States under the terms of the Act of March 11, 1941, entitled "An Act to Promote the Defense of the United States"; and serve as the central liaison office for the conduct of such scientific and medical research for such countries.

h. Perform such other duties relating to scientific and medical research and development as the President may from time to time assign or delegate to it.

3. The Director may provide for the internal organization and management of the Office of Scientific Research and Development and may appoint such advisory committees as he finds necessary to the performance of his duties and responsibilities.

4. In carrying out its functions, the Office of Scientific Research and Development shall utilize the laboratories, equipment, and services of governmental agencies and institutions to the extent that such facilities are available for such purposes. Within the limits of funds appropriated or allocated for purposes encompassed by this Order, the Director may contract with and transfer funds to existing governmental agencies and institutions and may enter into contracts and agreements with individuals, educational and scientific institutions (including the National Academy of Sciences and the National Research Council), industrial organizations, and other agencies, for studies, experimental investigation and reports.

5. The Director is authorized to take over and carry out the provisions of any contracts which fall within the scope of this Order heretofore entered into by (1) the National Defense Research Committee, established by order of the Council of National Defense on June 27, 1940, (2) the Health and Medical Committee, established by order of the Council of National Defense on September 19, 1940, and (3) the Federal Security Administrator in his capacity of Co-ordinator of Health, Medical Welfare, Nutrition, Recreation, and other related activities as authorized by order of the Council of National Defense on November 28, 1940. The Director is further authorized to assume any obligations or responsibilities which have heretofore been undertaken by the above agencies for and on behalf of the United States Government and which fall within the scope of this Order.

6. There is created within the Office of Scientific Research and Development an advisory Council consisting of the Director as Chairman, the Chair-

man of the National Advisory Committee for Aeronautics, the Chairman of the National Defense Research Committee (hereinafter described), the Chairman of the Committee on Medical Research (hereinafter described), one representative of the Army to be designated by the Secretary of War, and one representative of the Navy to be designated by the Secretary of the Navy. The Council shall advise and assist the Director with respect to the co-ordination of research activities carried on by private and governmental research groups and shall facilitate the interchange of information and data between such groups and agencies.

7. There shall be within the Office of Scientific Research and Development a National Defense Research Committee consisting of a chairman and three other members appointed by the President, and in addition the President of the National Academy of Sciences, the Commissioner of Patents, one officer of the Army to be designated by the Secretary of War, one officer of the Navy to be designated by the Secretary of the Navy, and such other members as the President may subsequently appoint. The National Defense Research Committee shall advise and assist the Director in the performance of his scientific research duties with special reference to the mobilization of the scientific personnel and resources of the Nation. To this end it shall be the responsibility of the Committee to recommend to the Director the need for and character of contracts to be entered into with universities, research institutes, and industrial laboratories for research and development on instrumentalities of warfare to supplement such research and development activities of the Departments of War and the Navy. Furthermore, the Committee shall from time to time make findings, and submit recommendations to the Director with respect to the adequacy, progress, and results of research on scientific problems related to national defense.

8. There shall be within the Office of Scientific Research and Development a Committee on Medical Research consisting of a Chairman and three members to be appointed by the President, and three other members to be designated respectively by the Secretary of War, the Secretary of the Navy, and the Administrator of the Federal Security Agency. The members so designated by the Secretaries of War and Navy and Federal Security Administrator shall be selected from the respective staffs of the Surgeons General and the Surgeon General of the Public Health Service with particular reference to their qualifications in the field of medical research. The Committee on Medical Research shall advise and assist the Director in the performance of his medical research duties with special reference to the mobilization of medical and scientific personnel of the nation. To this end it shall be the responsibility of the Committee to recommend to the Director the need for the character of contracts to be entered into with universities, hospitals, and other agencies conducting medical research activities for research and development in the field of the medical sciences. Furthermore, the Committee shall from time to time, on

request by the Director, make findings and submit recommendations with respect to the adequacy, progress, and results of research on medical problems related to national defense.

9. The members of the Advisory Council, the National Defense Committee, the Committee on Medical Research, and such other committees and sub-committees as the Director may appoint with the approval of the President shall serve as such without compensation, but shall be entitled to necessary and actual transportation, subsistence, and other expenses incidental to the performance of their duties.

10. Within the limits of such funds as may be appropriated to the Office of Scientific Research and Development or as may be allocated to it by the President, the Director may employ necessary personnel and make provision for necessary supplies, facilities, and services. However, the Director shall use such statistical, informational, fiscal, personnel, and other general business services and facilities as may be made available to him through the Office for Emergency Management.

FRANKLIN D. ROOSEVELT

THE WHITE HOUSE

	Number of Contracts	Total Dollar Value of Contracts
Monsanto Chemical Company	8	$4,222,044.00
Zenith Radio Corporation	3	4,175,000.00
Standard Oil Development Company	14	3,453,000.00
Hygrade Sylvania (Sylvania Electric Company)	17	3,093,451.16
Erwood Sound Company	1	2,875,000.00
Douglas Aircraft Company	3	2,592,500.00
M. W. Kellogg Company	2	1,915,000.00
Budd Wheel Company	2	1,655,000.00
Gulf Research and Development Company	9	1,601,450.00
Delta Star Electric Company	1	1,464,850.00
Emerson Radio and Phonograph Corporation	5	1,333,500.00
Ford, Bacon and Davis, Inc.	2	1,300,000.00
Globe-Union, Incorporated	2	1,275,000.00
Federal Telephone and Radio Corporation	13	1,211,390.00
Bowen and Company	1	1,160,000.00
National Carbon Company	4	1,076,000.00
Galvin Manufacturing Corporation	7	1,041,950.00

ACKNOWLEDGMENTS

THIS BOOK conforms to the security regulations of the Army and Navy in force in May 1946, when Joint Security Control cleared it for publication.

My thanks are due to the Trustees of Williams College for their permission to undertake this work on a part-time basis since February 1943, and during a leave of absence in the summer of 1945; and to the Secretaries of War and of the Navy for access to secret and confidential material and to various establishments of the services during tests.

Considerations of space prevent acknowledgment in detail of the kindness of friends in the Office of Scientific Research and Development and in the services who made material available or offered suggestions and criticism. Dr. Vannevar Bush and Dr. James B. Conant, who read the entire manuscript, have been unfailingly helpful. Each chapter has been read by one or more members of the divisions of the National Defense Research Committee or the Committee on Medical Research. I am grateful for the friendly criticism of Colonel Allen F. Clark, Jr., Deputy Chief of the Historical Division, War Department Special Staff; Colonel Clanton W. Williams, Historian of the Army Air Forces; Admiral Raymond A. Spruance, Rear Admiral Julius A. Furer, and the late Rear Admiral Ernest G. Small.

Dr. Arthur M. Walker, then attached to the Office of the Director, CMR, wrote chapters XX–XXIII, and Dr. Detlev W. Bronk contributed the chapter on *Aviation Medicine*. Dr. W. Albert Noyes, Jr., Chief of Division 10, NDRC, and now President of the American Chemical Society, wrote Chapter XVIII, *Why Not Gas?*, and the portion of Chapter XIX dealing with smokes.

I am indebted to Frederick J. Hovde, Dr. Dael Wolfle, and Dr. John E. Burchard, for help with the chapters on *Rockets*, *Selection and Training*, and *Operations Research and Field Service*, respectively; and to Dr. Henry Guerlac, the Historian of the Radiation Laboratory, President Karl T. Compton of M.I.T., Dr. Charles G. Suits, Vice-President of the General Electric Company, Dean F. E. Terman of Stanford University, Dr. James Stokley, and Mr. O. G. Villard, Jr., for help on the chapters dealing with *Radar and Loran* and *Radar Countermeasures*. Mr. T. E. Shea of the Western Electric Company, Dr. John T. Tate, Dr. E. G. Colpitts, and Dr. Philip M. Morse laid me under heavy debt for their generous assistance in the field of *Subsurface Warfare*; as did

Mr. Palmer Cosslett Putnam, Mr. Dennis Puleston, and my son, Lieutenant James P. Baxter, 4th, USNR, with regard to *Amphibious Warfare*, and Dr. J. Allan Hynek with regard to *Proximity Fuzes*.

Mr. Carroll L. Wilson, Dr. Irvin Stewart, now President of the University of West Virginia, Dr. Roger Adams, Dean Edward L. Moreland, and Dr. Frank B. Jewett, Member NDRC and President of the National Academy of Sciences, were of great assistance in matters concerning organization and administrative history.

For his extraordinary knack as a collector of photographs and documentary material, and for his friendly criticism, I am indebted to Mr. George R. Clark, my executive officer, whose efforts were ably seconded by Lieutenant Robert N. Cunningham, USNR, and Miss Emily Mitchell. Mrs. Helen Maxwell and Miss Jane Page, of my Washington office, and Miss Kathleen O'Connell, Mrs. Barbara Bradley, Miss Fay Grady, Miss Mary Rita Grady, Miss Ruth Larabee, and Mrs. Dorothy Smullyan of Williamstown were most helpful in the preparation of the manuscript. My friends Edward A. Weeks, Jr., and Stanley Salmen of the Atlantic Monthly Press gave me far more help and guidance as to the presentation of this material than authors have a right to expect from their publishers.

JAMES PHINNEY BAXTER *3rd*

WILLIAMSTOWN, MASSACHUSETTS

July, 1946

APPENDIX C

25 Principal Non-Industrial Contractors with OSRD[1]

	Number of Contracts	Total Dollar Value of Contracts
Massachusetts Institute of Technology	75	$116,941,352.05
California Institute of Technology	48	83,451,746.45
Harvard University	79	30,963,478.80
Columbia University	73	28,521,412.63
University of California	106	14,384,506.98
Johns Hopkins University	49	10,572,642.61
University of Chicago	53	6,742,070.64
George Washington University	2	6,561,650.00
Princeton University	17	3,593,446.51
National Academy of Sciences	19	3,164,531.14
Carnegie Institution of Washington	26	2,999,035.00
University of Pennsylvania	36	2,960,438.31
Northwestern University	29	2,568,628.00
Carnegie Institute of Technology	20	2,511,675.00
University of Michigan	30	2,159,035.00
Woods Hole Oceanographic Institute	5	2,110,000.00
University of Illinois	30	2,013,525.49
University of Iowa	7	1,933,350.00
Franklin Institute	13	1,923,025.00
Evans Memorial Hospital	4	1,920,960.00
University of Rochester	35	1,859,863.57
Duke University	11	1,210,579.50
Cornell University	31	1,147,836.50
University of New Mexico	9	1,141,550.00
Battelle Memorial Institute	15	1,141,500.00

25 Principal Industrial Contractors with OSRD[1]

Western Electric Company	94	17,091,819.00
Research Construction Company	2	13,950,000.00
General Electric Company	58	8,077,047.14
Radio Corporation of America	54	5,783,498.13
E. I. du Pont de Nemours and Company	59	5,704,146.54
Westinghouse Electric Manufacturing Corporation	54	5,122,722.26
Remington Rand, Incorporated	3	4,675,050.00
Eastman Kodak Company	29	4,509,200.00

[1]As of June 30, 1945.

INDEX

ABELSON, P. H., 441
Acoustics, see Harvard Psycho-Acoustic Laboratory; Sound, underwater; Torpedoes, guided
Adams, Roger, 22, 124, 254, 256, 279
Addison, Air Commodore, 168
Admiralty Signal Establishment, 144
Advisory Committee on Scientific Personnel, 129, 131 n.
Advisory Committee on Uranium, 423–426; see also S-1 Executive Committee; Uranium Committee
Advisory Council, OSRD, 28–29, 33, 129, 411 n.
Air Defense Research and Development Establishment, Great Malvern, 144
Air power, 4–6, 29, 31–36, 40, 44, 46, 53, 56, 63–65, 67, 69, 81, 83–99, 109, 141, 153, 179, 187–200, 221
Air warfare, 83–99, 187–200, 215, 223, 238, 241, 244, 282–285, 288–296, 369, 377–393, 406, 415; interception, 3, 6, 35, 57, 91, 223, 235; strategic bombing, 53–54, 83–92, 97, 157, 168–169, 240; tactical support of ground troops, 53, 83–92, 114, 153, 168, 210
Airborne Instruments Laboratory (Division 15), 34, 161–162
Aircraft, accidents, 183, 188, 379, 392–393; aerodynamics, aeronautics, 9, 13–16, 62, 187–188, 194, 197; B-29 research, 90, 217, 402–403; blind landing of, 57, 97, 153, 400; brakes, 187; VLR (Very Long Range), 44–46
Air-sea rescue, 42, 50, 64, 106, 153, 406
Alamogordo, New Mexico, 419–420, 446–447
Albanite, 261
Allegany Ballistics Laboratory, 210, 255
Allied Submarine Devices Investigation Committee (Asdic), see Sound, underwater
Allis-Chalmers Manufacturing Co., 441
Allison, S. K., 446
Alvarez, Luis W., 153, 155, 157–158, 444
American British Laboratory of Division 15 (ABL-15), 168–169, 408
American Can Co., 176
American Tel. & Tel. Co., 160
Amphibian jeep, 243
Amphibious warfare, 47, 67–82, 206–207, 243–251, 289, 296, 390, 398–399, 406; see also Dukw; Weasel
Anderson, Carl, 210
Anderson, General Orville, 87
Andrus, E. Cowles, 378
Antiaircraft (AA, flak), 11, 35, 45–47, 49, 58, 60, 73, 92–93, 114–115, 117, 140, 145, 147, 159, 165, 187, 194, 202–203, 205, 208, 212–216, 221, 224, 229–235, 237, 241, 265, 379, 404, 406
Anti-Jamming (AJ) Committee of Division 15, 168
Antimalarials, see Malaria
Antisubmarine devices, see Submarines
Antisubmarine Warfare Operations Research Group (ASWORG), 41, 177, 178 n., 184, 405–406, 408 n., 413
Anzio, 114–115, 246, 270, 282, 287
Applied Mathematics Panel, NDRC, 22, 41, 84, 90, 102, 125, 177, 216, 409–411
Applied Psychology Panel, NDRC, 22, 90, 125, 396–403
Arawe, 74
Archambault, Bennett, 411
Armour Research Foundation, 176
Arnold, General Henry H., 16, 83, 192, 199, 290, 406
Arthur D. Little, Inc., see Little, Arthur D., Inc.
Asdic sound gear, see Sound, underwater
Aston, F. W., 422
ASW (Antisubmarine Warfare), see Antisubmarine Warfare Operations Research Group; Submarines, antisubmarine devices
Atabrine, 107, 306–320, 338, 361
Atomic power, 3, 22, 51, 419–447; see also Bombs, atomic
"Aunt Jemima" explosive, 265
Aviation helmets, 190–191
Aviation medicine, 188–191, 377–393
Aydelotte, Frank, 129, 131 n.
Azon, see Bombs, guided

BACHER, R. F., 155, 157, 446
Bachmann, Werner, 22, 256–257
Bailey, George, 123 n., 131 n.
Bainbridge, Kenneth T., 155, 157, 446
Bakelite Corporation, 193
Baker, Rear Admiral Wilder D., 405
Ballistics, 14, 22, 193, 210, 261, 406; see also Explosives; Ordnance; Rockets
Barber-Colman Co., 217
Bartol Research Foundation, 155 n.
Barton, Henry A., 127
Baruch, Bernard M., 18
Bat, see Bombs, guided
Bathythermograph, 51, 180, 184
Battle of Britain, 5–6, 91, 121–122, 147, 158, 165, 323, 381, 387
Battle of the Bulge, 36, 113, 115–116, 249 n., 408
Bausch and Lomb, 218
Bazooka, see Rockets, bazooka
Beal, R. R., 141 n.
Beams, J., 429